Wimbledon Common & Putney Heath

A Natural History

Wimbledon Common & Putney Heath

A Natural History

Edited by

TONY DRAKEFORD and UNA SUTCLIFFE

Foreword by David Bellamy

Illustrations by Christiana Gilbert

Published by
Wimbledon and Putney Commons Conservators

© Wimbledon and Putney Commons Conservators 2000

Wimbledon and Putney Commons Conservators
Manor Cottage
Wimbledon Common
London SW19 5NR
Telephone: 0208 788 7655

British Library Cataloguing in Publication Data
Data available

ISNB 0 9501887 5 1

Frontispiece: courtesy of Aerofilms Limited

Design, typesetting and production by
John Saunders Design & Production, Reading, UK
Printed in Hong Kong on acid-free paper by
C&C Offset Printing Co., Ltd.

Contents

        Non-flying Mammals *Tony Drakeford*   184
        Bats *Pete Guest*   192

15 **Extracts from a Keeper's Diary**   196
        Dave Haldane

16 **Habitat Creation and Habitat Restoration**   204
        Habitat Creation – Ravine Pond *Tony Drakeford*   205
        Habitat Restoration *Pete Guest*   207

    Epilogue   213

    Further Reading   214

    Index   216

Acknowledgements

Our benefactors, the All England Lawn Tennis Club. Final Championships of the Twentieth Century, 1999.

The Editors would like to thank the following organisations and individuals for their financial assistance towards the publication of this book.

Our special thanks must go to the very generous support from our 'neighbours', the All England Lawn Tennis and Croquet Club, headed by its Chief Executive, Christopher Gorringe, whose substantial contribution has enabled us to produce a higher quality of book than was first envisaged.

English Nature has encouraged the project from its outset and provided a Grant towards publication.

Contributions have also been received from The Putney Society; Mr J. Leek and the Parkside Residents' Association; Wimbledon House Residents' Association; Wimbledon Common West Residents' Association; Tennis Umpires; Mrs J. Brinkman; Mr C. Walliker; and Mrs E. Marris. To all the above named we are extremely grateful.

The preparation of the book was a happy experience for the Editors, through the interesting people they met and the encouragement and help they were so generously given. Many people have assisted in various ways towards its production. Robert Boote, a past Conservator of the Commons, provided impetus during the initial stages; and we are indebted to Richard Hart who put us in touch with our Designer. James Reader, Clerk & Ranger of the Commons; Daphne Jones, Deputy Clerk & Ranger; Dave Haldane, Assistant Ranger; Sharon Dugdale, Secretary; and the Conservators, gave constant support and encouragement.

Practical scientific advice or help in the field was given by Russell Coope, Dennis Fullwood, Dave Haldane, Martin Henderson, Robert Holmes, Richard MacPhail, Frank Miller, Davinia Miln, Nigel Reeve, Paul Rhodes and John Weir. David Bridgland, David Evans, Brian Ferry, Phil Gibbard, Shirley Goodwin, John Hutchinson, David Keen, Richard Milward, Phil Palmer, Richard Preece, Antony Sutcliffe, Richard Thompson, Freda Turtle and Staff of the Environment Agency read and commented on parts of the typescript. Chris Jones, of the Scanning Electron Microscope Unit of the Natural History Museum, provided valuable help.

Simon Jennings and Christine Smyth allowed us to publish, for the first time, their study of the Farm Bog pollen sequence.

Marjorie Carreck discovered, among the archives of the Geologists' Association, the photograph of Walter Johnson.

Christiana Gilbert's palaeontological reconstructions; John Whittaker's re-examination of the Wimbledon Common London Clay foraminifora; and the photographing of a Daubenton's bat in flight over Queensmere by Frank Greenaway, were projects specially undertaken for the book.

Mr & Mrs P. Blacker and Octagon Developments Ltd. permitted the inspection of deposits exposed in temporary excavations near the Windmill and at Oxford Lodge, Parkside, respectively.

Alan Elliott and Anne-Marie Hill arranged availability of illustrations from the collection of the Wimbledon Museum. Stewart Nicol and Marisa Sarközi provided technical guidance.

To John Saunders, our Designer, we are especially indebted for assembling this book so skilfully and so congenially.

To those we have inevitably forgotten, we extend our apologies.

Foreword

I quote unashamedly from Graham Murphy's book *Founders of the National Trust* to which I was also honoured to contribute a Foreword. My reason is that the very existence of these hallowed 1140 acres of Wimbledon and Putney Commons, which are now in grave danger of being 'loved to death', are intimately wound up with the foundation of that august body.

> Since before the agricultural revolution of the eighteenth century, uncultivated commons had been described as the 'wastes' of manors. 'Wastes indeed!' declared the radical essayist William Cobbett. 'Give a dog an ill name. Was Horton Heath a waste? Was it a "waste" when a hundred perhaps of healthy boys and girls were playing there on a Sunday instead of creeping about covered with filth in the alleys of a town?'
>
> Cobbett's humanism did not prevail against economic arguments; (back in those days) poor children were small adults, useful for minding machines or crawling up chimneys; play belonged to the idyllic past: the future lay with towns and factories. There was no place in the urban environment for such a frivolity as a playground. When in 1847 the first northern municipal park, designed by Joseph Paxton, was opened in the township of Birkenhead to the financial benefit of those able to buy the building plots on its periphery, no provision whatsoever was made for children to play. . . . Only in the 1870s, with the publication of Octavia Hill's (herself one of the visionary founders of the National Trust) essays on urban improvement, was the right of working-class children to open-air recreation generally conceded.
>
> By that time the middle classes, the majority of whom already owned gardens or had access to a square, had become aware of the potential of urban remnants of common land as alternative places for relaxation. Romanticism in art and literature showed that a wilderness was beautiful and, if carefully managed – or rather, carefully neglected – could be as desirable as a tended garden or a park laid out to order. City clerks and accountants sought suburban property fronted by land which required neither costly purchase nor radical alteration. They moved to the defense of common rights and titles and the enactment of regulation schemes. . . . Their appreciation of open spaces strengthened their sense of community. The first rambling clubs comprised a number of middle-class men who met on Sunday afternoons for vigorous walks on the commons. On weekdays they and their children, as members of a naturalists' club, might use the same commons as their scientific laboratories.

Such clubs continued to keep a record of the natural history that had been kept, for over 6000 years, safe in the peat of Farm Bog. This timely book is the latest chapter in that history.

It is a miracle that there is anything left for this team of local natural historians to write about. The tiny minds of those whose vision goes no further than concrete, tarmacadam, wooden decking, patios and flowerpots dripping with preservatives, pesticides and short term profit; are still hell bent on smothering the little that is left of the world's living, breathing soil.

This soil was originally crafted by the wildwood that once covered these now sacred acres. Wildwood there was, even on these clays and nutrient poor acid lands; wildwood that was turned into a patchwork of heath and scrub by the necessity of many cycles of slash and burn, as Stone Age hunter-gatherers metamorphosed into farmers. With the evaporating power of the trees gone, the water table rose, creating the conditions for the development of the bog. The rest of the story of these last remnants of the wildscape of London is detailed in this excellent book.

As a botanist perhaps I should ask where have all the flowers gone, why no section specifically on the flora? Well, lists of plants do get boring for the uninitiated, so they are cunningly hidden in the chapters about habitat. Plants are the primary producers of food, soil, shade and shelter, the stuff of every living landscape. So when you use the Common and the Heath I beg you to treat them with the respect they deserve.

I will, if I may, select just one chapter for special comment and that is the account of Fungi and Lichens. The former are the original Wombles, litter pickers and recyclers without equal; the latter, the Lichens which, like the canaries used by miners, keep tabs on the purity of the air we breathe. The good news is, after two hundred years of decline, things are looking better. We all look to the day when Uncle 'Lobaria' is back on the scene and with fuel cell technology coming on line, who knows?

Their future is however not only threatened by the developers of property and parkland, but by a growing conflict between 'Mother Nature' and the urban temperament. While London still burned coal, acid rain helped keep the soils sour and unproductive. But now, nitrogen from grid locked exhausts, doggies doos and other wastes, are enriching the soils and helping to speed the growth of trees, which are no longer held in check by browsing animals and heathland fires. Without proper management the whole of this common land will turn itself into forest; a wonderful resource but not the landscape now enjoyed by the post Womble generation.

Jealously guarded by at least a million pairs of eyes and trodden by an army of feet shod in a diverse array of footwear, it should be the safest bit of urban greenscape in the world. But what if management threatened someone's favourite glade of invading birch, or suggested fire, or the introduction of grazing animals, or fences, or relocation of paths at irregular intervals, or the eradication of invading plants and animals? What about the reintroduction of the red squirrel, brown hare, water vole and beaver? Shock! horror!, the altercation of divided opinions, urban rage.

It will happen unless everyone who lives around or loves the freedom of these now sacred spaces (the smell of their rain washed living soil, the buzz of their insects, and the changing patterns and colours of the seasons of the natural world) take the trouble to learn the true facts of the life of this, their common heritage. Please buy and read this book, and in the full understanding of everything it contains, love it *not* to death, but back into the haphazard patchwork of biodiverse working order as it was in the days of my youth.

David Bellamy

Chapter 1

Introduction

Tony Drakeford

"He does not know Wimbledon Common who is not familiar with its labyrinths of leafy glades, its tangled thickets of wild red rose, bramble, and honey-suckle; who has not often traversed its turfy plateau and had the perfumes of odoriferous herbs borne in upon his senses; who has not pondered over its rusty pebble, and wondered whence they came; tried to acquaint himself with what may be gleaned of local history; . . . and rambled through the bird paradise of Beverley Vale" . . . "Judged broadly, the Wimbledon flora and fauna must be ranked very high for a suburban area" . . . "Sundry petitions must now be made. First of all, to the Conservators of the Common, to whom we really owe very much, one may appeal for the preservation of the heath in its wild state. . . . one prays earnestly that the Common be not 'vulgarised' . . . by making this lovely spot ordinary – a kind of level, well-ordered suburban park, . . . for this windswept Common is not ordinary; it stands alone, and is therefore priceless".

That eloquent statement was made way back in 1912 by Walter Johnson (Fig. 1.1), writing in his classic book, *Wimbledon Common; its Geology, Antiquities and Natural History*, until now, perhaps surprisingly, the only major work to be published, devoted entirely to the natural history of the Commons.

Figure 1.1 Walter Johnson, 1867–1950 (right of group photograph) during a Geologists' Association field excursion to Lyme Regis in 1906. The bearded gentleman (left) is William Whittaker, famous London Geologist and friend.

From the archives of the Geologists' Association, with permission.

Although so valid at that time, Johnson's sentiments carry even greater significance today, as increased urbanisation and major road building programmes all contribute to an ever shrinking countryside and to the destruction and fragmentation of irreplaceable wildlife habitats. Because of this, preservation and conservation of protected areas such as Wimbledon Common and Putney Heath is increasingly important and indeed vital if we are to safeguard Britain's wildlife heritage.

During the years since the publication of Johnson's book there have been many changes on the Commons. For example, it is certain that the area was then much less wooded than it is now, with heath and scrub predominating, thus having, I would venture to suggest, less diverse biota than that of today. The Commons now benefit from a wider range of habitats, which should lead to greater species diversity. Over the years there have been new arrivals to add to our species lists, some beneficial and welcome, others less so. Indeed, in these enlightened times with more and more people becoming interested in natural history, enthusiastic recorders have listed species which were probably overlooked in the past; and every year additional names are being added to our files. We also know from our records of a number of interesting species which have unfortunately disappeared, in line with national declines.

The proximity of the Commons to central London has placed tremendous human pressures on them but, notwithstanding, they still support a wealth of wildlife. This potential conflict of interests had already been recognised as a problem by 1871, when an Act of Parliament was passed decreeing that the Commons were forever to remain open, uninclosed and unbuilt upon, for the purpose of recreation and exercise.

In 1953 a large part of the 1140 acres of Wimbledon Common and Putney Heath was further protected by being designated a Site of Special Scientific Interest by the Nature Conservancy Council (now English Nature).

As Walter Johnson would have wished, the Commons continue to be administered and managed, as they were in his day, by a dedicated Board of vigilant Conservators and Rangers, pledged to uphold the provisions of the 1871 Act.

Figure 1.2 Hogweed growing in profusion in the meadow near the Windmill.
Photo: Tony Drakeford.

Figure 1.3 Horse riders on Gravelly Ride.
Photo: Antony Sutcliffe.

Figure 1.4 The magic of the Commons is carried into the homes of children worldwide by the 'Wombles of Wimbledon Common' books, television series and songs. This is Great Uncle Bulgaria with two of his pals.
Photo: Una Sutcliffe.

Furthermore, as a result of increased awareness of the natural world, of the problems which beset it and the urgent need to conserve what is left, we are assisted in our efforts by many of the thousands of people who value and enjoy the Commons. These open spaces are a vital lung for Londoners participating in all manner of recreational pursuits from walking, running, horse riding, cycling, kite flying and organised sports, to simply relaxing and unwinding in the open spaces and woodland rides. For children there is even the possibility of encountering a Womble!

A walk on the Commons today will reveal a veritable patchwork of mature mixed woodland; prime heathland; grasslands offering a mixture of long and short sward; scrub; a number of ponds and meres, plus some fine bogs, streams and, of course, the Beverley Brook.

For the naturalist, whatever his or her speciality, the Commons cater for it. Orchids grace the grassland in summer. The secretive and colourful kingfisher can sometimes be seen as an electric-blue blur flashing along the Beverley Brook. Hobbys occasionally hawk above Kingsmere for dragonflies, and in July the heady aroma of Spanish broom pervades 'the hills', which in turn come alive during August to the sound of grasshoppers and crickets stridu-lating in the sunshine.

Monster pike lurk in some of the meres, and the Commons support an encouraging number of butterflies, moths, dragonflies and damselflies, all reliable indicators of a healthy environment. Rabbits, foxes and badgers live on the Commons and timid voles and wood mice leave tell-tale traces of their feeding habits among fallen hazel nuts. Species lists for wildflowers and trees are impressive.

Nearly ninety years have elapsed since the appearance of Johnson's excellent

Figure 1.5 A Common
Spotted Orchid growing on
the Common.
Photo: Tony Drakeford.

Figure 1.6 Harebells can still
be found in a few places.
Photo: Tony Drakeford.

book. Much has happened since then. The natural history of the Commons
has continued to be extensively studied, with prominent observations
published as notes in the *Quarterly Journal of the Wimbledon Natural History
Society*, a section of the then John Evelyn Society (now The Wimbledon
Society) which flourished between 1911 and the outbreak of the Second World
War. Then in 1971, the centenary year of the 1871 Act, a fascinating booklet
entitled *Walks on Wimbledon Common* was published which contains worthwhile facts about the flora and fauna.

It is nevertheless timely for a new book to be published. To make this
possible we have gathered around us a team of authors and an illustrator, every
one an expert in his or her own particular sphere of interest, and each having
as great a love of the Commons as we have. To all of them, we are deeply
indebted. This combination of knowledge will, hopefully, give readers as
complete a picture as possible of the natural history of the Commons in the
late 1990s, showing too, how past events have shaped the present.

Technology has made tremendous advances since 1912. Photography was
in its infancy in Johnson's day; even so his work does include some excellent
monochrome pictures. Modern colour photography, however, allows us much
greater scope to record accurately all that we see around us and full advantage
is taken of this facility within these pages. Of equal significance, modern scientific techniques present us with a unique opportunity to reconstruct the
vegetational history of the Commons and probable human influence on past
environments, through studies of fossil pollen, dated by the Carbon 14
method. The sample core for pollen analysis was taken from Farm Bog, the
most important bog in the London area.

The book begins with chapters on geology, drainage and palynology,
followed by an account of past disturbance on the Commons; thus opening a
window into the past and building a foundation upon which we can examine
the present.

As will be seen in the following pages, the Commons harbour a great variety
of wildlife. We have endeavoured to document the aspects that have been

Figure 1.7 Scene with badgers.
Artist: Christiana Gilbert.

most intensively studied and those that are most 'visible' to people visiting the Commons, thus regrettably, there are groups of flora and fauna that have not been covered in this book. Where faunal groups have been comprehensively recorded, the chapters have been written in the form of field guides, to help with identification of species, when walking on the Commons. In general we have tried to avoid over-burdening readers with too much detail, seeking instead to present a balanced picture of the ecology, which will stimulate interest and encourage awareness and appreciation of the fascinating natural world which we in south-west London are so very fortunate to have on our doorsteps. In the concluding index plants and animals have been listed under English names, with Latin names given secondarily, except where no English names exist.

It is intriguing to speculate on how the Commons will look and what species will still be around in another ninety years! If global warming becomes a reality, then who knows what exotic creatures will move in?

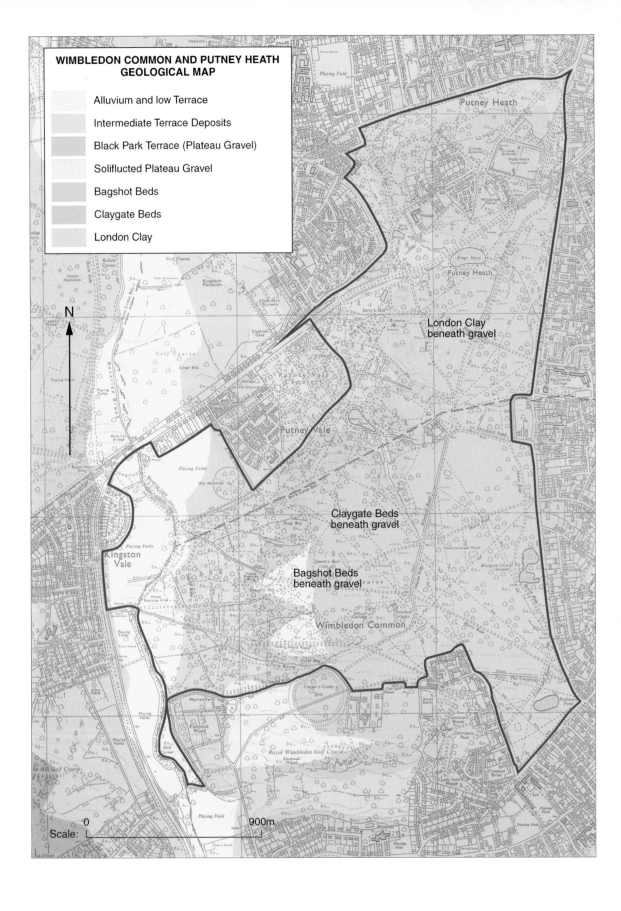

WIMBLEDON COMMON AND PUTNEY HEATH GEOLOGICAL MAP

Alluvium and low Terrace

Intermediate Terrace Deposits

Black Park Terrace (Plateau Gravel)

Soliflucted Plateau Gravel

Bagshot Beds

Claygate Beds

London Clay

N

Putney Heath

Putney Heath

London Clay
beneath gravel

Putney Vale

Claygate Beds
beneath gravel

Kingston
Vale

Bagshot Beds
beneath gravel

Wimbledon Common

Royal Wimbledon Golf Course

0   900m
Scale:

Chapter 2

Geology and Drainage

Antony and Una Sutcliffe

Before looking more widely at the Natural History of Wimbledon Common and Putney Heath, it is important first to consider the underlying rock structure, soils and present day drainage pattern, which together give the Commons their unique variety of habitats.

Geology

Antony Sutcliffe

Two main types of rock (in the geological sense) outcrop on the Commons. The lowest and earliest of these, underlying the entire area, is the London Clay; laid down in the sea, under sub-tropical to tropical conditions, during Eocene times, about 54–52.5 million years ago. Much of the oak woodland that mantles the lower western slopes of Wimbledon Common grows directly upon the London Clay. Resting upon an eroded surface of this (and locally on an overlying sand deposit – the Bagshot Beds) is a layer of pebbly sand and gravel, only a few metres thick, laid down in the bed of the River Thames about 430,000 years ago. This outcrops across the plateau top, where it supports predominantly heath and birch woodland. That Wimbledon Common and Putney Heath survive as an open space today can be attributed directly to this deposit, its poor agricultural quality causing it to have been left in times past as Manorial wasteland, for the use of Commoners. Cut into the London Clay foundation of the Common is a geologically controlled pattern of small streams fed by springs from the overlying gravel aquifer, with associated *Sphagnum* bogs.

Let us look at this geological structure in a broader context and in greater detail. South-east England is a classic example of rock folding, giving rise to the London Basin syncline and Wealden anticline – the former, bounded on the north and south by the Upper Cretaceous Chalk ridges of the Chiltern hills and North Downs respectively; the latter, by the same North Downs and the Chalk ridge of the South Downs along the coast. Erosion of the Wealden anticline now exposes in its core Greensand and other rocks of earlier Cretaceous age, below the Chalk, and a small fault-emplaced area of Jurassic limestone (Figure 2.2).

Overlying the Chalk in the London Basin is a series of fossiliferous deposits of Palaeocene and Eocene Age, of which the London Clay, upon which the Commons are situated, is only part. In ascending order these are:- the Thanet Sand and Upnor Formations, the Woolwich and Reading Formations (which merge laterally, the last mentioned not represented beneath Wimbledon Common), the Harwich, London Clay and Bagshot Formations. There is much local variation among these various deposits which, laid down during times of constantly changing shore line, include sediments of shallow marine, lagoon, estuarine and fluvial origin.

Figure 2.1 Geological map of the Wimbledon Common area. On the west the alluvial deposits of the Beverley Brook occupy a valley cut into the London Clay. River gravels (the Black Park Gravel Spread / Terrace), which mantle the plateau top of the Common, rest on an eroded surface of westward dipping London Clay, Claygate Beds and Bagshot Beds.

Adapted from the 1:10,000 map of the British Geological Survey; base map reproduced from the Ordnance Survey, with the permission of H.M.S.O. Crown Copyright MC 100031556. Draughtsman Mike Parson.

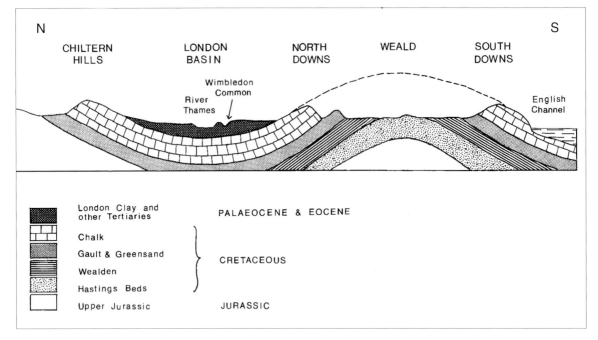

Figure 2.2 Schematic geological section across the
London Basin and Wealden
anticline, greatly simplified,
faulting omitted, showing the
location of Wimbledon
Common.
Drawn by Una Sutcliffe.

The London Clay represents the greatest transgression of the Eocene seas,
with water depths of up to several hundred metres (though not its deepest in
the Wimbledon area) indicated by the fossil shells of single-celled foraminifera.
Five sedimentary cycles have been recognised, each recording an initial transgression, followed by a gradual shallowing of the sea.

Throughout most of its thickness of up to 150 metres the London Clay is
composed of a stiff bluish clay that weathers brown at the surface (Fig. 2.3). In
its uppermost part it changes to a series of alternating beds of clay and sand –
the Claygate Member of the London Clay Formation – lithologically transi-
tional to the overlying yellow-brown sands of the Bagshot Formation. With the

Figure 2.3 London Clay,
exposed in 1996 during
foundation excavations for
new flats on the site of former
Oxford Lodge, Parkside,
adjacent to Wimbledon
Common. Fresh blue clay in
the lowest part of the excavation is weathered brown in its
uppermost part. The light
coloured deposit on the right
of the excavator is builder's
spoil.
Photo: Antony Sutcliffe.

climate still tropical, the Bagshot sands represent the youngest part of the London Basin Eocene sequence.

A study of the pebbles and other rock fragments present in the deposits described above provides some information about the date of development of the London Basin syncline and Weald anticline. Being of marine origin, the Chalk, which extends from East Anglia across to France, must originally have been laid down as a horizontal deposit. The occurrence of rounded pebbles of flint from the Chalk in the Upnor Formation shows that by Palaeocene times there had been upwarping of the Chalk somewhere, although emergence in the region of the present day Chiltern Hills and Isle of Wight may have preceded the formation of the Wealden anticline itself. The occurrence of fragments of Greensand chert in the Bagshot deposits shows that by then erosion had penetrated the Chalk into the underlying Greensand. The evolving northern flank of the now up-doming Wealden anticline is likely to have been one of the sources of Greensand fragments into the London Basin. Continued uplift into late Miocene and Pliocene times is indicated by the presence of fossiliferous marine deposits at up to 190 metres above sea level at Lenham, in Kent, and Netley Heath, Surrey, on the North Downs.

Although fossils tend to be difficult to find at inland exposures of and excavations in the London Clay, the natural sorting of shells, bones and fossil wood from the clay by the sea, at such coastal localities as Herne Bay and the Isle of Sheppey, has enabled geologists to compile lengthy lists of the plants and animals that lived in and around the London Basin in London Clay times. Marine animals include crocodiles and turtles, fish, crabs and lobsters, nautilus, many other species of mollusca and foraminifera. Washed from the land into the sea are rare bones of mammals, including *Hyracotherium* (an early ancestor of the same approximate lineage as the horse), birds and remains of plants. Some five hundred plant species have been described, including mangroves, palms, magnolia and cinnamon, giving a picture of tropical rain forest bordered by a swampy coastal plain. The London Clay flora is similar in many respects to that of the present day Bay of Bengal.

We can now examine the sequence of deposits beneath and in the region around Wimbledon Common and Putney Heath. Since the London Clay is the earliest deposit exposed there, it is necessary to examine records from wells and bore-holes for what lies below. Both Reading Beds and Thanet Sands have commonly been reached; Chalk in the deeper bore holes. A well and bore hole sunk at the Atkinson Morley Hospital near Wimbledon Common, in 1869, encountered Chalk at a depth of 165 metres after passing through approximately 132 m. of London Clay, 23 m. of Reading Beds and 7 m. of Thanet Sand.

At the surface there is widespread development of Claygate Beds, overlain by Bagshot Sands. Exposures of these on the Commons are at present extremely poor. A pit (Fig. 4.1) that in the past was excavated in the London Clay, for brick making, near Brickfield Cottage, since demolished, has long been abandoned; its sides degraded. Exposures along stream beds show only clay that has become oxidised and brown, with little likelihood of fossils surviving in it. Johnson records that, during the early 20th century, Bagshot sands were exposed in the bottoms of several pits being excavated for sand for the golf course and in overlying river gravels in the south west part of the Commons. These have all long since been abandoned, but a small exposure of Bagshot sands may still be seen in the bank of the old pit adjacent to Gravelly Ride, which is now used as a horse ring (Fig. 2.4).

Figure 2.4 Plateau gravels overlying Bagshot Beds, exposed in the bank of a former sand and gravel pit, beside Gravelly Ride, Wimbledon Common, now used as a horse ring. The miniature pick axe has a length of 40 cm.
Photo: Antony Sutcliffe.

Fig. 2.5

Fig. 2

Fig. 2.7

Fig.

It is nevertheless good fortune that a series of commercial excavations for wells, pipe trenches and at building sites on and near the Commons, during the last 130 years, have provided useful access to the fossil fauna that lies beneath.

In 1996 excavation for an underground car park beneath a new block of flats being constructed on the site of former Oxford Lodge, on the east side of Parkside, only the distance of the width of the road from Wimbledon Common (Fig. 2.3), provided a valuable opportunity to examine a new exposure of the London Clay and overlying river gravels. Thanks to the goodwill of the Contractors, Octagon, who allowed access to the site over a period of several months, the deposits were recorded in detail; and a small number of fossils retrieved from the London Clay by sharp-eyed building workers.

These showed a number of interesting features. A fragment of plant stem of unidentifiable species (Fig. 2.5) was found to be almost entirely concealed within a nodule of pyrite (iron sulphide, often known as iron pyrites or fool's gold), with octahedral crystal structure on its surface (Fig. 2.6).

The occurrence of pyrite in the London Clay, where it had been formed below the sea bed soon after deposition, is a widespread phenomenon. Since this mineral is relatively unstable, however, it readily oxidises when exposed to

Figure 2.5 Pyrite nodule, from the London Clay of the Oxford Lodge building site, encrusting a fragment of fossil plant stem. Scale in cm.
Photo: Tony Drakeford.

Figure 2.6 Octahedral crystals of pyrite on a fossiliferous nodule from the London Clay of the Oxford Lodge site.
Scanning electron photomicrograph, Natural History Museum. Scale x 3200.

Figure 2.7 Fossil gastropod, *Acteon* species, in a pyrite nodule from the London Clay of the Oxford Lodge site. Length 2.5 mm. This is an internal mould, with pyrite-infilled former cracks showing as ridges.
Scanning electron photomicrograph, Natural History Museum.

Figure 2.8 Fossil nautilus, *Cimonia imperialis*, incomplete, from a boring for a pile in London Clay near the bottom of Edge Hill, south east of Wimbledon Common, in 1977. Scale in cm. Compare with Fig. 2.10.
Photo: Tony Drakeford.

Figure 2.9 Foraminifera, excavated from a depth of 33 metres in a well dug into London Clay on Wimbledon Common, about 1860, now preserved in the Natural History Museum.
1. *Lenticulina rotulata*, with pyrite crystals on the outside.
Magnification x 43.
2. *Lenticulina cultrata*. Part of the original shell has disintegrated, revealing the pyrite infillings of the chambers.
Magnification x 33.
3. *Nodosaria latejugata*.
Magnification x 16.
4. *Marginulinopsis wetherellii*.
Magnification x 50.
5. *Nodosaria* species.
Magnification x 25.
This is an assemblage of foraminifera typical of the upper part of the London Clay.
Re-identifications and scanning electron photomicrographs by John Whittaker, Natural History Museum.

air and moisture, with disintegration of any associated fossils, and it does not occur in the surface layers of the Commons. Figure 2.7 shows a fossil marine gastropod *Acteon* sp. from a similar nodule from the same locality, which also contained shells of the bivalve *Nuculina* sp.

In 1977 part of a fossil nautilus (*Cimonia imperialis*), Fig. 2.8, was found by a Mr Monk in London Clay in a boring for a pile near the bottom of Edge Hill, south east of the Common. The specimen was presented by Professor John Hutchinson, on behalf of Mr Monk, to the Geology Department of Wimbledon Girls High School, where it is safely preserved. The present day nautilus is typically an inhabitant of deep water, but with local temperature-related behaviour variations. In regions where average sea temperature is less than about 27° it rises nearer the surface at night; but in equatorial regions it remains below 100 metres. It is not known in what manner *Cimonia* behaved.

Probably the most important discovery of fossils in the London Clay of the area around the Commons was made more than a century ago. About 1860 large samples of clay, obtained from the depth of about 33 metres in a well being dug on Wimbledon Common (its precise whereabouts has not so far been established) were carefully examined for foraminifera by Professor T.

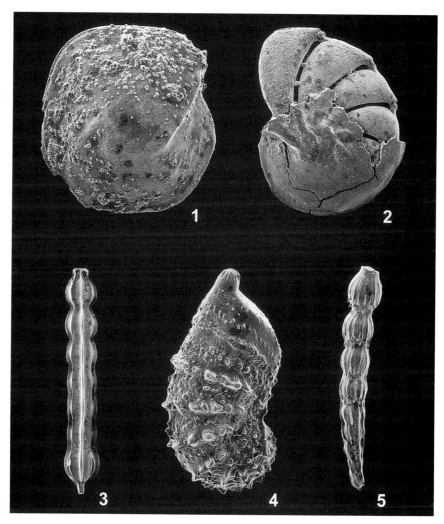

Figure 2.10 Artist's reconstruction, by Christiana Gilbert, of how the place that is now Wimbledon Common may have appeared in Eocene, London Clay, times, about fifty million years ago. Tropical vegetation, bordering the shore, includes mangrove, *Nipa* (left, overhanging the water) and *Bruguiera* (right). In the sea are turtles, *Puppigerus*, and a nautilus, *Cimonia imperialis*. Scene reconstructed from plant and animal remains described from various localities in the London Basin; the nautilus from the Edge Hill specimen (compare with Figure 2.8). With acknowledgements to Richard Moody.

Wimbledon Common and Putney Heath during the Ice Age

Rupert Jones and W.K. Parker. Their findings were published in the 1864 number of *The Geologist*. In their paper they listed nearly forty species – "probably a nearly complete local Foraminifera fauna" – indicating a depth of about 100 fathoms (200 metres) for the sea in this district. The collection is still preserved in London's Natural History Museum, where the 19th century names have been up-dated by Dr John Whittaker, who has provided the scanning electron photomicrographs reproduced in Figure 2.9. Jones and Parker's estimate of sea depth, he confirms, would still be regarded as fairly accurate by modern authors. In other parts of the London Clay, fossil mollusca indicate shallower conditions.

From palaeontological evidence such as that outlined above, our artist, Christiana Gilbert, shows how the place that is now Wimbledon Common, may have appeared in London Clay times, slightly more than fifty million years ago.

Following the deposition of the Bagshot Beds, nearly fifty million years ago, there occurred a long period of denudation in the Thames Valley. Although something of what happened during this time is known from deposits of later Eocene, Oligocene and Pliocene Age in other parts of the British Isles (notably in East Anglia, Hampshire and Devon and from the high altitude marine deposits of Lenham and Netley Heath, on the North Downs, previously mentioned), for Wimbledon Common we must pass on now well into the Quaternary, the time of the Ice Ages, extending over the last two million years or so. It was not until less than half a million years ago that the gravels that cover the flat plateau top of the Commons (the Black Park Gravel Spread / Terrace, to be discussed in greater detail below) were laid down in the former bed of the River Thames. They rest upon an eroded surface of westward dipping London Clay, its Claygate Member and the Bagshot Beds (Fig. 2.11).

Wimbledon Common does not represent the entire outcrop of this plateau gravel. A further remnant, isolated from it by the later downcutting of the Beverley Brook, survives on nearby Kingston Hill. Both have the same surface altitude, at about 53 metres O.D. The gravels reach their greatest thickness (up to 7 metres) on Kingston Hill, decreasing to less than two metres on the east side of the Commons. Although, in geological terms, they are quite young, the amount of valley downcutting that has occurred since they were laid down, is dramatic. A substantial change of river base level has subsequently taken place.

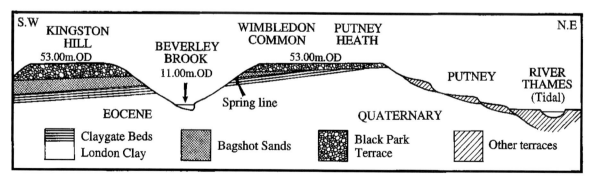

Figure 2.11 Schematic section across Kingston Hill and Wimbledon Common (total distance about eight kilometres), not to scale, vertical scale greatly exaggerated. Gravels of Black Park Terrace of the River Thames, thicker on Kingston Hill than on Wimbledon Common, rest on an eroded surface of gently south-westward dipping Bagshot Sands, Claygate Beds and London Clay. A series of sand and gravel terraces of age later than the Black Park plateau gravels form a series of steps to the present River Thames, where Putney is now situated. Draughtsman Phil Rye.

Figure 2.12 Plateau gravels (Black Park Terrace of the Thames) exposed during excavations at Oxford Lodge, adjacent to Wimbledon Common, 1996. Pebbles seen are predominantly flint. Length of trowel, 22 cm.
Photo: Antony Sutcliffe.

The Wimbledon Common and Kingston Hill plateau gravels have long been a place of pilgrimage by visiting geologists. Their study has contributed not only to the understanding of the evolution of the River Thames itself, but also to the broader picture of the repeated and extreme fluctuations of climate now known to have characterised the Ice Age.

From an early date the abundance of foreign pebbles in gravels predominantly composed of flint derived from the chalk, attracted attention. Monckton, writing in 1893, concluded that these deposits represented the southern boundary of the area over which glacial gravel debris had been distributed, beyond the limit of an ice sheet coming from the north. Johnson, writing in 1912, proposed that, at the time of deposition of the plateau gravels, the outlet of the Thames with its feeder tributaries into the North Sea was situated further north-east than at present. He further concluded that a huge ice sheet, which was already melting, spread from the north almost to Wimbledon. Far away, out in the North Sea, what should have been the river mouth was choked by an ice mass overriding the opposing land (i.e. continuous from Essex to somewhere on the Continent of Europe); with the creation of an ice-dammed lake in the Lower London Basin, extending as far as Wimbledon. The plateau gravels became a resting place for pebbles derived from both the glaciated area north of the Thames and from the unglaciated, but deeply frozen area to the south.

More than eighty years have elapsed since Johnson wrote about the plateau gravels, during which time Ice Age studies have progressed dynamically, especially in the Thames Valley, through the work of Wooldridge, Gibbard, Bridgland and others. Only now does it become fully apparent how far ahead of his time Johnson was. Let us now look at this most recent work. Until about thirty years ago there was general belief that, although the Quaternary had been a time of repeated climatic change, relatively few such cycles had occurred; and reliable absolute dates were available for only the most recent ones. With the advent of deep sea oxygen isotope studies in the 1950s and 1960s this picture was greatly changed. Varying proportions of isotopes 16 and 18 of oxygen in fossil foraminifera from continuous cores of sediment, obtained from the floors of the world's oceans, provided a method of reconstructing past variations of the amount of water in the sea. From this, working on the assumption that a low sea level represents a cold episode (when water is taken up on the land as ice), a long glacial – interglacial chronology, with dates extending back for two million years, was established. Surprisingly it was found that many more such cycles had occurred than had previously been recognised – about eighteen during the last 1.8 million years, or one every 100,000 years. Many minor climatic fluctuations were found to be superimposed upon major ones.

This new method of establishing a dated record of past climatic change provided a valuable yardstick to which events during the Quaternary could be related and most present day studies are based upon it; with even numbers assigned to cold stages, odd numbers to the interglacials (Fig. 2.13). The present interglacial is Oxygen Isotope Stage 1.

Let us now consider how the Wimbledon Common story fits into this chronology. As further new methods of study are devised and as new field work is undertaken, details face constant revision but, at the turn of the Millennium, the following sequence of events seems a likely approximation. We are concerned here only with the last 500,000 years or so – back to about Stage 13. The huge ice sheet to which Johnson referred is believed to represent Oxygen Isotope Stage 12, the Anglian Glaciation. This was the most extensive of all the Quaternary ice advances over the British Isles, reaching north London, north Devon and probably the Isles of Scilly. The River Thames, which was flowing along a line north of its present course, reaching the North Sea at Clacton, was overridden by the ice between St Albans and Colchester and was displaced southwards to near its present route through London (Fig. 2.14). East of London it found its way into the valley of the northward flowing River Medway, which then extended across Essex; and thence to the North

Figure 2.13 Table showing position of the Wimbledon Common and Putney Heath plateau gravels and Farm Bog peat, in the context of a broader Quaternary chronology. Only the mammalian faunas of the Brentford, Isleworth and Kempton Park sites, living geographically close to the Commons, are indicated here. Mammals of Oxygen Isotope Stages 11–6, known only from sites further afield, would also have found their way to the Commons. Draughtsman Phil Rye.

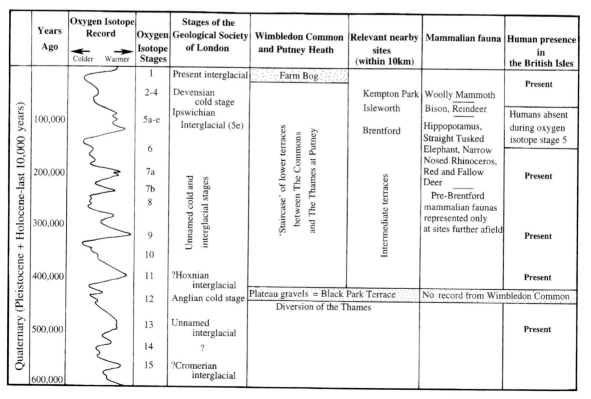

Years Ago	Oxygen Isotope Record (Colder ← → Warmer)	Oxygen Isotope Stages	Stages of the Geological Society of London	Wimbledon Common and Putney Heath	Relevant nearby sites (within 10km)	Mammalian fauna	Human presence in the British Isles
		1	Present interglacial	Farm Bog			Present
		2-4	Devensian cold stage		Kempton Park	Woolly Mammoth Bison, Reindeer	
100,000		5a-e	Ipswichian Interglacial (5e)		Isleworth		Humans absent during oxygen isotope stage 5
		6			Brentford	Hippopotamus, Straight Tusked Elephant, Narrow Nosed Rhinoceros, Red and Fallow Deer	
200,000		7a		'Staircase' of lower terraces between The Commons and The Thames at Putney	Intermediate terraces		Present
		7b	Unnamed cold and interglacial stages				
		8				Pre-Brentford mammalian faunas represented only at sites further afield	
300,000		9					Present
		10					
400,000		11	?Hoxnian interglacial				Present
		12	Anglian cold stage	Plateau gravels = Black Park Terrace		No record from Wimbledon Common	
				Diversion of the Thames			
500,000		13	Unnamed interglacial				Present
		14	?				
600,000		15	?Cromerian interglacial				

Quaternary (Pleistocene + Holocene-last 10,000 years)

Figure 2.14 Map showing the relationship of Wimbledon Common to the River Thames; in its pre-Anglian course through St Albans; after diversion and at the present day. After Bridgland and Gibbard 1997.

Draughtsman Mike Parson.

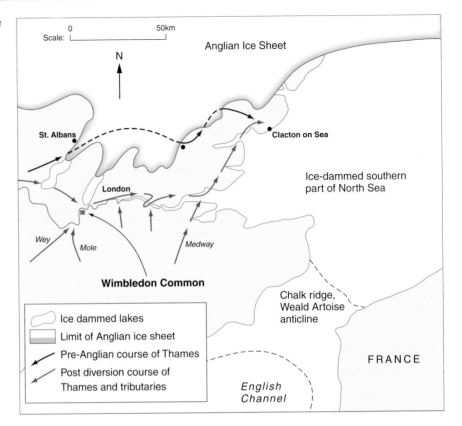

Sea basin offshore from its original outlet near Clacton. The northernmost parts of tributary rivers flowing into the earlier Thames from the south thus became the southern parts of tributaries flowing into it from the north, with reversed direction of flow. At the same time ice from Scandinavia became confluent with the Anglian ice of the British Isles, forming a continuous barrier from Norfolk to the Netherlands. With a Chalk ridge still intact across the Straits of Dover, an ice-dammed lake built up in the southern part of the North Sea, later to be released by the (probably catastrophic) downcutting of the overflow channel into the English Channel. This apparently occurred before the northern ice barrier had decayed. Both the Thames and Rhine, which had previously flowed into the North Sea, now had a new outlet for their waters into the English Channel. Once deglaciation set in water would also have been able to escape northwards.

We can return now to the plateau gravel on Wimbledon Common and Kingston Hill. Gibbard, from his detailed study of these deposits and from the proportions of various rock types represented by the pebbles in them, concluded that they were indeed of fluvial origin and had been laid down at the confluence of the then Wey, Mole and Thames rivers, at the time when there may still have been ice in the St Albans valley. The gravel structure was characteristic of a braided river, with a wide expanse of shallow interweaving channels subject to variations of water flow (Fig. 2.15).

Since the Wimbledon Common and Putney Heath plateau gravels (part of the Black Park Terrace) represent the earliest deposits of the Thames in its present course, we cannot take the Quaternary history back earlier into post-Eocene time. Unfortunately no fossil mammalian remains or any human

Figure 2.15 A present day braided river, Banks Island, arctic Canada. Similar conditions – interweaving channels with fluctuating water flow – probably prevailed at the time of deposition of the Wimbledon Common and Putney Heath plateau gravels.
Photo: Wighart von Koenigswald.

artefacts have been found in the plateau gravels, so that we have no picture of life or lack of it in the area at this time. Archaeological excavations at Boxgrove in Sussex, only 70 kilometres south-east of the Commons and at other sites show, nevertheless, that humans were present in southern England during Oxygen Isotope Stage 13 and during at least part of Stage 12. Artefacts have been found elsewhere in the Black Park Terrace, for example at Hillingdon, West London.

Following the melting of the Anglian ice, substantial downcutting by the river systems of the lower Thames indicates that a substantial fall of base level occurred. The Thames moved its outlet into the North Sea southwards across Essex to its present location; and the cutting of a valley by the Beverley Brook isolated the gravels of Kingston Hill from those on the Commons. Several factors may have contributed to this change of base level. Draining of the ice-dammed southern part of the North Sea would have caused a fall of water level (but compensated to some extent by melt water returning to the sea – further fluctuations of sea level would have accompanied subsequent glacial events and deglaciations); depression of the land by the Anglian ice may have been followed by upward recovery; and uplift of the Wealden anticline may still have been continuing. Whatever the combination, their combined effect was to leave Wimbledon Common and Putney Heath high and dry as the flat hilltop that we know today, flanked by the Beverley Brook, the Wandle and the Thames, at levels nearly 40 metres lower.

Although we cannot carry the geological history of the Commons into later time from direct evidence, a clear picture of life that would have existed there on several occasions up to the present day is readily available from evidence to be found in the immediate neighbourhood, most notably from the stair-case of river terrace deposits lying between the Commons and the Thames at Putney (Fig 2.11) and from Brentford, Isleworth, and Kempton Park. The Commons would have been a grazing and hunting ground for animals obtaining their water lower down; and humans would have found their way there too, potentially to leave their artefacts on top of the plateau gravel.

Evidence that humans were present near the Commons several hundred

Isleworth reconstruction overleaf. Legend p. 20.

Figure 2.16 (pp. 18–19)
Artist's reconstruction of how
Wimbledon Common may
have appeared during Oxygen
Isotope Stage 3, about
50,000 years ago; based on
the evidence of fossil
mammal, plant and insect
remains found in 1959 in a
commercial gravel pit near
Isleworth, only 6 km distant.
Illustration by Christiana Gilbert .

Christiana Gilbert

thousand years ago, possibly in Oxygen Isotope Stage 11 or 9, is provided by the rare discovery of hand axes and other worked flint artefacts in lower level terrace gravels from Dover House Road (British Museum), Chartfield Avenue and Keswick Road, Wandsworth (both London Museum).

Ipswichian (oxygen isotope sub-stage 5e, c.120,000 years ago) terrace deposits of the Thames at Brentford, seven kilometres from the Commons, revealed a rich interglacial mammalian fauna, including hippopotamus, straight-tusked-elephant, narrow nosed rhinoceros and red and fallow deer. Associated plant remains, from sites with a similar fauna further down the Thames, indicate a climate warmer than the present day. Hippos would have been frequent visitors to the Commons at this time. Concurrently humans were apparently absent from the British Isles.

Slightly later terrace deposits at nearby Isleworth, Oxygen Isotope Stage 3, about 50,000 years old, contain an abundance of bones of bison and reindeer, associated with plant and insect remains indicating treeless but not very cold conditions (Coope & Angus 1975; Kerney, Gibbard *et al.* 1982). In Figure 2.16 our artist, Christiana Gilbert, shows how Wimbledon Common, with topography not greatly different from that of today, and with these animals present, may have looked at that time. In the foreground is the Beverley Brook. Beyond is the hill on which the Windmill is situated today. Bison, reindeer and a bear co-exist on an almost treeless landscape. The season is late September. The reindeer bulls have fully developed antlers, which have already lost their velvet; dwarf birch, *Betula nana*, has become red. Some other plants shown include grasses, rushes and sedges, hogweed, thistles, reed mace and bur-reed. Although the treeless landscape might be interpreted as evidence of cold conditions, the insects suggest otherwise. Climate had apparently warmed rapidly after a phase of severe conditions.

Deposits with remains of woolly mammoth and plants in a gravel pit at Kempton Park demonstrate a subsequent cooling of climate, probably Oxygen Isotope Stage 2. Mammoth remains have also been found in low level terrace deposits near Kingston upon Thames.

The mammalian remains from the three above mentioned sites are preserved in the Natural History Museum.

Palaeontological evidence does not provide the only means of reconstructing later stages of the history of the Commons. Signs of past permafrost conditions, mostly dating from the last glacial advance, oxygen isotope stage 2, about 18,000 years ago are close at hand. Fossil ice-wedges, cutting through the Isleworth reindeer-bison deposits, indicate a substantial subsequent deterioration of climate. The Commons would have been frozen to some depth. With drainage impeded by ground ice, sludging on the hillsides during the summer thaw – a process known as solifluction – would have been widespread. The gravels that mantle parts of the slopes on the western side of the Commons, between the plateau and the Beverley Brook, are apparently plateau gravels displaced by this process. The most recent episode in the history of the Common is provided by Farm Bog, situated in a spring-fed valley, cut into the soliflucted gravels. It will be discussed in greater detail in the following section.

Drainage

Una Sutcliffe

Although the great diversity of habitats found on the Commons is related to the underlying geology, also important are topography and the water regime (Fig.2.17). It can be seen that the floras of the dry and wet areas differ greatly. Therefore let us follow the drainage pattern through from the time rain falls; to its subsequent run off or infiltration into the ground; re-emergence from springs; and finally to streams flowing mainly in a westerly direction towards the Beverley Brook, and thence to the Thames (Fig. 2.18).

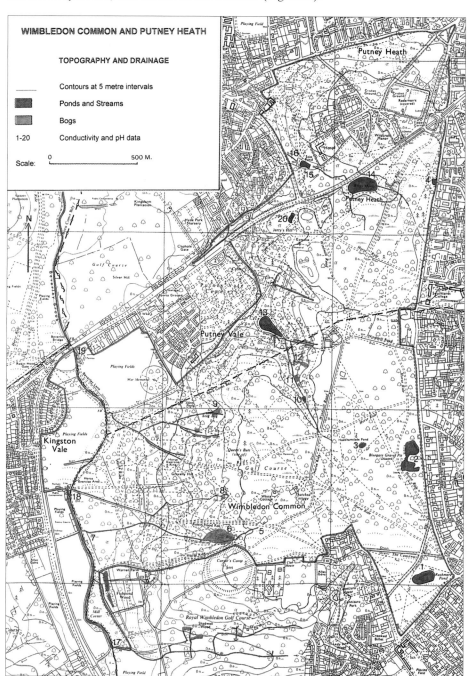

Figure 2.17 Map of Wimbledon Common and Putney Heath showing bogs, streams and ponds. For names of numbered sites, see Table 2.1, p.27.

Base map reproduced from the Ordnance Survey map 1:10,000, with the permission of H.M.S.O. Crown Copyright MC 100031556. Adapted by Una Sutcliffe.

Figure 2.18 Schematic block diagram of the western part of Wimbledon Common, illustrating its drainage pattern. Ice Age (Black Park Terrace) gravels rest on a gently westward sloping erosional surface of westward dipping London Clay, Claygate Beds and Bagshot Sands. Springs creating streams leading into the Beverley Brook are concentrated along the western side of the Commons.
Draughtsman: Mike Parson.

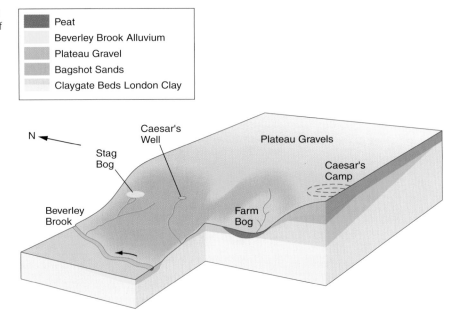

Peat
Beverley Brook Alluvium
Plateau Gravel
Bagshot Sands
Claygate Beds London Clay

N
Caesar's Well
Stag Bog
Plateau Gravels
Caesar's Camp
Beverley Brook
Farm Bog

The Plateau

The flat plateau, surrounded by lower ground, is the principal catchment for water falling on the Commons. Consequently, most of the streams and ponds carry water originally falling there. Past management of the Commons has been less nature orientated than at present and, throughout, drainage ditches are to be found that carry water away from the paths. Many of the main paths are flanked by ditches carrying surface run-off to further ditches and streams and ultimately to the Beverley Brook, but attempts are now being made to slow down the rate of water leaving the Commons. Much of the water, other than that lost by evaporation and evapotranspiration, however, finds its way into a perched water table that underlies the plateau, from which (especially along the western side of the Commons) it re-emerges as springs feeding streams on the hillside below.

The Commons have many ponds, all thought to be man-made. They fall into two principal categories – water table ponds on the plateau, and, to be discussed later, ponds created by the artificial damming of streams. Rushmere Pond, near Wimbledon Village, already documented as early as 1617, Bluegate Gravel Pit, Hookhamslade and 7 Post Pond, all created by past gravel extraction, are the most important ponds of the former category. Measurements of the level of the water in them and in dip wells positioned on the plateau show the water table to have a domed shape, with water nearest to the ground surface in the centre of the plateau, becoming lower towards its margins. The water table itself is not of constant elevation (Fig. 2.19), but fluctuates by up to one metre in response to variations of rainfall, which in turn affect the levels of the water table ponds, some of which even dry out at times of extended drought (Figs. 2.20, 2.21). The flooding of house basements in Peek Crescent, Wimbledon, not far from Rushmere Pond, resolved by the installation of sump pumps, is apparently a manifestation of the plateau water table.

Examination of the gravel plateau of the Commons reveals considerable local variability in ground permeability. It is noticeable that in winter, after severe rain, there are areas on the plateau, to the north and east of the Windmill,

Figure 2.19 Water level measurements on four of the Common's water table ponds and in one temporary excavation, showing variation from drought to moderate rainfall conditions. The top of each column represents ground surface. The water table has a dome shape and is also marginally higher at the southern end of the Common (Rushmere Pond) than at its northern end (7 Post Pond).
Draughtsman: Mike Parson.

Figure 2.20 Rushmere Pond: (a) High rainfall conditions, February, 1995. (b) Drought conditions, September, 1995.

Figure 2.21 Bluegate Gravel Pit: (a) High rainfall conditions, December, 1992. (b) Drought conditions, June, 1997.

Photos: Antony Sutcliffe.

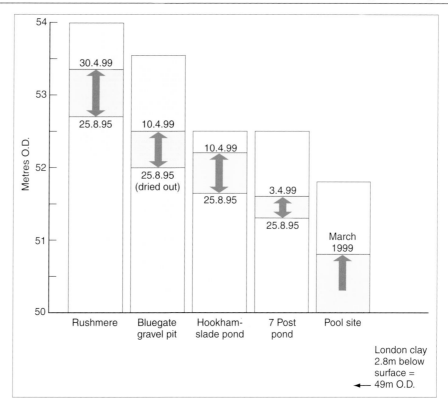

2.20(a)

2.20(b)

2.21(a)

2.21(b)

Figure 2.22 (left) Section
exposed during excavations at
the former Oxford Lodge site,
Parkside, opposite Windmill
Road, 1996. In descending
order (below concrete layer);
humic layer, bleached white
sandy gravel, ferruginous
sandy gravel. Shovel rests on
surface of underlying London
Clay.

Figure 2.23 (right) Old
soakaway discovered in 1996
during excavations at the
former Oxford Lodge site,
Parkside, for an underground
car park for a new apartment
block.

Photos: Antony Sutcliffe.

where the ground can become very waterlogged, leading to temporary pools.
These ephemeral wet areas can be identified by wetland plants, such as rushes,
grey willow (*Salix cinerea*), purple moor grass (*Molinia caerulea*), creeping
willow (*Salix repens*), and in a few areas there are patches of cross-leaved heath
(*Erica tetralix*). Such wetland heath areas are rare in Greater London and
appropriate management is now geared to maintain them.

We are fortunate that two excavations have recently provided opportunities
for studying the nature of the deposits and associated water regime under the
plateau surface, the substrate for roots of the plants growing above. In 1996,
excavations for the foundations of a new apartment block on the site of Oxford
Lodge on Parkside (previously mentioned), only 500 metres east of the
Windmill, followed in March 1999 by excavations for a swimming pool in an
enclosed garden adjacent to the Windmill, exposed almost identical sequences
of deposits. These were, in descending order (Fig. 2.22), a brown humic layer,
a bleached sandy gravel merging into a weakly cemented ferruginous sandy
gravel (both part of the Terrace sequence) and, at a depth of about three
metres below the surface, the eroded top of the London Clay.

Two important lines of evidence, concerning the drainage of the Commons,
became apparent from these excavations. Penetrating the gravels at the Oxford
Lodge site, almost to the London Clay, were discovered the remains of an old
soakaway (Fig. 2.23), confirming poor natural surface drainage. At the
swimming pool site the water table was encountered only one metre below the

surface, making pumping necessary for the work to proceed. Meanwhile water continued to seep from the face of the ferruginous sandy gravels into the excavation. This last mentioned deposit was seen to correspond to the zone of saturation, the white sandy gravel to the unsaturated zone above it. A fluctuating high/perched water table, resting on the London Clay, has produced the bleached gravels by the combined process of vertical podsolic leaching and gleying (a process by which iron compounds in a soil are depleted of oxygen by soil bacteria under anaerobic conditions).

On the south west part of the plateau the ground is considerably drier, with absence of many of the wet indicator plants, apparently because the water table is deeper there.

Springs, streams and the Beverley Brook

As previously observed, water from the plateau water table emerges as a series of springs feeding streams. These occur at approximately the boundary between the Terrace deposits and the underlying Eocene beds. These springs, however, are confined almost totally to the western slope below the plateau. They have no equivalent on its eastern side. Two factors apparently contribute to this situation. Firstly, the eroded surface of the Eocene deposits is not quite horizontal, but slopes gently westward (50 m. O.D. at Oxford Lodge, 49 m. at the Swimming Pool site), directing water movement westward. In addition, since the underlying beds dip westward, the Terrace gravel rests directly upon impervious London Clay along the eastern side of the Commons, whereas on the western side it overlies the more pervious Claygate Beds and Bagshot Sands (Figs 2.4, 2.11, 2.18). Some of the spring water emerging there comes not from the base of the gravels, but from these last mentioned deposits. Several of the springs have associated *Sphagnum* bogs. The best known of these is Farm Bog, to be described later.

In clock-wise order, from the south west to northern parts of the Commons, the principal springs are those arising on the Royal Wimbledon Golf Course; at Farm Bog; Caesar's Well; Stag Bog; at bogs in 'The Ravine'; and at a conduit building which formerly existed on Putney Heath, near Roehampton (Figs 2.17, 4.1). There are also some springs in stream beds, for example in 'The Ravine' and at Scio Pond, which become obvious only at times of drought. Water issuing from these springs supports small streams, all of which flow into the Beverley Brook. Many of these streams, for example those flowing from Stag Bog and from Caesar's Well (Fig.6.25) are very picturesque with liverworts and mosses adorning their banks. At times of drought, flow from the springs is greatly reduced and the lower parts of the stream channels dry out completely (Fig. 2.24).

Similar geological conditions on neighbouring Kingston Hill, previously described, support a further series of springs flowing westwards, the water from which was carried in lead pipes to Hampton Court Palace from the early sixteenth to the late nineteenth century, crossing the beds of the Hogsmill and Thames rivers on the way. The associated conduit buildings still survive today, in various states of repair.

In addition to the water table ponds on the Commons there are also other ponds and meres created by the artificial damming of streams. They are generally deeper than those on the plateau, and, since they lie directly upon the London Clay, they are more permanent. The two largest are Kingsmere and Queensmere. The latter, created in 1887 by damming a naturally boggy area, remains the deepest of the ponds and thus provides an important stable environment for wildlife, particularly fish. Scio Pond, on Putney Heath, is

Figure 2.24 Reduced stream flow from Farm Bog and Stag Bog at times of drought. Solid and dotted lines, August 1989; solid line only, September, 1995 (Stag Bog stream dry). Compare with Fig.2.17.

Base map reproduced from the Ordnance Survey map 1:10,000, with the permission of H.M.S.O. Crown Copyright MC 100031556. Adapted by Una Sutcliffe.

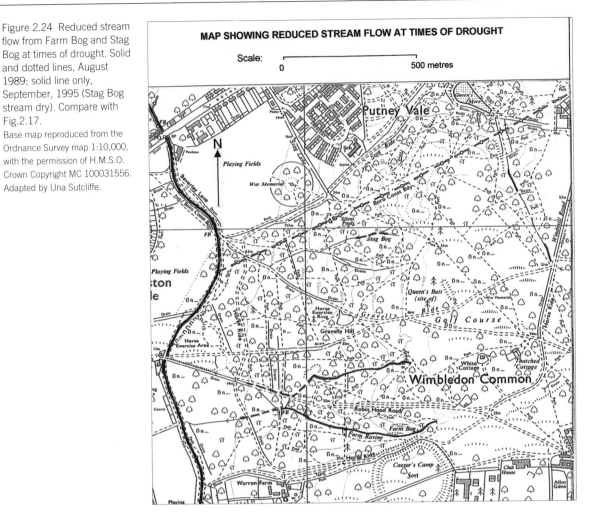

smaller in area, but is spring fed and so never dries out. Only recently constructed, in 1998, is Ravine Pond.

The area beyond Parkside, immediately east of the Commons' boundary, is now extensively built-up, so that it is impossible to define the original pattern of streams and ponds; but certainly there do not seem to have been any major springs there with output of the magnitude seen to the west of the plateau. Two small ponds (both almost dry at time of inspection in November 1999) in Tilford Gardens and Victoria Drive may be spring fed; and a small surface run-off stream formerly flowed from the Common along the line of Queensmere Road into Wimbledon Park Lake and thence to the River Wandle. This now disappears down a drain alongside Parkside and there is little sign of its former course through what are now gardens below.

Old maps show numerous lakes on the sloping ground east of the Commons, but it seems likely these were artificial features in the large estates that formerly existed there. Alas, with urban development, most have since been drained and built upon. The largest of these lakes, constructed during the 1770s and surviving into the 20th century where Margin Drive is now situated, could only have been maintained with the aid of a dam. For a time the lake

Table 2.1 Conductivity and pH of Ponds, Bogs and Streams

	Conductivity (µ S cm)	pH		Conductivity (µ S cm)	pH
1. Rushmere Pond	107	6.5	**11.** Ravine Bogs	167	6.3
2. Bluegate Gravel Pit	102	5.3	**12.** Ravine Bog, above Queensmere	223	4.6
3. Hookhamslade Pond	206	6.6	**13.** Queensmere	207	6.3
4. 7 Post Pond	129	6.6	**14.** Kingsmere	110	6.0
5. Farm Bog, stream head	508	5.1	**15.** Scio Pond	502	6.1
6. Farm Bog		4.6–5.8	**16.** Stream below Scio Pond	630	6.2
7. Farm Ravine, lower part	329	6.0	**17.** Beverley Brook, Mill Corner	896	6.1
8. Caesar's Well	208	5.7	**18.** Beverley Brook, Brook Cottage	975	6.2
9. Stag Bog	134	5.7	**19.** Beverley Brook, A3 Bridge	809	6.2
10. Ravine Pond	314	6.0	**20.** Curling Pond	192	6.0

was the property of Sir Henry Peek, M.P., to whom we owe so much for saving the Commons for posterity by the 1871 Act. The pond in the grounds of the Buddhist Temple in Calonne Road is a small surviving arm of this formerly extensive lake. Its water is anaerobic, with no evidence of any pattern of flow.

The acidity of the various ponds and streams on the Commons varies considerably (Table 2.1), in turn reflected by the relative abundance of invertebrates living in them and diversity of associated flora. The spring-fed streams (Farm Bog Stream Head, Caesar's Well, Stag Bog and Ravine Bog above Queensmere) are acid, partly because they carry groundwater from the acidic heath and partly as a result of the decay of pyrite in the underlying London Clay. As the streams progress downhill towards the Beverley Brook, they collect humus from the woodland formed on the more nutrient rich London Clay, with a consequent increase in pH. Lower Farm Ravine has a pH of 6.0. The Beverley Brook, still slightly acid, averages a pH of 6.2; but the results that are really interesting are those for conductivity – ionic content of the water. These were extremely high for the three samples taken (896, 975 and 809), much higher than in any of the streams or ponds. This can only reflect poor water quality (see Chapter 8).

Farm Bog

The conservation of boggy areas created by springs forms part of the management plan for the Commons. In fact Farm Bog, which covers an area of approximately 100 x 70 metres, now has its own five-year Management Directive. Its topography and drainage are worthy of special study. They are shown on a map accurately surveyed and contoured by the writer in 1990 and which is used as a yardstick for future management (Fig. 2.25). To the north and north-east of the bog is a steep embankment, formed by soliflucted Pleistocene gravels. The bog itself, cut into this gravel, slopes gently in a south-westerly direction, finally draining into a small stream (the Farm Ravine) which flows into the Beverley Brook. It is fed both by spring seepage, causing gullying and pool formation (though many of the pools are ephemeral and may have developed from previous conservation work) and by direct infiltration of rainwater. Continuous movement of the groundwater containing nutrients at low concentration through the soil gives rise to a mesotrophic

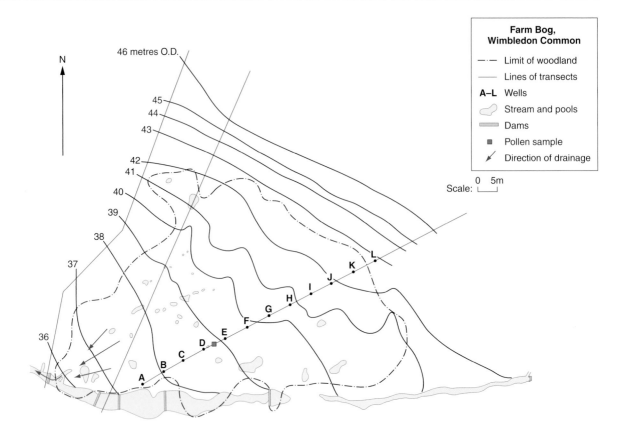

Figure 2.25 Topographical map of Farm Bog, surveyed in 1990. Arrows indicate the general direction of drainage. Stations A – L are dip wells that provided quantitative hydrological data. Site of pollen core (Chapter 3) indicated.

Draughtsman: Mike Parson.

(moderately nutrient rich) mire vegetation. Two metres of peat, resting on the underlying Claygate Beds, lies beneath the surface. Farm Bog is fairly acid, its pH ranging from 4.6 to 5.8. It will be further described in Chapters 3 and 8.

By measuring water levels in dip wells on a transect along the line of drainage it was possible to monitor fluctuations of water table height. The response to rainfall episodes was rapid, indicating that whereas the continuous high water level of the bog was maintained mainly by spring fed water, at times of storm, the levels would rise and overflow into the stream from the flatter and wetter south-west corner of the bog. The rate of discharge from the Farm Bog catchment could be calculated by measuring the rate of water (in litres per minute) flowing over one of a series of dams, constructed across the stream by the London Wildlife Trust in order to maintain a high water table on the bog. The results showed a similar rapid response to rainfall.

Chapter 3

Six Thousand Years of History Preserved in Farm Bog

Simon Jennings and Christine Smyth

In addition to providing information on present-day characteristics of bog plant communities and hydrology, bogs, such as Farm Bog, preserve a record of past environments. Examination of fossil pollen taken from Farm Bog demonstrates vividly the nature of past conditions.

Remains of plants lying on the ground surface normally soon decay. However, under anaerobic conditions, typical of a peat bog, the remains gradually build up as layers of peat because the processes of decay are slowed down. Since the plant assemblages represented are likely to vary from layer to layer, their study provides a valuable tool in the reconstruction of past environments. One of the main methods of identifying past vegetation is the study of fossil pollen – the science of palynology. Pollen grains are highly resistant to decay in peat bogs, and their distinctive shape, surface texture and other morphological features allow ready identification. The successive layers of peat in a bog can be radiocarbon dated, providing a time scale for the floral changes represented. This type of study is commonly referred to as 'pollen analysis', and the results are depicted graphically in a 'pollen diagram'.

Peat bogs with long pollen sequences are rare in the London area, and Farm Bog, on Wimbledon Common, is one of the finest known examples. This chapter is an account of pollen analysis undertaken from a two metre peat core extracted from the bog.

The Principles of Pollen Analysis

Before the results are described, it is important to appreciate some of the ideas which underpin the technique, and to recognise a number of problems which can influence the interpretation of the resultant pollen diagram.

The examination of a sequence of pollen and spores is a study of plant succession or plant community changes through a considerable period of time, which is part of the science of palaeoecology. A pollen diagram is therefore a powerful tool to illustrate changes to the vegetation of an area, and by identifying which taxa expand or are lost from the vegetation, it is often possible to suggest reasons for these changes. The time-scales over which these changes occur will be determined by the age of the sediments (usually peat) from which the pollen and spores are extracted. The sequence from Farm Bog covers the period from approximately 6,000 years ago to the present day, and therefore falls within the geological time-period known as the 'Holocene', which covers the last 10,000 years following the end of the last glaciation.

Since pollen analysis is the study of the pollen and spore record, the technique relies upon the establishment of a stratigraphy (or sequence) from

Figure 3.1 The authors extracting the peat core from Farm Bog. For location of the core, see Fig. 2.25.
Photo: Antony Sutcliffe.

which interpretations concerning environmental change can be proposed. The methodology employed in pollen analysis requires the recognition of three specific types of stratigraphy. First, because the pollen must be extracted from sediment, a lithostratigraphy is established, which is a detailed description of the sequence of sediments from the site investigated. For Farm Bog, this was achieved by coring the bog (Fig. 3.1) along a number of transects using a hand-auger. One of the core-sites was then chosen for pollen analysis, on the basis of depth and type of sediment found. By identifying the sequence of pollen and spores from this one core, the second type of stratigraphy is then established, which is a biostratigraphy. Finally, by dating important changes within the biostratigraphy, for example through radiocarbon dating as at Farm Bog, a chronostratigraphy is provided. All three types of stratigraphy are illustrated on a pollen diagram.

During the process of establishing the stratigraphic framework, it is apparent that a pollen diagram is the result of a considerable degree of sub-sampling of the pollen and sediment. For small sites such as Farm Bog, sediment samples of approximately 1 cm³ are taken for pollen analysis from a single core, at approximately 5 cm intervals. The samples are then treated with a series of chemical processes in the laboratory to concentrate and isolate the grains. Following staining of the grains to make identification easier, a small amount of the resultant pollen-rich residue is placed upon a microscope slide, and then a sub-sample of the grains on each slide is identified. The size of this final sub-sample is called 'the pollen sum', which for Farm Bog was usually around 300 pollen of dry land and marsh taxa, although pollen of aquatics and spores of ferns, mosses and horsetails were also recorded. Due to the vast numbers of pollen and spores released, this degree of sub-sampling does not significantly jeopardize the reliability of the results.

Although the sub-sampling inherent in pollen analysis does not present a significant problem when interpreting a pollen diagram, there are three more specific features of palynology that can be problematic.

1. *Pollen production and release:* The amount of pollen produced and released by some plants is greater than that produced and released by others. As a consequence, some taxa will be over-represented on a pollen diagram, while others will be under-represented. One of the main reasons for this differential representation is that plants use different mechanisms to release their pollen. The function of the pollen grain is to transport the male gametophyte from the anther to the stigma, and this may be achieved in a number of different ways. The most common mechanism of pollen release and transport is by wind. This mechanism lacks any direct targeting of the pollen from anther to stigma, so very large quantities of pollen are released to ensure successful pollination. Not surprisingly, wind pollinated taxa, for example pine (*Pinus*) and oak (*Quercus*), tend to dominate pollen diagrams, which is in contrast to insect pollinated taxa which release relatively small amounts, as a host is used to transport the pollen. An important example of an insect pollinated tree is lime (*Tilia*), which is therefore under-represented on pollen diagrams. This differential release of pollen has fundamental implications for the interpretation of pollen diagrams. For example, the dominant tree in the native lowland British woods prior to extensive forest clearance for agriculture from the mid-Holocene was lime, although it seldom reaches more than 10-20% on pollen diagrams. This recognition of the importance of lime is possible due to studies of contemporary pollen production and release, allowing corrections to be made of pollen data of past communities, overcoming the problems of under- and over-representation of taxa due to differential pollen production and release.

2. *Pollen dispersal:* In addition to the amounts of pollen released by plants, the distance over which the pollen has travelled between its release and its deposition on the land surface is an important consideration when interpreting pollen diagrams. Again, using results from studies of contemporary pollen dispersal, it can be assumed that, for small bogs such as Farm Bog, most of the pollen deposited on the surface originated from plants that were growing either on the bog or in the immediately surrounding area. Most of the pollen from further afield is filtered-out by surrounding woodland, although some particularly aerodynamic grains from wind pollinated trees, especially pollen from pine, may become embedded amongst the dominant, locally-derived pollen. Therefore, the pollen data from Farm Bog can be used only to infer vegetational or palaeoecological changes that have occurred on and close to the bog during the period covered by the pollen diagram. It would be unwise to extrapolate these inferences to include all of Wimbledon Common.

3. *Pollen preservation:* Pollen and spores are composed of resilient materials which normally survive fossilisation and chemical treatment in the laboratory. However, the deposit most conducive to the preservation of fossilised pollen and spores is peat, due to its anaerobic nature. Also, peat bogs tend to be quiescent environments, so that once pollen is deposited on a bog surface and subsequently buried by progressive peat growth, it remains undisturbed,

Figure 3.2 A selection of pollen grains and spores (stained red) extracted from the Farm Bog core.

A. Horsetail *Equisetum* sp.
B. Grass Poaceae
C. Pine *Pinus* sp.
D. Alder *Alnus* sp.
E. Lime *Tilia* sp.
F. Bracken *Pteridium* sp.
G. Birch *Betula* sp.
H. Sedge Cyperaceae
I. Bog Moss *Sphagnum* sp.
J. Daisy Compositae
K. Heather Ericaceae

Magnification approximately x400.

Photos: S. Jennings and C. Smyth

Digital editing: Natural History Museum.

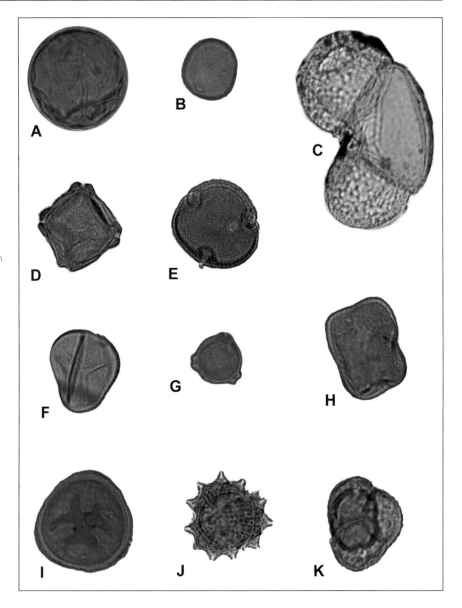

enhancing its preservation potential and maintaining the sequence in which the pollen was deposited; that is, it remains in its original stratigraphic context, which is vital for the accurate interpretation of a pollen diagram. Farm Bog has provided just such an environment.

A selection of pollen grains and spores identified from the bog is illustrated in Fig.3.2.

Radiocarbon Dating

Two radiocarbon dates have been obtained for the Farm Bog pollen diagram, establishing a sequence that covers approximately the last 6,000 years. However, as with pollen analysis, the technique of radiocarbon dating has limitations which should be recognised when discussing the age of plant communities and vegetational changes. Most radiocarbon age determinations are reported as being 'before present' (BP), which is taken as being the year

1950. These 'conventional' radiocarbon age determinations are affected by a number of factors, which result in the age quoted being in error in the order of a few hundred years, or possibly more. In order to give a more reliable age determination, the BP results are converted to calendar years via a calibration technique which utilises the known age of tree rings. The two age determinations from Farm Bog have been calibrated, and are reported in this chapter as 'cal. BC' or 'cal. AD' years. However, both conventional and calibrated radiocarbon age determinations cannot provide a specific age, and both are reported with an age range. The radiocarbon laboratory code for the samples is also given.

Pollen Diagram Construction and Characteristics

The pollen diagram is the result of initially fieldwork, then laboratory preparations and finally the identification of pollen grains and spores to achieve the pollen sum. For the Farm Bog sequence, pollen was identified at either x400 or x1000 magnification. All pollen and spore types recorded in each sample were converted to a percentage of the pollen sum. Because some pollen and all spores lie outside of the pollen sum, when they reach individual totals in excess of the pollen sum they obtain percentage frequencies greater than 100%.

Since the main function of a pollen diagram is to represent graphically the percentage frequency of taxa through time at the site under investigation, changes in pollen frequencies are interpreted as being the result of ecological responses by the vegetation to changes in factors such as climate, soil conditions and human impacts. To ease interpretation, pollen diagrams are divided into 'local pollen assemblage zones' (lpazs). These can be seen on the right-hand side of the Farm Bog diagram and represent discrete episodes in the vegetational development of the site. Zone boundaries are drawn where a significant and sustained change in the pollen record occurs, heralding the next phase in vegetational development.

The main pollen diagram for Farm Bog (Fig. 3.3) has been constructed conventionally, with depth, conventional radiocarbon dates and the lithostratigraphy of the core-site depicted down the left-hand side. This is followed by the percentage frequencies of taxa, drawn by horizontal bars which can be matched against the percentage scale either at the top or bottom of the diagram. Botanical and common English names are given for each of the taxa. In additon, a summary diagram (Fig. 3.4) depicting only plant groups (trees plus shrubs, herbs and spores) is provided. This illustrates the main changes to the vegetation over time.

The Interpretation of The Farm Bog Diagram

Following extensive coring of Farm Bog, one core-site was chosen for detailed pollen analysis. This site (shown on Fig. 2.25) has approximately two metres of uninterrupted organic material. The upper 15 cm was poorly decomposed *Sphagnum*, from which no pollen samples were extracted. From 15 cm to 190 cm, samples were taken every 5 cm, with a final sample taken at 200 cm. Below this depth, the sediment is a grey sand or sandy silt which contains very few pollen grains.

The main pollen diagram (Fig. 3.3) is described below. This has been divided into six local pollen assemblage zones. Each will be examined in turn with a description of the main features, inferences drawn as to the type of community(ies) represented and the main causes of change discussed.

Figure 3.3 (pages 34 and 35) The main Farm Bog pollen diagram, with sediments and radiocarbon age determinations. The diagram includes only the main pollen types found, and it is expressed as percentages of the sum of dry land and marsh pollen. Cartographer: John Gibbs, Univ. of North London.

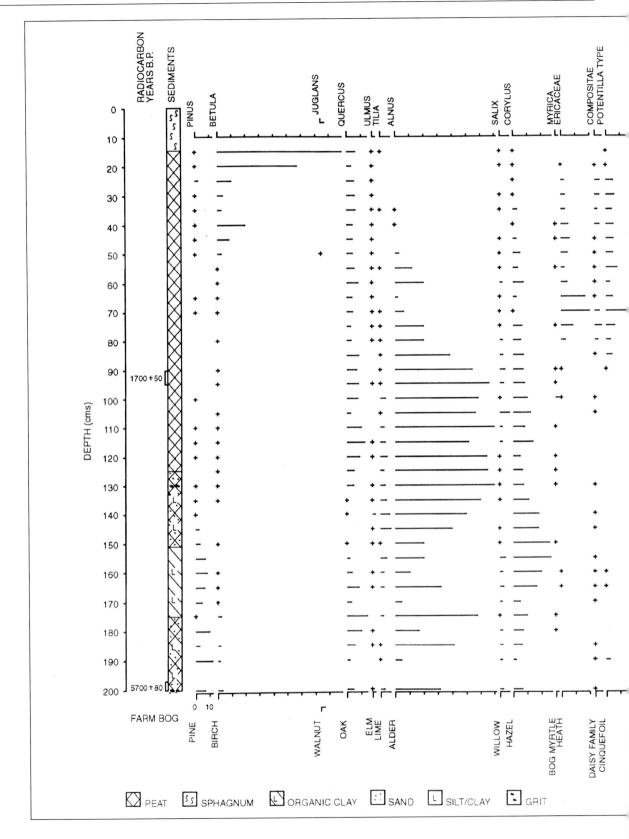

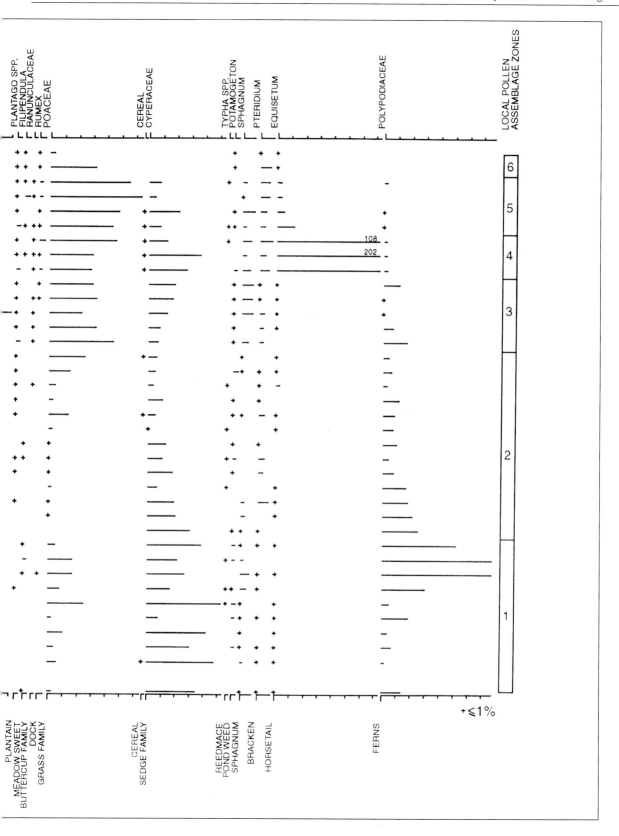

Figure 3.4 A summary pollen diagram from Farm Bog showing main plant groups and changes in vegetation on Farm Bog through the last 6000 years.
Cartographer John Gibbs, Univ. of North London.

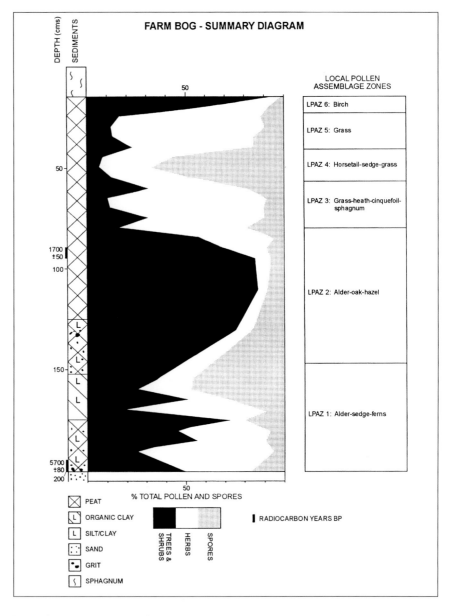

Lpaz 1: alder – sedge – ferns

The base of the sequence, which rests upon a sandy - grit substrate, has been dated to 5,700 ± 80 BP (cal. BC 4750 to 4360 - Beta-69266). The vegetation of the bog alternated initially between alder (*Alnus*) and sedge (Cyperaceae), but towards the top of this zone hazel (*Corylus*) and ferns (Polypodiaceae) became established. Concurrently, there was an expansion of *Sphagnum* and, to a lesser extent, grasses (Poaceae). Willow (*Salix*) was also present on the bog. Pine (*Pinus*) reaches its highest frequencies during this zone, and was probably part of the local woodland community, although this is always an over-represented tree on pollen diagrams. Nonetheless, it is likely that lpaz 1 represents the last vestiges of native pine trees at Farm Bog. The very low frequencies of pine pollen in the other lpazs probably represent long-distance transport of pine pollen, but this may include pollen from sources on the more acidic soils of Wimbledon Common. If this is the case, then Wimbledon Common may have played host to pine throughout the Holocene, which is in contrast to much of England where pine probably died-out in the early Holocene due to competition from taller growing trees.

Lpaz 1 represents a phase of mixed communities at Farm Bog. The presence of pondweed (*Potamogeton*) suggests pools of open water surrounded by alder and willow, with pine, oak and hazel growing on drier areas surrounding the bog. The expansion of hazel and ferns in this zone indicates a drying-out of the bog surface, with the expansion of *Sphagnum* suggesting a phase of increasing acidity. It is possible that this represents a limited development of raised bog, and it coincides with a small representation of heath (Ericaceae) and cinquefoil (*Potentilla*) type pollen. The single cereal pollen grain recorded implies that limited cultivation was taking place close to the bog during late-Mesolithic or early Neolithic times. The periodic decline in alder and its replacement with sedge and grass suggests episodes of disturbance to the bog, while the sand and silt recorded in the sediments indicate the inwash of material from the surrounding slopes. It is unclear whether this disturbance and inwash of material was the result of human impacts, or rather a reflection of the sensitivity of the young bog to other external factors such as storm events washing material onto the, then lower, bog surface.

Lpaz 2: alder – oak – hazel

The vegetation of the bog 'settles down' during this zone into an alder carr, in association with willow. The low frequencies of herbaceous pollen suggest a dense canopy of alder and willow on the bog. The decline in hazel pollen from the previous zone may be explained by competition from taller trees, both on the bog (from alder and willow) and on the drier surrounds (from oak and lime). Hazel may not have declined in number, as it can survive as an under-storey tree, but in that situation it produces less pollen.

On the bog itself, *Sphagnum* had a limited and sporadic presence, but although pondweed pollen declines, its occasional appearance on the pollen diagram indicates the presence of small and perhaps temporary pools on the bog surface. Reedmace (*Typha* spp.) and bracken (*Pteridium*) were also present on the bog occasionally. On drier areas, notably surrounding the bog, there was deciduous woodland comprising oak, bracken and lime with some elm (*Ulmus*). Taking into account lime's under-representation on pollen diagrams, it is likely that it was at least as important as oak in the woodland community.
The lpaz 2/3 boundary is drawn at the point where alder begins to decline, opening up the bog and allowing a greater variety of plants to grow. The initial phase of the alder decline is radiocarbon dated to 1,700 ± 50 BP (cal. AD 240 to 440 - Beta-69265), which is late- to post-Roman in age.

Lpaz 3: grass – heath – cinquefoil – *Sphagnum*

The dramatic reduction in alder was followed by an expansion of grass (Poaceae), heath (Ericaceae), cinquefoil (*Potentilla*) type and other herbaceous pollen with *Sphagnum*. This marks a significant change to the environment of the bog, with an acid heath replacing the alder and sallow carr. Surrounding the bog, oak, hazel and particularly lime decline, which suggests widespread floristic changes to this part of Wimbledon Common at this time. The three most likely explanations for these changes are human impacts, succession to an acidic, possibly raised bog, or a combination of both.

(a). Human impacts: The timing of these vegetational changes is interesting as they occurred at the end, and immediately after the Roman Occupation of Britain. The archaeological site of Caesar's Camp is close to Farm Bog, but is something of a misnomer, as it is Bronze Age to Iron Age in origin with only scant evidence for Roman activity. This dearth of archaeological evidence for Roman activity in the area correlates well with the stratigraphic evidence from Farm Bog. The Roman Period on the Farm Bog pollen diagram is represented by lpaz 2, which, as discussed above, was a period of mostly undisturbed alder carr. Two cereal pollen grains were found in this part of the diagram, indicating occasional agricultural activity close by (cereal pollen is dispersed only locally), but this apparently had no impact on the bog. Archaeological evidence suggests that it was not until the late Saxon Period (about the 9th century) that Wimbledon Common experienced significant human activity, which is at variance with the pollen record which indicates activity soon after the end of the Roman Occupation; that is in the early Anglo-Saxon period. That substantial impacts on the vegetation at Farm Bog did not take place until the Anglo-Saxon period establishes an interesting link with Epping Forest, where the main period of lime woodland decline has been dated to the middle Saxon Period.

(b). It is possible that the alder decline had nothing to do with human activity, but rather represents a natural succession on the bog from alder carr to an acidic (raised?) bog as peat continued to accumulate, resulting in the bog becoming nutrient deficient. If there had been extensive human impacts, then it is surprising that the sediment remained as peat with no inclusion of silt and sand eroded from areas surrounding the bog. Although this explanation may account for the changes on the bog, it does not explain the decline in oak and lime that were probably growing around the margins of the bog. Some form of woodland management, rather than the complete removal of trees was probably taking place there.

(c). A combination of human impacts and succession to an acidic (raised?) bog: Increased acidification of soil can occur following forest clearance, as has been noted at a number of locations in the British Isles. If the forest clearance at Farm Bog was associated principally with clearing land for grazing rather than for cereal production, then trees may have been cut back rather than removed, allowing the spread of lower-growing vegetation on an increasingly acidic bog surface. The trees may have been coppiced or pollarded (both of which limit flowering and therefore pollen production), minimising disturbance to the bog surface and surrounding area. In support of this grazing hypothesis is the expansion of daisy (Compositae) family, plantain (*Plantago* spp.), buttercup (Ranunculaceae) family, dock (*Rumex*) and bracken, following the removal of alder.

Lpaz 4: horsetail – sedge – grass

Alder, and to a lesser extent willow and hazel, make a small and temporary recovery around the lpaz 3/4 boundary, which is associated with a decrease in the frequency of heath and other herbaceous pollen, presumably as a direct consequence of increased competition from the renewed growth of trees. However, the main feature of lpaz 4 is the explosion in the representation of horsetail (*Equisetum*), and this coincides with the elimination of alder from the bog. Sedge, dock and bracken also peak during this stage. There is a continuous presence of cereal pollen, although peat was still forming on the bog, indicating that cereal production was taking place in the vicinity of the bog, but not on the bog surface.

This pollen zone may represent a period when there was less grazing on the bog and more cereal production in the surrounding area. However, this would not explain the very low frequencies of tree pollen especially from trees such as alder which had been growing on and close to the bog. It is likely, therefore, that wood was being collected from Farm Bog, perhaps by coppicing and pollarding, but the first small rise in birch (*Betula*) at the top of lpaz 4 shows that woodland regeneration was possible. The absence of alder during the rise in birch indicates either that alder was being managed, or that it had died out on the bog, perhaps through deliberate clearance.

Walnut (*Juglans*) was introduced into Britain by the Romans, but the stratigraphic position of its pollen on the Farm Bog diagram is well above the zone ascribed as Roman. The position of walnut pollen on the diagram probably relates to part of the Medieval Period.

Lapz 5: grass

The decline in horsetail was as dramatic as its increase, leaving the bog to be dominated by grass during this zone. Sedge was still a reasonably important but declining component of the local vegetation, and many low growing herbaceous plants were present on the bog. The very high frequencies of grass, and the very low values of tree pollen show that the bog was treeless, but with oak and elm growing nearby. The absence of trees on the bog during this zone suggests continuing human exploitation, with perhaps a resurgence of grazing on the bog itself.

Lpaz 6: birch

Within the upper 20 cm of the bog, there is clear pollen evidence for a rapid colonisation of the bog by birch, with some willow, the competition from which brought about a major decline in grass and a decrease in floristic diversity overall. Surrounding the bog, oak, and elm with an understorey of hazel continued to grow. The high birch pollen frequencies allow a connection to be made between the palaeoecology of Farm Bog, and the present environment. The sawn birch trunks that can be seen today on Farm Bog, as a consequence of recent management, may well be the same birches, or their immediate descendents, that produced the pollen found in this zone.

Conclusions

The Farm Bog diagram is one of the most extensive pollen records from the London area, and illustrates vegetational changes from the mid-Holocene to the present day. It comprises a sequence of marked changes to the flora of the bog and surrounding area. Human impacts on the bog and its surrounds have been particularly significant since the end of the Roman Occupation of Britain, which raises important archaeological issues relating to the impact of Anglo-Saxon and Medieval activities on Wimbledon Common. It is perhaps surprising, given its close proximity, that the establishment of Caesar's Camp apparently had such a limited impact on Farm Bog.

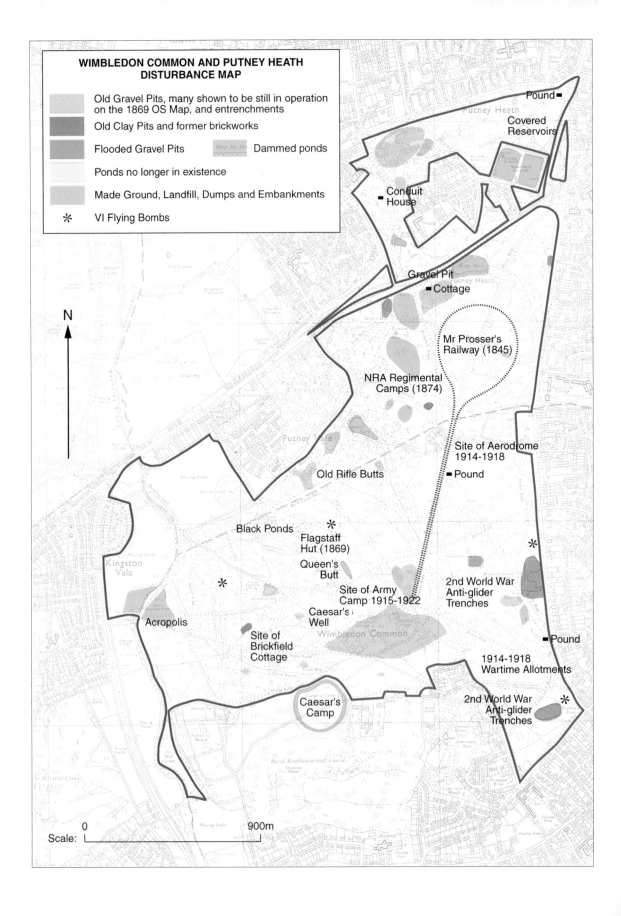

**WIMBLEDON COMMON AND PUTNEY HEATH
DISTURBANCE MAP**

Old Gravel Pits, many shown to be still in operation
on the 1869 OS Map, and entrenchments

Old Clay Pits and former brickworks

Flooded Gravel Pits   Dammed ponds

Ponds no longer in existence

Made Ground, Landfill, Dumps and Embankments

✱ VI Flying Bombs

Pound

Putney Heath

Covered
Reservoirs

Conduit
House

Gravel Pit
Cottage

Putney Heath

N

Mr Prosser's
Railway (1845)

NRA Regimental
Camps (1874)

Site of Aerodrome
1914-1918

Pound

Old Rifle Butts

Black Ponds

✱

Flagstaff
Hut (1869)

Queen's
Butt

✱

2nd World War
Anti-glider
Trenches

Kingston
Vale

✱

Site of Army
Camp 1915-1922

Caesar's
Well

Wimbledon Common

Acropolis

Site of
Brickfield
Cottage

Pound

1914-1918
Wartime Allotments

Caesar's
Camp

2nd World War
Anti-glider
Trenches

✱

Royal Wimbledon Golf Course

0   900m

Scale:

Chapter 4

A Disturbed Landscape

Una Sutcliffe

Figure 4.1 Map of
Wimbledon Common and
Putney Heath showing the
locations of some of the
past and present anthro-
pogenic disturbances.
Base map reproduced from the
Ordnance Survey map1:10,000,
with the permission of H.M.S.O.
Crown Copyright MC
100031556.
Draughtsman: Mike Parson.

When we look at Wimbledon Common and Putney Heath today, with its cover of heath and woodland, it might be thought that here is an area of land that has survived change, while houses sprang up all around it. Although this is to some extent true, in that very few permanent buildings have ever been constructed there, the amount of disturbance, by diverse causes, that has occurred in the past, is immense. There is barely a place where the ground has not been broken or the vegetation growing on it destroyed at some time or another.

Disturbance of the Commons can be classified into four broad categories:

(1) Its flat plateau surface, at 53 m. O.D. on the Black Park Terrace, has in the past made it ideal for use as an army parade ground, for landing small aeroplanes and even for the construction of an experimental railway. An obelisk erected on Putney Heath in 1961 proudly commemorates the formation of the Queen's Royal Surrey Regiment, which held its first parade there three hundred years earlier. From 1860 until 1889 organised rifle shooting dominated much of the Commons. All these activities resulted in massive destruction of vegetation and trampling of the ground.

(2) When the Plateau was found to be becoming water-logged, a series of shallow drainage ditches were cut across it, feeding into existing streams.

(3) There has been widespread excavation at places across the Commons for the extraction of gravel and, to a lesser extent, clay for brick making. Army trenches and Second World War bomb craters, now mostly filled in, caused further disturbance to the ground.

(4) Lastly, there are several artificial hills on the Commons, composed of spoil derived from nearby building and road construction operations.

Although such disturbances might be expected to have had a lasting deleterious effect on the Commons, often they have created additional habitats and have in fact substantially added to their ecological interest.

Early Disturbances

No attempt is made in this chapter to provide a detailed study of the history of the Commons, so thoroughly covered by Richard Milward and Norman Plastow (see Further Reading). We are concerned here only with past disturbance likely to have influenced what we find today.

To set the scene, there is evidence of human occupation on the Commons from at least Bronze Age times and possibly much earlier. A cluster of Bronze Age Barrows is recorded on Putney Heath, south of the A3, close to Tibbet's Corner. Unfortunately, most of these were flattened and the material used for road repairs in the early 19th century. Only one barrow now remains, overshadowed between the two artificial hills - to be described later. The most famous archaeological feature, however, is Caesar's Camp, earlier known as Bensbury Camp. It is a large circular structure with banks and ditches which have subsequently been partly flattened. Today, this fort, which is not Roman, but Late Bronze / Early Iron Age, dating around 500 B.C., lies just outside the southern boundary of Wimbledon Common. It is likely that the water supply for such a large camp came either from the nearby spring feeding Farm Ravine or, more likely, the spring feeding what we now know as 'Caesar's Well'. We know from the previous chapter on the palynology of Farm Bog that there appeared to be woodland clearances in Late Roman / Early Saxon times in the region of Farm Bog.

Establishment of the Commons

Wimbledon Common and Putney Heath, like so many other Commons, owe their preservation as open land to the fact that this was the waste land of the Manor, on account of its poor acidic soil. Tenants had Commoner's Rights which included digging turf; collecting gravel, sand or loam and wood; grazing a specified number of animals, mainly sheep; collecting thorns, brambles, briars, ferns, furze, etc. for fuel. During the 15th and 16th centuries the Manor Court Rolls showed numerous prosecutions for exploiting the Commons, such as grazing too many animals, failing to ring pigs (to stop them rooting up trees) and cutting too much wood. Oxen and horses were grazed on the Commons for pulling the ploughs in the arable fields that were springing up east of Wimbledon Common, below the Ridgeway. Throughout the 18th and 19th centuries, weak management from successive Lords of the Manor, together with a rapidly expanding local population, had led to serious abuse of the Commons. In 1864 the 5th Earl Spencer, Lord of the Manor, drew up a plan for restoring control by making the land, south of the present A3, into a Public Park. He planned to sell off the rest of the Commons to pay for this and he had plans for demolishing the Windmill to build a private residence in that area for himself. However, he underestimated the strength of the local opposition, spear-headed by Henry Peek, M.P., who were determined that the whole

Figure 4.2 Rushmere Pond and grazing cattle. Painting: Elizabeth Phillips, 1838. Wimbledon Society Museum.

area should be preserved as Common land. This came about with the passing of the Wimbledon and Putney Commons Act of 1871. The duty of the newly elected Conservators was to keep the Commons open, uninclosed and unbuilt on; to protect the turf, gorse, heather, timber and underwood; and to preserve it 'for public use for the purpose of exercise and recreation. For this we must be eternally grateful. The Conservators, nevertheless, inherited many serious problems and a difficult time still lay ahead.

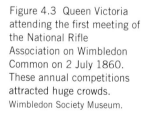

Nineteenth and Twentieth Century People Pressure

The closeness to the Commons of densely populated urban areas has long been a cause of wear and tear by people. Old photographs show how, before the days of car travel, popular landmarks, such as Caesar's Well, Queensmere and Kingsmere, drew hoards of people at weekends. Some of the other major causes of disturbance will be described here.

National Rifle Association

From 1860 - 1889 the newly formed National Rifle Association and Volunteer Rifle Corps virtually dominated the Commons, their activities being encouraged by the 5th Earl Spencer, Lord of the Manor. Shooting ranges were set up south of the Windmill, running approximately north east to south west across the Common. The first meeting on 2 July, 1860, was attended by Queen Victoria who, with a little guidance, fired the first shot from the Grandstand alongside Parkside to the 'Queen's Butt' 400 yards away. The butts were a permanent feature and for twenty nine years four or five hours of firing took place on every weekday except Wednesday. In addition, there were the annual N.R.A. summer meetings when, in June and July, the Plateau around the Windmill was fenced in and a huge enclosure with marquees and tents set up on a massive scale. These events drew thousands of competitors and spectators and a horse-drawn tramway at the rear of the firing points was constructed to carry people from the Pound to the Windmill.

In spite of the Wimbledon and Putney Commons Act, the N.R.A. and Volunteer Corps continued to use the Commons extensively for training and

Figure 4.3 Queen Victoria attending the first meeting of the National Rifle Association on Wimbledon Common on 2 July 1860. These annual competitions attracted huge crowds.
Wimbledon Society Museum.

summer meetings for a further eighteen years, so that the terms of the Act regarding public and local use, were not being respected. The turf, gorse, timber and underwood suffered a set-back when a massive fire broke out during a Volunteer Field Day exercise in 1874, involving 8,000 personnel. This left hundreds of acres burned. However, the heath recovered from this and it was not until 1889 that the N.R.A. eventually moved their headquarters from Wimbledon to Bisley. Firing practise, however, continued for a few years longer, but was finally stopped in 1894 following an unfortunate accident, when a stray bullet killed a grave digger in Putney Vale Cemetery. The Queen's Butt, a legacy from the days of N.R.A. dominance, is still a landmark on the Common.

The Two World Wars

During the First World War training camps were set up for troops about to be sent overseas; and an aerodrome was built on the flat Plateau between Parkside and the Windmill. A large army camp set up in 1915, with its entrance by Springwell Cottage, occupied a huge area on Wimbledon Common and remained there until 1922. As part of the war effort allotments sprang up opposite West Place (looking towards Parkside). It is amazing that vegetables could grow on this poor ground, but they did!

In spite of the military activities, most of the Commons were still a haven for wildlife. A resident of West Place, shortly after the war, who remarkably still lives there, recalls 'a Common full of wild flowers, buttercups, daisies, celandine, crowfoot and harebells, and in the woods, kingcups, cowslips, primroses, violets and bluebells'. Sadly, today, not all of these remain.

Even more disturbance took place during the Second World War. Trenches were dug over large areas of the Commons. These could still be clearly seen from later aerial photographs. Rows of posts were positioned across open spaces to stop the landing of enemy aircraft, and 'dragon teeth' were erected as barriers for tanks. Close to the Windmill was an army camp which carried heavy anti-aircraft guns. Parts of the Golf Course and gravel pits (to be described later) were used for bren gun carrier practise, the tracks remaining for years after. Many bombs were dropped on the Commons during the war

Figure 4.4 First World War Army Camp, with practice trench, on Wimbledon Common, December, 1918. Wimbledon Society Museum.

and a few craters are still discernible. In Figure 4.1, only the large V1 Flying Bombs are indicated.

Testing Inventions

The openness and flat topography made the Plateau an ideal place for testing new inventions.

One rather extraordinary construction was a railway track, designed by William Prosser in 1845 for his Experimental Train, which ran from the Windmill in a straight line (now Inner Windmill Road) to Thatched Cottage. A large turning circle was constructed north of the Windmill, part of which is

Figure 4.5 Prosser's Experimental Wooden Railway, 1845, which ran from the Windmill to Thatched Cottage. There was a turning circle (still visible) north of the Windmill. Illustrated London News, 8 November, 1845.

Figure 4.6 Passat's Ornithopter – a flying machine, built in 1912 in the garden of a nearby house and tested on the Commons. Photo: courtesy of Richard Milward.

still clearly visible as present paths partially follow the line. William Prosser used an engine whose main wheels dispensed with flanges, but instead had guide-wheels running against the inside of the track to give stability. Although the engine claimed to be more economical than the iron railway, due to lack of friction, it never took on!

Prior to the First World War, the Commons were on occasions unofficially used for testing proto-type 'flying machines', including, in 1912, Passat's Ornithopter, literally meaning 'winged bird', but looking more like a giant beetle!

Golf

The Commons suffered more pressure when the Golf Course was set up - first a 7-hole course for the London Scottish Volunteers in 1865; then, after the 1871 Act, the Conservators permitted the Course to be extended to 18 holes. Today, the Golf Course covers much of the Plateau, south of the Windmill, and is used by two golf clubs – the London Scottish and the Wimbledon Common. The construction and maintenance of bunkers (utilising in some cases depressions left from old gravel workings), fairways and greens, has given that part of the Common an artificiality, distinct from the rest.

Artificial Drainage

By the beginning of the twentieth century, according to eye-witness reports, the Commons seemed rather neglected. They were overgrown with furze (gorse) and very boggy in parts 'making it a hazardous place for walking'. Some of the water-logging was undoubtedly the result of soil compaction, through destruction of vegetation and trampling. The main policy of the Conservators at this time was to endeavour to make the Commons a safer place for walking by creating shallow ditches which linked with existing streams to take surface run-off, and by deepening the existing streams. Although very narrow, many of the ditches now provide an attractive habitat with willows, rushes and ferns growing in them. The deepening of the streams, however, has resulted in natural boggy areas, such as Farm Bog and Stag Bog, becoming drier. Current management is towards reversing this trend (see Chapter 5).

Mineral Extraction

Evidence of old gravel workings is to be found at many places on the high ground of the Commons. Their depth varies according to the local thickness of exploitable gravel - only about a metre alongside Parkside, but nearly three metres near Springwell Cottage. Many of these pits were still active in 1869 (Fig. 4.1), but by 1912, when Walter Johnson wrote his book, major gravel extraction had ceased.

The remains of a very large pit is evident just east of Springwell Cottage. Along Parkside the most important area for extraction was the now flooded Bluegate Gravel Pit, earlier known as 'The Swamps'. The southern part of the pit was excavated more recently than its northern part. Hookhamslade and 7 Post Pond also owe their existence to gravel extraction. All these ponds have added scenic diversity to the Commons and have formed, over the years, biologically rich habitats. The area of Putney Heath from Tibbet's Corner, following the line of the A3 towards Putney Vale Cemetery, is riddled with old gravel workings, resulting in an undulating topography. The building known as 'Gravel Pit Cottage', south-west of Kingsmere, is a survival from this time. The northern artificial hill, which will be described later in this chapter, covers a large pit shown on the Ordnance Survey map of 1869.

Figure 4.7 Early gravel pits, incorporated into bunkers on Golf Course.
Photo: Antony Sutcliffe.

Putney Heath, north of the A3, also has its share of gravel diggings. There is a large pit between Putney Heath Road and Telegraph Road which holds water at times and has marshy vegetation. Growing on the banks of the pit are some fairly mature trees, indicating many decades of abandonment.

Gravel was not the only material extracted from the Commons. Sand was also removed with the gravel and used locally for the bunkers on the Golf Course. Also important, were pits in the London Clay, from which tiles and bricks were fired on the spot. A map of 1787 shows a brick kiln on the slopes north west of the Windmill. The best known old clay pit, however, is situated in woodland, close to Robin Hood Road, in the south west of Wimbledon Common. A building known as 'Brickfield Cottage', demolished only a few decades ago, formerly existed here. A laundry on this site is remembered by local people. The pit is described in the 1860s as 'a large brickfield with kiln near Caesar's Well'. Ostensibly, the kiln was erected to make tiles for drainage of the Commons, but soon it became apparent that it was also for brick making on a wide commercial scale. After some time in operation adverse public opinion led to the closure of the brickyard. There is still a degraded section of clay to be seen behind the site of Brickfield Cottage.

Putney Heath Reservoirs

During the nineteenth century four covered Reservoirs were constructed by the Chelsea Water Company on an enclosure within Putney Heath, the first about 1858, others during the 1880s. Figure 4.8 shows the earliest Reservoir under construction, leading to the temporary dumping of huge amounts of spoil, displaced by the operation, on the adjacent heath. The Reservoir was subsequently covered and grassed over to become a cricket pitch. In 1996 the oldest two cells were demolished and completely reconstructed in a major project by Thames Water, the present owners. It was sad to see the demise of such a magnificent Victorian construction. Although the Reservoirs are not part of the Commons, a pipeline had to be constructed on the adjacent heath, which necessitated the removal of some trees. After the work was completed small-scale landscaping and replanting was negotiated between Thames Water and the Conservators.

Figure 4.8 Artist's impression of the construction of the first Putney Reservoir. The Reservoir was demolished and rebuilt in 1996. From the *Illustrated Times*, 8 May, 1858.

Artificial Hills

As recently as the 1960s a huge amount of spoil from widening the A3, widening and diverting Roehampton Lane and excavating Tibbet's Corner Underpass was allowed to be dumped on the Commons. Altogether, the Commons lost several acres and the destruction of many trees through this. Financial compensation was given to rehabilitate the damaged land and, in addition, a parcel of land of equal extent on Putney Lower Common was acquired by the Conservators. The two main areas of 'made ground' are at opposite ends of the Commons.

The first, and less conspicuous, known as 'the Acropolis', is situated between the Beverley Brook and horse ring at the foot of Robin Hood Road. A

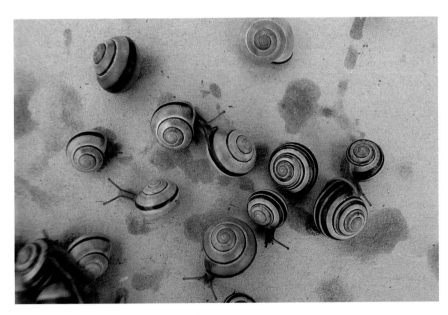

Figure 4.9 The made ground on the Commons increases biodiversity and favours species, such as these banded snails (*Cepaea nemoralis* and *C. hortensis*), collected from nettles. Photo: Una Sutcliffe.

Figure 4.10 Stinging nettles, so abundant on the areas of made ground, provide habitat for caterpillars of the peacock butterfly. Photo: Tony Drakeford.

resident living on the Kingston By-Pass, opposite the Common, remembers seeing lorry load after lorry load of material being taken to this site. What must have seemed an ecological disaster at the time has now developed into an additional interesting habitat, with grassland herbs (particularly legumes) and shrubs, attracting birds and invertebrates. Especially conspicuous amongst the insects, flitting from flower to flower in the summer months, are the colourful butterflies. Snails are also abundant in this nutrient enhanced habitat. Nettles (*Urtica dioica*) cover large areas, and sizeable populations of the very attractive banded snails (*Cepaea nemoralis*) and (*C. hortensis*) can be seen feeding on these plants, together with the less abundant Kentish snail (*Monacha cantiana*). Nettles are also the food plant for peacock butterfly larvae and it is worth a brush with the nettles to observe these spectacular nests of black caterpillars at close range.

The second, and more obvious areas of 'made ground', are the two hills situated north west of the Windmill and close to the A3. An enormous amount of material must have been dumped here to create hills 10 metres above the adjacent Plateau. Naturally, there was much opposition at the time to this radical artificial topography and introduction of foreign soil, but fortunately landscaping has been successful and created a habitat much more calcareous than the surrounding heath, with a rich and interesting flora and fauna, described in Chapter 6.

In conclusion, it is understandable that Wimbledon Common and Putney Heath, so close to central London, should have a history of disturbance of various kinds. In a way this is part of the evolution of the place we all enjoy today. It has kept the Commons open, created new habitats and possibly increased the biodiversity. Fortunately, through all this, the naturalness and wildness of the Commons remain. Nature is very resilient.

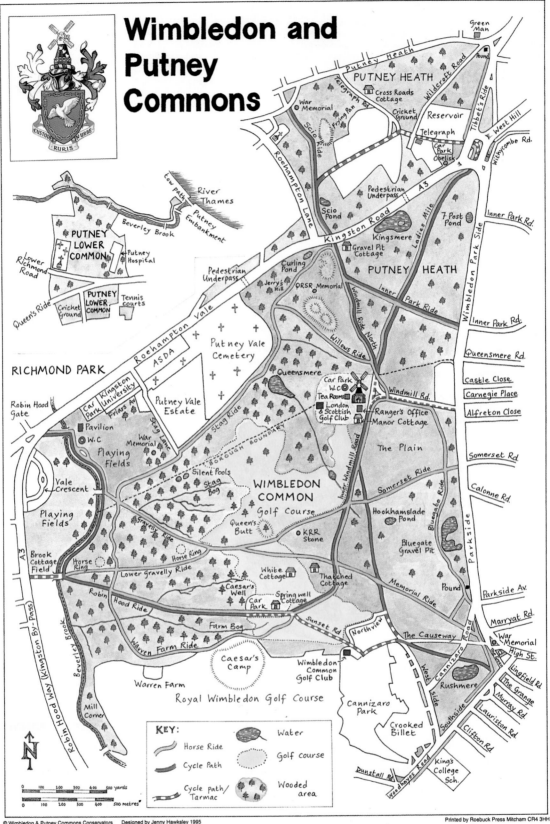

Wimbledon and Putney Commons

KEY:

- Horse Ride
- Cycle Path
- Cycle path/ Tarmac
- Water
- Golf course
- Wooded area

Printed by Roebuck Press Mitcham CR4 3HH

Chapter 5

Wimbledon and Putney Commons Management

James Reader, Clerk and Ranger

As we have seen in the previous chapter, Wimbledon Common and Putney Heath, surrounded by the urbanisation of Wimbledon, Putney and Kingston, have experienced such widespread disturbance in the past, that they might be expected to be massively degraded today – a 'far cry' from natural countryside. Yet, as so vividly introduced in the first chapter, here is an enclave of remarkable beauty and biological interest, much of it scheduled as a 'Site of Special Scientific Interest'. The survival of this open place in such pristine condition, in spite of the potentially conflicting activities of a suburban environment, has not happened by chance, but through careful management. How this has been achieved is the subject of this chapter.

Wimbledon and Putney Commons Act, 1871

By the late 1860s, the Lord of the Manor of Wimbledon, Earl Spencer, had gradually acquired the 'common rights', which had entitled the tenants of the Manor, known as 'Commoners', to share and use the natural produce of the Commons. Earl Spencer had bought back the majority of these rights over the years, intending to enclose about 700 acres of the Commons as a park, and to sell off another 300 acres as a means of paying for the development of a Manor House on the land on which the Windmill and adjoining buildings currently stand. A further two acres of land surrounding these buildings would have been used for private grounds to the Manor House. The Common at this time was classed as "land that was boggy with noxious mists and fogs arising from it." Furthermore the problems that were caused by gypsies, vagrants and travellers camping on the Commons meant that some changes had to be made.

However, Lord Spencer's ideas were thwarted by the local residents of the properties around Wimbledon Common and Putney Heath, who formed a Committee called the Wimbledon Common Committee, with the objective of preserving the whole of the Commons for the benefit of the neighbourhood and the public. Their first Chairman, Henry Peek, who was later knighted as MP for Mid Surrey, strongly opposed Lord Spencer's proposals. Finally, after years of negotiations, a Bill was passed which saved the Commons for posterity; and in August, 1871 the Wimbledon and Putney Commons Act received Royal Assent. Henceforth, ownership of the Commons was conveyed to eight Conservators. Earl Spencer was made to relinquish all rights over the Commons in return for an annual payment in perpetuity of £1,200, a price based upon the average income received by him over the preceding ten years. This was paid off by a lump sum payment of £22,500 in 1958.

The 1871 Act of Parliament ensured that the land, known as Wimbledon and Putney Commons, remained open, un-enclosed and available for the

Figure 5.1 Map of Wimbledon and Putney Commons, 1995, showing golf course, horse rides and cycle tracks.
Designed by Jenny Hawksley.

Figure 5.2 Occasional events, such as this annual Fair, near Rushmere, can be accommodated on restricted areas near the edge of the Commons.

Photo: Antony Sutcliffe.

purposes of exercise and recreation for the public and local people. It is this edict that is so important to the Conservators in any decisions that they make in managing the Commons.

Of the eight Conservators, three are appointed and five elected: one Conservator is appointed from each of three Government Departments – the Home Office, Ministry of Defence and the Department of the Environment, Transport and the Regions. Five Conservators are elected triennially by levy payers.

Under the provisions of the 1871 Act the Conservators were empowered to raise a revenue for managing the Commons by levying rates upon occupiers of dwelling houses, which had a rateable value of more than £35, within a radius of three quarters of a mile (approximately one kilometre) of some part of the Common, which included Putney Lower Common and the old parish of Putney. The rate levied varied in accordance to the distance of the property from the Commons in quarter mile bands. This was the method of financing the Commons working funds until the early 1990s when rateable values of property were displaced by the Community Charge and latterly the Council Tax. The variable quarter mile charges ceased with these changes and the three Borough Councils, in which the Commons lie, were instructed to act as levy collectors for the Conservators. This simple alteration to the system ensured that the Conservators received all their working capital in regular payments and eliminated the accelerating problem of bad debt. Seventy five percent of the money required annually to manage the Commons is derived from levy payers. The remainder is raised by charging various users, such as rents on properties, football, golf, film crews and annual fairs.

Staffing

Currently the Conservators have an administrative staff of three full time and one part time employees, who together ensure that someone is 'on call' every day. The Clerk and Ranger has a Security staff of seven Keepers, mainly mounted on horses, who patrol the Commons every day of the year. In addition there are seven Maintenance staff who provide the physical workforce required in looking after the Commons and also ensure the maintenance of the Commons' properties. The administrative headquarters is at Manor Cottage, near the Windmill.

In the 1920s a further 42 acres of land was added to the Commons as playing fields for public use, following an appeal made by Mr Richardson Evans to preserve land near the Robin Hood Roundabout that had been scheduled for urban development. Now known as the Richardson Evans Memorial Playing Fields, these fields provide rugby and football pitches, together with a grass running track in the summer months. The site, in spite of limited changing facilities and the constraints of the 1871 Act which prevents further development, hosts the Shell UK Rugby Schools Sevens Competition and is one of the training grounds for the Wimbledon Football Club. The pitches are maintained to the highest standards and competitively priced for other local users. A full-time staff of three is required to manage and maintain the Richardson Evans Memorial Playing Fields.

Figure 5.3 Mounted Keeper chatting to member of the Maintenance staff.
Photo: James Reader.

Administration and Communications

How do the Commons work? Who pays for the maintenance? How much does it cost each household and are they getting value for money? How are the needs for bio-diversification met? These are some of the questions regularly asked at Open meetings. The Conservators, who are unpaid, act as custodians of the Commons during their period of office. Having been elected or appointed, as the case might be, they meet at Manor Cottage on the second Monday of the month to discuss issues relating to the Commons and to dictate policy. The monthly meetings, although open to the public, do not allow public participation. The chance for the public, elector or levy payer, to voice his or her opinion is at the Annual Open Meeting, usually held in June at one of the local venues within three quarters of a mile radius of the Commons.

Good relations with the public are of paramount importance if we are to expect co-operation. All levy payers receive an annual Newsletter and the

Figure 5.4 Keepers' Open Day, a popular annual event.
Photo: James Reader.

Figure 5.5 Theme walks attract a large gathering. Here, on the made ground, known as 'the Acropolis', Tony Drakeford is leading a butterfly walk.
Photo: Antony Sutcliffe.

Figure 5.6 The focal point on Wimbledon Common is its Windmill, now including a Museum.
Photo: Una Sutcliffe.

Commons' accounts are available at Manor Cottage for inspection. The Keepers' Open Day, held in July each year, is a happy family occasion where the public are invited behind the scenes to view exhibits, see the horses and chat informally with the Rangers and Keepers. Through the year there are regular conducted walks on the Commons for the public to enjoy on specified themes, butterfly walks during the summer being particularly popular.

A major new venture that has just been completed is the Windmill Trail, a short circular trail which the physically disadvantaged can also enjoy. Audio equipment, available at the Ranger's Office, enables those with impaired vision to enjoy the trail more fully. The path is quite flat and is suitable for wheel chairs. It covers a variety of habitats; starting in woodland, it passes over a small stream before finally opening out on to the heather clad heath. All this lies within a few hundred metres of the Windmill Car Park.

Properties on the Commons are largely occupied by employees, apart from the Mill House, the Tea Rooms, the London Scottish Golf Club and of course, the focal point of Wimbledon Common, the Windmill. The latter has, over the years, provided accommodation for up to six families at one time but, following major refurbishment, was converted into a Museum. In 1999, following further major improvements with money from the Heritage Lottery Fund, the entire Windmill became a museum.

Pressures – A Balancing Act

Unlike agriculture the Commons are unique in that they have not succumbed to the national demand to be more productive. Hopefully they have remained much the same as they were decades ago. None the less, there is a constant pressure from Local Authorities, Highways' Authorities, and public utilities, for services such as electricity, gas, water and telephone, to allow encroachment of, and onto, the Commons. All these pressures are resisted by the Conservators, who uphold the 1871 Act of Parliament under which the Commons are managed.

Times have changed and so too has our concept of 'Management'. Management according to the Oxford English Dictionary is defined as "the people responsible for running an organisation, or the technique or practice of managing or controlling." We, the Managers, are sometimes targeted by members of the public as failing in our duty to manage the Commons. When asked why we have failed, the response is usually that the Commons are untidy and dirty or that the grass is too long! The modern idea of Management by the average person is 'everything in its place, neat, tidy, mown or swept', to conform with the increasingly sterile world that we live in. Cleanliness has been carried to the extreme and it is for this reason that there are some users of the Commons, who are not local, and without an understanding and affinity of the value of the Commons, who regard them as unmanaged.

According to the 1871 Wimbledon and Putney Commons Act the management duty of Conservators and their employees is simple "to keep the Commons for ever open and uninclosed and unbuilt on, and to protect the turf, gorse, timber, and underwood thereon, and to preserve the same for public and local use, for purposes of exercise and recreation, and other purposes".

Most of the area of the Commons, south of the A3 is designated a Site of Special Scientific Interest (S.S.S.I), and as such we, the Managers, have an agreement with English Nature that clearly lays down the operations that we are permitted to carry out there. The most obvious objective, as agreed with English Nature, is to maintain the natural state and beauty of the Commons while preserving and fostering the wildlife. Yet simultaneously there has to be an element of compromise, taking into consideration the activities on the Commons such as walking, running, cycling, horse riding, golf, football, picnicking and many others. All these activities can be categorised as "exercise and recreation" as stated in the 1871 Act, and may conflict with other users.

Figure 5.7 (left) The 1871 Wimbledon and Putney Commons Act decreed that the Commons were to be preserved "for public and local use, for purposes of exercise and recreation". Walking the family dogs. Photo: Una Sutcliffe.

Figure 5.8 (right) Recreational cycling on designated paths. Photo: Dave Haldane.

Succession

Preserving the 'natural aspect' of the Commons, as laid down in the 1871 Act, can be interpreted in many ways. Does 'keeping the natural aspect' refer to the natural state of the Commons as and when the 1871 Act was established, or 100 years ago, or 50 years ago, or as the Commons are today? It is self evident that some changes are bound to occur when one considers that we are dealing with the growth of grass, shrubs and trees. A fundamental principle of ecology is 'succession'. If the private garden is neglected for any length of time, say a year, it takes a considerable amount of time and effort to restore it to its original status. The change that can and does occur within the time frame of twelve months of unrestricted growth, especially in good climatic conditions, is staggering.

Obviously the Commons cannot be left totally unattended otherwise birch scrub, bracken, holly and other invasive plants would engulf the reasonably open aspect of the Plateau. These open areas are invaluable and a vital element in maintaining the diversity of flora and fauna and also the leisure activities on the Commons.

For more than a century the Commons have been managed without the benefit of livestock. It was the livestock, strictly controlled in numbers, which ate the herbage, the young saplings and limited the encroachment of invasive species such as birch, bramble, holly and bracken, thus keeping the Commons open. Today, with the absence of grazing and rooting animals such as the cow, sheep or pig, we, as managers are forced to rely upon control of the natural vegetative growth by unnatural mechanical means.

Were it not for the presence of the London Scottish and Wimbledon Common Golf Clubs (the former was already in existence before the establishment of Wimbledon and Putney Commons under the 1871 Act), one might not have the benefit of the vistas created by the 18 Fairways which are the backbone of the golf course and which have thus allowed Wimbledon Common to remain open. However, the open spaces and vistas that once stretched from Parkside and North View to the Windmill are no longer there. These areas are fast becoming areas of impenetrable birch scrub. Some members of the Thames Hare and Hounds Running Club recall that they used to run from North View to the Windmill by the shortest route using the Windmill as a visual point of reference. This is no longer possible as the Windmill is now obscured by trees and scrub and only seen with some difficulty when about 250 yards away.

One reason for the loss of these open spaces is the speed with which we and the Fire Brigade, attend any fire on the Commons. Today we are too efficient! Fires are extinguished almost before they are lit. Fire, although apparently destroying the beauty of the countryside can have a beneficial knock on effect. This has been demonstrated all too clearly in Australia and the USA where bush fires have destroyed vast areas. Historically these areas were burnt or allowed to burn on a regular basis. When the fires were extinguished nature quickly regenerated the area as the heat of the fire encouraged dormant seeds to germinate. Added to this was the fact that the canopy had been reduced, allowing the sun to penetrate and woodland flowers to flourish. The same principle applies to the survival and continuity of heather regeneration. Fire, if controlled, can be beneficial. Nature cannot be 'left to itself', otherwise we will lose the 'natural aspect' that we seek. So we have to interfere in the guise of management.

Gradually, with improved investment in machinery and well trained employees we are able to constrain the encroachment of the scrub. We are able to annually cut and thus stimulate the growth of heather. In future years the

Figure 5.9 Although ragwort is an attractive plant for insects it is poisonous to horses; therefore some control of its spread is necessary.
Photo: James Reader.

heather probably could expand and cover a larger area than it does today as trees and scrub that currently overshadow it either die or are physically removed.

When the total area of heather on the Commons was catalogued in 1992, it was estimated that it covered about 92 acres, that is more than the total acreage of heather for the whole of the County of Essex. Today we believe that we have nearly 100 acres of heather. The aim now is to establish and maintain a variety of growth stages ranging from one to twenty years, after which the heather degenerates. This will ensure the continuance and survival of the heath, as it will the wildlife that needs these different environments provided by the heather at different stages of growth. One of the control measures for dry heath, apart from cutting, is to burn areas selectively. Fire removes the dried dead wood and litter which, if left in situ, will alter the acidity of the heath soil and reduce the survival of the heather.

People Management

When considering the 'Management of the Commons' one tends to think and relate only to the physical and mechanical methods applied to mowing grass, felling trees, clearance of litter and repair of roads and pathways. There is, however, another form of management which is superseding the above, and that is the 'Management of People'.

With the ever increasing pressures put upon open spaces by the public, coupled with the decline in open spaces elsewhere around London, the Commons have become an extremely busy place for exercise and recreation, as intended by the Act. It is quite conceivable that at a weekend or Bank Holiday, with favourable weather conditions, the Commons could be host to more than 10,000 people a day. In order to avoid excessive trampling, we have, over the years, established footpaths, horse rides and cycle tracks (Fig. 5.1) to alleviate the pressure on more sensitive areas.

The very fact that there is a hard path does focus our orderly minds to use them rather than force ones way through the undergrowth. This is a form of subliminal management. Restricting the public, unconsciously, in this manner to specific routes does give the wildlife greater freedom to survive. An example of this is the management of one of the open areas where we are trying to encourage more skylarks to visit, nest and breed on the Commons. To achieve this we are mowing areas of open grassland to a variation of heights in order to encourage this beautiful bird to return and breed in greater numbers than in the last decade. Alas these birds, which were once so abundant, yet now classed as 'at risk', are regularly disturbed by the public and their dogs. Hopefully over the next few years the skylarks will not only survive but also increase in numbers. We ask the public to respect this 12 acre site and to restrain their dogs from the area, also to walk along the well worn footpaths rather than through the rough grass. We are hopeful that, with current concern over the decline of several bird species, the public will take heed, and respect the area, thus allowing the skylarks more freedom.

The numbers of users of the Commons possibly has not changed significantly over the years. It is the manner in which the public use it that has altered. For example, in recent years the popularity of the four-wheel drive motor vehicle has transformed it from being the workhorse of the countryman to that of a symbol of affluence for the urban dweller. The inevitable outcome, particularly as these vehicles become cheaper and more available, is the excitement of using the four wheelers on a surface more challenging than tarmac. Consequently, we have been forced to apply a form of control along our 10 miles of unenclosed boundary of the Commons to limit access for such vehicles.

Figure 5.10 Although large groups of dogs were formerly brought to the Commons by commercial dog walkers, a new bye-law now prohibits more than four dogs with any one person.
Photo: James Reader.

Until the mid 1980s the mountain bike was a luxury for a few dedicated cyclists. Today the mountain bike has almost replaced the conventional cycle. In the early 1980s the Conservators were pressurised into creating a few simple cycle tracks for leisure. Today, with the emphasis on reducing pollution, exercising to keep fit and a government policy for restricting car use by charging excessively for parking, the cycle in one form or another is becoming increasingly popular as a mode of transport and recreation. As a result, a minority of cyclists try to go everywhere at speed, and fail to restrict their activities to just the authorised cycle routes. This has required the Conservators to take radical action and to consider Court action on persistent offenders.

Other instances of misuse of the Commons in recent years have occurred with the changing lifestyle of the young families who both work and consequently employ someone else to exercise their dogs. The dog walking business has grown to unforeseen proportions and has resulted in packs of up to forty dogs being exercised on the Commons by one person. The impact of such a business required the Conservators to compile a new bye-law, as they did for the user of the metal detector, to protect the Commons from actions of this nature. The compilation and enactment of the new bye-law took months of work before enforcement could be applied. But, once in place, it restored the Commons to the pleasant, quiet, safe and enjoyable place that it was originally intended to be in 1871.

Regrettably, almost one third of our Maintenance staffs' working time is spent on ensuring that the Commons are clear of the debris and litter generated by the public. By this I refer to the volume of paper, plastic, garden waste, domestic waste, such as mattresses and kitchen equipment and on occasions materials left by fly tippers. The removal of waste material is possibly the most expensive and labour consuming element of the Commons' costs. If only the public could be educated to take their litter home or to a recycling centre then not only would the Commons' Levy be reduced, but the maintenance employees could actually do what they are employed to do. Unfortunately, some 8-9% of the Commons' Levy is expended upon the cost of clearing up and disposing of waste from the Commons.

Conservation in Action

Bearing in mind that about 900 acres of the Commons south of the A3 is an S.S.S.I., management of this area has to be monitored by English Nature. A Management Plan is drawn up every five to seven years to consider how best to manage the Commons and ensure that it remains as natural as possible.

The Maintenance Department, managing 1140 acres, only remove trees and shrub growth that are either dangerous or encroaching onto the limited open spaces that we have on the Commons. Trees that are felled are left to decompose naturally. Others that die and are regarded as not being a hazard to the public are left to decompose in their vertical state. The reason for this is that the upright dead tree serves as a host to a variety of species that would not colonise a fallen tree. The decomposition of the fallen tree is from the outside towards the centre. On the other hand the decomposition of the standing tree is the reverse, centre to outside. A tree that is dead is left for birds and invertebrates until it is regarded as unstable. At this point it is felled and invariably left on site to decay naturally. Inevitably there are some instances where trees have been removed or cut back, again either to preserve the tree or to allow vehicular, equestrian or pedestrian access, such as along the rides or the public highway. This always causes concern to someone, but management of this nature is vital.

Every consideration is given when a project such as creating a new pond or even cleaning out an existing pond is undertaken. Will the work be of benefit, or could it disturb and reduce the natural cycle of wildlife? To date, the changes and works undertaken have both improved the amenity value and appear to have increased the potential of the Commons for biotic diversity.

For some time electro fishing of some ponds has taken place to remove the

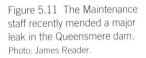

Figure 5.11 The Maintenance staff recently mended a major leak in the Queensmere dam. Photo: James Reader.

Figure 5.12 Pondside notice requesting the protection of amphibians.
Photo: Antony Sutcliffe.

less desirable and more predatory fish such as pike. This has been undertaken at about five yearly intervals because fishing is against the bye-laws and the larger fish survive at the expense of the smaller. It is noticeable that the number of tadpoles, frogs and toads decline over the years. The effect of one large predator is understood when a pike weighing 10 kilos (22 lbs) was removed from one of our ponds in December, 1993 and whilst at an investigation centre it regurgitated a fully fledged black headed gull. Another pike was removed with a fish weighing over 2 kilos in its belly. The destruction to a small pond by one fish can be catastrophic (See also Chapters 8 and 12).

The collecting of tadpoles by children could become a hazard to the amphibian populations of the Commons. Friendly notices on trees beside ponds will hopefully deter this.

Over the last 125 years, with the occupation of the Commons first by the National Rifle Association and then by troops during the two World Wars (see Chapter 4), there has been a progressive tendency to drain the Commons and accelerate the removal of standing water. Wimbledon Common and Putney Heath are important for their wet heath, a habitat which is rare in Greater London, but gradually the 'improvements' made by draining the Commons, and the apparent change in our climate to drier seasons, is putting the wet heath species at risk. We are therefore trying to reverse this process by slowing the existing drainage systems. To achieve this, the Maintenance staff are blocking some ditches and allowing others to silt up, in an attempt to allow more rainwater to infiltrate the heath rather than run into ditches.

The dry periods experienced since the late 1980s have resulted in seasonal lowering of water level or even drying out of ponds such as Kingsmere and Bluegate Gravel Pit (Fig.2.21). The drying out of ponds may also be the result of silting. About 50% of Queensmere was recently cleared of debris (leaf litter, branches, stones and a miscellany of items thrown in by passing users of the Commons) that had accumulated since the last clearance in the 1930s.

The ponds also suffer from the problem of invasive and unwanted flora and fauna. The Canada goose has gradually increased in numbers from about seven ten years ago to nearer fifty at the Millennium. The goslings produced each year suffer from predators within the ponds and also the dogs and foxes frequenting the Commons. Despite these natural hazards, the numbers of geese increase and further control measures will inevitably have to be undertaken to limit numbers to their present levels.

In the ponds themselves the past decade has seen a rise in the turtle population (see Chapter 12), as children become bored with their pets, or the pet outgrows its limited accommodation. The turtle, together with the content of the aquarium, is deposited into one of the ponds, and the cycle of change begins. The turtle grows rapidly without any predator other than man. The speed of growth of the turtle, however, is nothing compared to the growth of the plants that were within the aquarium. Australian Stonecrop and Parrot's Feather seem to spread at phenomenal speeds. The Parrot's Feather is being contained and gradually reduced using chemical applications approved by English Nature and the Environment Agency.

Water on the Commons is at a premium, not only for nature, but also as a visual amenity. We have therefore, with the consent and assistance of the Countryside Commission, established another pond (see Chapter 16). This is the first pond created on the Commons since Queensmere was constructed in 1887. The new pond (Ravine Pond) was completed in November 1998 and is positioned in one of the ravines near the golf course. The water supplying this pond is from a stream which flows eventually into Queensmere and the overflow from the new pond will continue to supply Queensmere. The pond has been created by simply building a dam across the ravine. The clay used to make the dam was excavated from the base of Putney Heath reservoir when it was rebuilt in 1996; so all the materials used are of local origin. The dam has been reinforced with sandbags and then covered with coir matting to assist the establishment of vegetation.

Figure 5.13 Two problem alien species in Kingsmere – Canada geese, whose population is increasing; and, beyond, Parrot's Feather, which clogs the pond and has to be controlled.
Photo: Ray Grimwood.

Figure 5.14 Wide woodland tracks give a better sense of security for those using them.
Photo: Ray Grimwood.

Public Safety

Another aspect of the Management of the Commons that has, and will continue to be addressed, is the increasing need for us to maintain and improve the safety of the general public. By this we do not only refer to the obvious removal of hazards, such as dangerous trees, but to the increasing pressure of personally feeling safe on the Commons. In recent years major improvements have been made to widen the horse rides, cycle tracks and footpaths. This widening process enables the user of these paths to feel at ease and to see where he or she is going without the feeling of being boxed in. There are, and always will be, areas where one can feel restricted, but at least the choice of where one goes is left to the individual user.

We will continue to widen and improve these main arteries on the Commons in the future for the benefit of the public. Coupled with this, we have increased the number of Mounted Keepers on patrol on the Commons each day and we have also increased the number of mounted patrols. This ensures that our Security staff not only cover a larger area of the Commons in the day, but also provide a greater security presence at all times. All employees of the Conservators and the Golf Course employees have been equipped with short wave radios linking them directly with the main office. This provides us with about twenty staff on the Commons with radios acting as the ears and eyes of the Management. It is regrettable that it is necessary to do this but it is essential that public safety is not compromised. Closer liaison with the Police Service and the additional security changes 'in house' have made the Commons as safe a place as possible for those who wish to enjoy the freedom and tranquility offered by our magnificent open spaces.

In conclusion, the 1871 Act of Parliament may have appeared over the years to be very restrictive to both the management of the Commons and users. It has prevented the National Utilities from erecting poles and pylons, the Highways and Railways from establishing shortcuts and the local Borough Councils from building car parks. This all might seem academic but it has meant that the Commons have basically remained the same. Some people have argued that the Conservators and the Commons have not kept pace with modern thinking, but adhering to the provisions of the 1871 Act, with all its safeguards, is still accepted as appropriate management. Why is this?

The reason is that the prudent actions of the Conservators, Managers, and the way that the Act is so restrictive, has meant that detrimental changes to the Commons have NOT been made. We know that the Commons are unique and must be protected. Their value to nature and mankind is priceless. Biodiversity, the current buzz word, is the key to the Commons' success. It still supports a wide range of habitats. There are wild areas, mowed amenity areas, unmowed grassland, dry and wet heathland, mixed deciduous woodland and wetlands, all with a surprising diversity of flora and fauna.. The truth is that, even after 129 years, the conservation policy for Wimbledon Common and Putney Heath really seems to be working, hopefully providing security for a further hundred years, and more!

Finally, it must be made clear that within the auspices of the 1871 Act, the management can still be forward looking. New ideas are aired at the meetings of the Natural History sub-committee. One such project, which is backed by the Environment Agency, is to improve, where possible, the stretch of the Beverley Brook which runs through the Commons, thus making it a more attractive and healthy river for wildlife and also a river walk for people to enjoy.

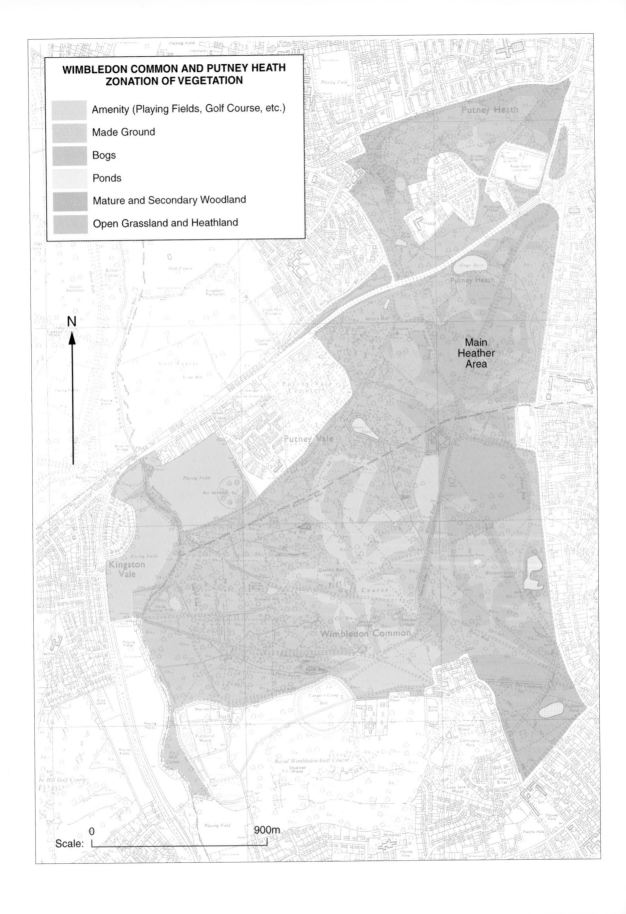

WIMBLEDON COMMON AND PUTNEY HEATH
ZONATION OF VEGETATION

Amenity (Playing Fields, Golf Course, etc.)

Made Ground

Bogs

Ponds

Mature and Secondary Woodland

Open Grassland and Heathland

N

Main
Heather
Area

Putney Heath

Putney Heath

Putney Vale

Kingston
Vale

Wimbledon Common

Scale: 0   900m

Chapter 6

Terrestrial Habitats of Wimbledon Common and Putney Heath

The Plateau *Una Sutcliffe*
Made Ground *Una Sutcliffe*
Woodland on the western slopes *Irene Kettle*

The noble provisions of the 1871 Wimbledon and Putney Commons Act were to ensure that the Commons remain open and unbuilt upon, and are preserved as far as possible in their natural state for people to enjoy. Inevitably, exploitation of the Commons continued after the 1871 Act. During both wars they were intensively used for camps and training exercises, so it was not until after World War II that real thought returned to how the Commons should be managed.

With such varied geology, topography, drainage patterns and soils, influenced also by past land use, the Commons offer a diversity of habitats with surprises around every corner. It was for this reason that in 1953 most of the land south of the A3 (856.2 acres or 346.5 ha.) was designated as a Site of Special Scientific Interest by English Nature (then the Nature Conservancy Council).

The discussion of the various plant communities in this and the following chapters will set the scene for later chapters on the fauna of the Commons. In this brief summary, no attempt is made to provide a comprehensive list of plant species, but rather to try to present 'the feel' of the habitat, so that the reader might be encouraged to explore for his or herself.

The Plateau
Una Sutcliffe

Figure 6.1 Map showing vegetation zones of Wimbledon Common and Putney Heath.
Base map reproduced from the Ordnance Survey map 1:10,000, with the permission of H.M.S.O. Crown Copyright MC 100031556. Draughtsman: Mike Parson.

For visitors arriving at the Windmill, the most obvious feature of the Commons is the large expanse of heather-clad heath and grassland, broken by small copses of mainly birch and oak and a scattering of isolated mature trees; which grow on the gravel capped plateau described in Chapter 2.

The Plateau has traditionally been kept open by destructive past land use on an already impoverished soil. Ironically, it is because the land has a history of abuse that we have today a comparatively open landscape. This covers a large area, which is also readily accessible, and is the one that most people associate with Wimbledon Common and Putney Heath.

The present distribution of vegetation, with vistas across open areas, is therefore not a natural one. Succession from grass and heather to birch woodland and finally to oak climax woodland would occur in less than a century, were these open spaces not being artificially maintained. The acid soil favours birch, with its shallow rooting system and, if allowed to colonise, the humus produced from its dead leaves will gradually improve the soil structure and encourage colonisation of the more deeply rooted oak.

Today, even though many thousands of people enjoy the relaxation of the open space the Commons provide, there is less trampling than in the recent past, and the grazing of domestic animals is no longer permitted. Only the rabbits remain; flourishing, but insufficient to keep the forest at bay! Hence, the natural tendency for succession towards scrub and secondary birch/oak woodland. Everywhere there are tree saplings (mainly birch, oak, aspen and willow) waiting to dominate the field flora, and the Rangers fight a constant battle to stop this happening on the existing open areas.

Although the gravels which cover the Plateau might be expected to be well drained, for geological reasons already discussed in Chapter 2 and probably in consequence of previous land use (Chapter 4), there are local areas where water-logging occurs at times of high rainfall. In the past drainage ditches have been constructed to drain away excess water. Most of these lead into natural streams that eventually join the Beverley Brook. Willow saplings thrive in the wetter areas and many drainage ditches are conspicuous for their mass of young willows. Also common in this habitat are species of rush and sedge. The south west part of the Wimbledon Common Plateau tends to be better drained than the rest of the area, possibly because the gravel is deeper. Here, there is greater development of gorse and bracken and less willow and purple moor grass.

The habitats to be found on the Plateau are:- unimproved acid grassland, *Calluna* heath; and secondary woodland. The area near the Windmill, known as 'the Plain' (where some of the grass is kept mown for informal recreational pursuits such as picnicking, ball games and kite flying) and the large area taken up by the 18 hole Golf Course would have looked much the same as the rest of the Plateau, if not developed as an amenity.

Golf Course

Although the Golf Course is a purely artificial habitat, it does cover a large part of the Plateau area south of the Windmill, supporting an important recreational activity; therefore deserving brief mention. It has capitalised on the uneven topography created by earlier gravel excavations, which challenge the golfers and add to the scenic attraction (see Chapter 4). The existence of the Golf Course certainly increases the general openness of this part of the

Figure 6.3 The vibrant gold of common gorse adds colour to the Plateau.
Photo: Una Sutcliffe.

Plateau. Within it there are nevertheless scattered clumps of trees, mainly birch, oak and a few pines. Common gorse (*Ulex europaeus*) is an abundant shrub in the roughs; and its golden glory in flower adds dimension to this part of the Common, which the golfers share with walkers and runners. There is a grassland community in the roughs and sparse heather still exists in places. Irrigation and fertilisers are required to maintain the greens, but these are kept to a minimum in order to prevent groundwater contamination of the boggy areas on the hillside below.

Unimproved Grassland and *Calluna* Heath

It is unrealistic to separate the grassland from the heather (*Calluna vulgaris*) heath, for in many areas they merge. In some places heather is to be found in small patches amongst the grass, but in others there are large pure stands of *Calluna* dominated heath, only interrupted by the occasional tree sapling. There are also pockets of wet heath, which will be described later. This plant community is very rare in Greater London and so requires careful management.

But first let us think about the grasses, for they too have their own individual beauty, especially with the light shining through on a summer's day. The different species are often to be found in discreet blocks, probably because of subtle differences in soil property or water regime. Purple moor grass (*Molinia caerulea*) is one of the most abundant grasses on the Commons and is always present in wet areas, where there is impeded drainage. It grows in huge leafy tussocks, and the inflorescence, which appears in late summer, has an attractive purplish tinge. Another important grass, although less common, is mat grass (*Nardus stricta*). It is densely tufted, with needle thin leaves, and its inflorescence has the one-sided appearance of a comb. A most beautiful heathland grass, and one that grows in abundance in areas of the Commons where the soil is acid, is wavy hair grass (*Deschampsia flexuosa*). The spreading panicles have shining silvery spikelets which sway gracefully in the wind (hence the name). Growing among the heather are sheep's fescue (*Festuca ovina*) and fine-leaved sheep's fescue (*F.tenuifolia*). Common grasses, less typically associated with heath, but forming conspicuous and extensive stands, include common bent (*Agrostis capillaris*), with its silky pink inflorescence, and the

Figure 6.4 A great diversity of grasses is to be seen on the Plateau.

Figure 6.5 Adder's tongue fern.

Photos: Antony Sutcliffe.

contrasting soft but coarser textured Yorkshire fog (*Holcus lanatus*), straw coloured in the July sun. Meadow foxtail (*Alopecurus pratensis*) is an easily identifiable early grass, to be followed by a similar looking grass, Timothy (*Phleum pratense*), the inflorescence forming a dense spike, resembling a pipe cleaner. Two other prominent groups of plants in this acid grassland community are rushes – the ubiquitous soft rush (*Juncus effusus*) and heath rush (*J. squarrosus*), a shorter but extremely tough little plant. Sedges are important components of this community too. The common sedge (*Carex nigra*), hairy sedge (*C. hirta*), spiked sedge (*C. spicata*), oval sedge (*C. ovalis*) and brown sedge (*C. disticha*), can all be found amongst the grasses.

Also to be seen are some attractive wild flowers – common sorrel (*Rumex acetosa*), sheep's sorrel (*R. acetosella*), common cat's ear (*Hypochoerus radicata*), ragwort (*Senecio jacobaea*), yarrow (*Achillea millefolium*), creeping thistle (*Cirsium arvense*), rose-bay willowherb (*Chamaenerion angustifolium*); and early flowering plants such as buttercups, clovers and vetches. Three other members of the pea family, bird's-foot-trefoil (*Lotus corniculatus*), meadow vetchling (*Lathyrus pratensis*) and the dainty red coloured grass vetchling (*L. nissolia*), lighten up the meadows in the early summer. These plants and many more, together with the grasses, provide habitat for a myriad of invertebrates (to be described in Chapters 10 and 11). There are some rarer plants too. Spring vetch (*Vicia lathyroides*) has been identified on one sandy spot by the Golf Course. Common spotted orchids (*Dactylorhiza fuchsii*) are to be seen on the Plateau meadows most years and, though hard to find amongst the tall grass, there is a small patch of the very beautiful adder's tongue fern (*Ophioglossum vulgatum*). Marsh cudweed (*Gnaphalium uliginosum*), with its narrow woolly leaves, used to be a speciality of damp hollows on the Plateau, but now it holds on tenuously in only a few places.

Currently, there is more grass than heather on the Commons, although heather areas do seem to have increased slightly in recent years. The large expanses of purple heather are at their best in August and September and are indeed a sight to behold. This mainly dry heath is a very important habitat for nectar feeding insects, particularly bees, butterflies and moths.

Figure 6.6 One of the delights of the Commons in late summer is the profusion of purple heather *Calluna vulgaris*.
Photo: Antony Sutcliffe.

Figure 6.7 An area of wet heath with cross-leaved heath *Erica tetralix* and creeping willow.
Photo: Una Sutcliffe.

The dominant plant, heather or ling (*Calluna vulgaris*), is an evergreen dwarf shrub which has tiny leaves and spikes of small purple bell-shaped flowers. It is to be found on acid heaths and moorland throughout north west Europe. In recent years summer drought has caused scorching of some *Calluna* on the Commons. Hitherto the management policy has been to mow the heathland area annually so that the heather never reaches a straggly degenerate stage, but plans are currently afoot to stagger the heather cutting so that a mixed age structure can develop (Chapter 5).

Most of the grasses mentioned previously are to be seen growing amongst the heather. So, also, are the two species of rush, heath rush being particularly abundant. Other plants found amongst the heather are tormentil (*Potentilla erecta*), a small creeping plant with yellow flowers, and occasionally heath bedstraw (*Galium saxatile*), a dainty plant with leaves in whorls of four to six, and white flowers with a rather sickly scent. Sheep's sorrel is also an important component of the heather community.

In some parts of the Plateau *Calluna* forms large stands and the only other plants to be seen are tree saplings, particularly birch and oak. Young pines can also occur where there are parent trees nearby. In less well-drained areas young willows are abundant, mainly goat and grey willow, but creeping willow (*Salix repens*), a low spreading shrub of wet heaths, bogs and dune slacks, is present in a few places. Some cross-leaved heath (*Erica tetralix*) is present on one area of Putney Heath, growing alongside the *Calluna*. Also a member of the Ericaceae family, this is a plant characteristic of wet heath or moorland. It looks quite different from *Calluna*, with whorls of four small leaves and a head of globular pink flowers. Star Moss (*Polytrichum commune*), which has the appearance of miniature Christmas trees, is also to be found in these wetter parts. In fact, a recent survey has shown that the wet heath indicators described above, together with purple moor grass, rushes and sedges, have a strong correlation with areas of the Commons where the water table is locally close to the surface.

In the drier mixed grass and *Calluna* heath, bracken (*Pteridium aquilinum*) and common gorse are important components; and bell heather (*E. cinerea*), which used to be more abundant, is hanging on in only one locality.

Secondary Woodland

We have seen how, everywhere on the unimproved grassland and *Calluna* heath, tree saplings are trying to establish themselves and convert the landscape to woodland. Scattered birch, oak, aspen, poplar, and locally pines project above the field layer, and young willows are common in the damper areas and drainage ditches. Sapling development is naturally especially prevalent around isolated mature trees. 1995 was an exceptional year for acorn production and, where there is sufficient light, oak saplings occur in abundance around such parent trees. At least a few are surviving.

At present considerable areas of immature woodland are developing on the Plateau. These small patches of woodland consist predominantly of young birch trees of roughly even age, growing close together and allowing insufficient light for much shrub or field flora to develop. A typical and attractive grass of this habitat, conspicuous for its bright, hair-like green leaves, is wavy hair grass, also encountered on the open heath. These woods can sometimes be quite dense, which can be unwelcoming to the pedestrian.

Towards the north east, on Putney Heath, these Plateau woodlands become more frequent and the trees tend to be of greater maturity and of mixed age. In some there are as many oaks as birch. The oaks are slower growing, but live longer, and will eventually out-compete the birch under favourable conditions. In some of these woodlands a structure is beginning to develop, with a few additional tree species, for example, rowan, sycamore and sweet chestnut; and with an understorey of holly, bramble and some bracken. In the wetter areas hummocks of purple moor grass are abundant.

Along Parkside, the obvious vigour of a line of mature trees, mainly lime, sycamore, oak and hawthorn, planted some time ago, may reflect the thinness of the gravel there, or perhaps the removal of gravel by past commercial digging has permitted rooting in underlying deposits.

Although the current management policy is to keep the Plateau as open as possible, it is important to maintain some woodland as it provides habitat for insects, birds and other animals; foxes can commonly be seen there.

Figure 6.8 Without control secondary birch woodland, such as this, would soon replace heather.
Photo: Antony Sutcliffe.

Made Ground
Una Sutcliffe

As we have seen in Chapter 4, during the 1960s three extensive areas of Common were buried by hills of spoil that had been brought there as a by-product of road 'improvements'. One of these areas 'the Acropolis' is situated north east of the Beverley Brook bridge, when approached from the Brook Cottage Car Park. In addition, two prominent artificial hills were created north of the Windmill and close to the A3 trunk road, partly from spoil excavated from the Tibbet's Corner Underpass. They were humorously described by Graham Nicholson, author of *Walks on Wimbledon Common*, 1971, as 'Great Tibbet' and 'Little Tibbet'; Great Tibbet (60 m. O.D.) rising all of ten metres above the adjacent Plateau!

Today, such disposal of foreign material on the Commons would be unthinkable, because of the sensitivity of the Conservators and the fact that these areas are part of a Site of Special Scientific Interest, but, in the event, its arrival was not as disastrous as might have been expected. Landscaping has been very successful, with the establishment of herb rich grassy slopes, thickets of shrubs and small trees. From the hilltops there are now greatly improved views of the surrounding Commons, with glimpses of the built up area around. Most far reaching, however, of all the effects of this dumping has been the establishment on the heath of an entirely new habitat, gradually becoming colonised by its own plant and animal communities, bringing greater biotic variety than existed there before. Whereas most of the gravel-capped plateau is acidic, the dumped material contains old bricks and broken fragments of concrete, creating a more alkaline environment.

The hills constitute a predominantly grassy habitat, with a high rabbit population. The rabbits keep the turf short, which makes walking pleasant. Human trampling, however, has in some places caused serious erosion by exposing fragments of rubble – a poignant reminder of an artificial landscape. The flora contains a weird mixture of plants. Most are native wild species, many indicative of a disturbed environment, but there are also a few exotics, together making this artificial habitat very different from the surrounding heath.

Figure 6.9 'Great Tibbet', one of the now vegetated areas of spoil dumped on the Commons. In the foreground is plateau surface heathland. Photo: Tony Drakeford.

In 1997, in order to compare the floras of the hills of made ground and the Plateau heathland, a small survey was carried out by random sampling 20m. square areas of the larger hill and of the adjacent heath. Although the pH on the hill was 7.0 (neutral) that on the heath was only 4.5 (very acid). Interestingly, in this survey, there was no overlap at all of the plant species recorded at the two sites. The results also showed far greater diversity on the hill, which was not unexpected, as heathland is renowned for its low species diversity (Table.6.1).

Taking a general overview of the vegetation of the two hills, it was found that, in addition to a number of grass species typical of disturbed ground, for example, wall barley (*Hordeum murinum*), cocksfoot (*Dactylis glomerata*) and

Table 6.1 Mean Abundance – (based on random sampling using 0.5 metre quadrats) in two 20 m² enclosures on Putney Heath

Date: 31.05.1997   Weather: Sunny and warm

Species	Hill (0–50 %)	Heath (0–50 %)
Wall Barley	——— (≈10)	
Sheep's Fescue	———————————— (≈40)	
Cut–leaved Cranesbill	-	
Yarrow	—————— (≈20)	
Bird's–foot–trefoil	—————— (≈20)	
Ribwort Plantain	———————— (≈30)	
Grass Vetchling	-	
Lesser Trefoil	—— (≈5)	
Common Vetch	-	
Creeping Thistle	-	
Field Bindweed	————— (≈15)	
Hoary Cress	-	
Soft Brome	—	
Red Clover	-	
Ragwort	-	
Dandelion	-	
Heath Bedstraw	-	
Hogweed	-	
White Clover	——— (≈10)	
Sticky Mouse-ear	-	
Ling		———————— (≈30)
Mat Grass		—
Fine–leaved Fescue		———————————— (≈40)
Birch		-
Wavy–Hair Grass		-
Heath Rush		——
Moss sp.		—————— (≈20)
Oak		-
Bent Grass sp.		· —

Figure 6.10 Vegetational survey team, with quadrats, in action on the Hill.
Photo: Tony Drakeford.

false oat-grass (*Arrhenatherum elatius*), sheep's fescue was also present in abundance over large areas, an indicator perhaps of a maturing habitat.

Especially strongly represented on the hills is the pea family (Leguminosae). Not only do its members help to bind the soil by their complex rooting systems, but they also improve the soil by their ability to fix nitrogen. In fact, the vibrant colour and heady aroma of Spanish broom (*Spartium junceum*) in the early summer seems to symbolise this unique man-made habitat. Goat's rue (*Galega officinalis*) and everlasting pea (*Lathyrus latifolius*) give colourful displays in early summer, as does the gold of bird's-foot-trefoil, one of the main food plants of the Common Blue butterfly. Meadow vetchling is also abundant here. Less conspicuous is the very beautiful yellow vetchling (*L. aphaca*), with its clasping leaves and the dainty little pinky red coloured grass vetchling, tucked away amongst the grasses. Many of these plants are scarce or absent on the surrounding Plateau. Red and white clovers (*Trifolium pratense* and *T. repens*), which can also be seen in other parts of the Commons, are particularly abundant on the hills.

The ephemeral nature of the flora of man-made habitats is to be expected as the coloniser species are succeeded by other plants. The showy yellow flowers of colt's-foot (*Tussilago farfara*) once smothered the hills, heralding spring, but, alas, they have now diminished to a few small patches. Today, there are large stands of field bindweed (*Convolvulus arvensis*), white campion (*Silene alba*), horse radish (*Armoracia rusticana*), burdock (*Arctium lappa*), common comfrey (*Symphytum officinale*) and the ubiquitous ragwort, to name but a few of the conspicuous invaders of this disturbed landscape. Japanese knotweed has been a problem alien in the past, but fortunately it has since been eradicated.

Herbs enjoying a long growing season such as bird's-foot-trefoil, yarrow, creeping cinquefoil (*Potentilla reptans*) and meadow cranesbill (*Geranium pratense*) are joined in early summer by the spectacular yellow spikes of weld (*Reseda luteola*), a plant more often seen on chalk grassland. Teasel (*Dipsacus fullonum*) is another attractive plant found in abundance on these grassy slopes and in some years there have even been bee orchids. Among the wild plants is

Plants on the Made Ground.

Figure 6.11 (top left) Spanish broom.

Figure 6.12 (top right) Everlasting pea.

Figure 6.13 (lower left) Bird's-foot-trefoil.

Figure 6.14 (centre) Colt's-foot.

Figure 6.15 (lower right) Field bindweed.

Photos: Antony Sutcliffe.

a scattering of garden escapes. One conspicuous, but incongruous escape is a large clump of white irises, certainly worthy of first prize in a horticultural show!

A succession of flowering shrubs, hawthorn, bramble and dog rose, attract insects and birds through the seasons; the berries being a valuable food source for birds. Also scattered about the hills are some small trees, mainly common and Turkey oak and some fruit trees, providing perches and shelter for birds.

Not only do the hills carry their own distinctive flora, but some of the invertebrates are also restricted to this habitat. In general there are relatively few land snails on the natural habitats of the Commons, although slugs are numerous. This is because much of the substrate is too acid for shell production. It is significant, therefore, that two closely related species of banded snail, the brown-lipped snail (*Cepaea nemoralis*) and the white-lipped snail (*C. hortensis*), more typical of calcareous grassland, occur here. A cache of broken shells, the work of a thrush, was found beneath a tree on the smaller hill. Stems of grass, carrying the yellow cocoons of the Burnet moth are reminiscent of chalk downland; and so rich is the insect fauna that conducted walks on the Commons, to look for butterflies, grasshoppers and bush crickets, are usually concentrated on these areas of made ground, where the greatest diversity of species is likely to be found.

Woodland on the western slopes of the Commons

Irene Kettle

Examination of the aerial photo of the Commons (frontispiece) shows what appears to be dense woodland along its western margin, locally interrupted by Queensmere and by several artificially cleared golf fairways. In extent this woodland closely matches the sloping ground which descends from the flat plateau top of the Commons to the Beverley Brook. The underlying geology changes downslope from the Claygate member of the London Clay (locally overlain by Bagshot Sands); to the London Clay proper; and to river alluvium (Figures 2.1, 2.11). Soliflucted (plateau) gravels, with flora similar to that of the Plateau, locally mantle the upper and middle parts of the slope.

The predominant canopy trees of the woodland on the western slopes are pedunculate oak and silver birch; with holly and hazel as the principal shrub vegetation.

Walter Johnson, writing in 1912, implies that about one hundred years before this there was widespread tree clearance on Wimbledon Common. However, when looking at very early maps of the area it can be seen that there were then only scattered trees on the western slopes, indicating, perhaps, that prior to the felling episode, this part of the Common was maintained as wood pasture rather than high forest. A few veteran trees (mainly oaks) that must have survived the devastation some two hundred years ago can still be found. There is no evidence of the Commons having been used for arable farming, so it can be assumed, for the most part, that the forest has grown back through natural regeneration.

Although principally oak/birch woodland, many additional tree species are to be found here. Some, such as beech, hornbeam and sweet chestnut are locally quite abundant. The more mature woodland formed on the London Clay differs from that found on the drier soliflucted gravel ridges by its greater species diversity and its well developed shrub layer. In the stream valleys, where more light can penetrate, there is a rich field and ground flora, quite different from other parts of the woodland.

Figure 6.16 A veteran oak.
Photo: Una Sutcliffe.

Figure 6.17 Mature oak/birch woodland, showing canopy, shrub and field layers.
Photo: Antony Sutcliffe.

Figure 6.18 Map showing
routes of two walks described
in the text (green line); alternative return route (red line).
Base map reproduced from the
Ordnance Survey map,1:10,000,
with the permission of H.M.S.O.
Crown Copyright MC 100031556.
Draughtsman: Una Sutcliffe.

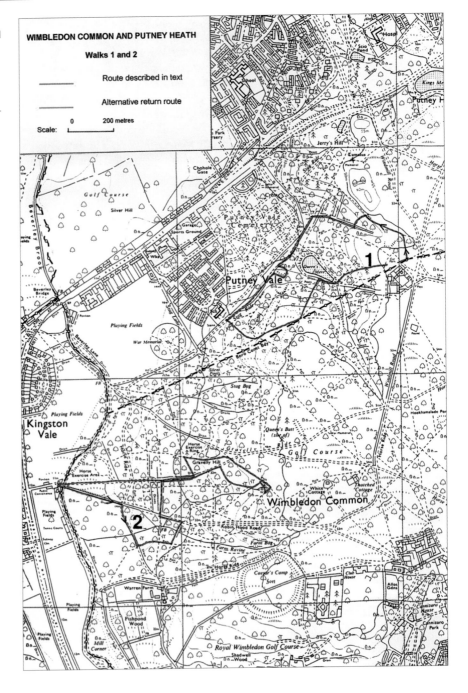

Figure 6.18 Map showing routes of two walks described in the text (green line); alternative return route (red line). Base map reproduced from the Ordnance Survey map,1:10,000, with the permission of H.M.S.O. Crown Copyright MC 100031556. Draughtsman: Una Sutcliffe.

Most of the woodland flora consists of native species but inevitably some aliens have found their way in. There are a few planted areas, but on the whole the woodland has the appearance of being 'natural' and the management policy is one of 'minimal intervention'.

The woodland is very beautiful at all seasons of the year. It is not easy to generalise about an area of this size and this complexity, so why not take a walk through the woods and witness for yourself some of its many surprises?

Two woodland walks are described below – the first on the north western slopes, the second on the south western slopes. The routes are indicated in Figure 6.18.

Walk 1

On entering the woodland, about 200 metres to the north west of the Windmill, we find ourselves in a wooded valley (documented in the archives of the National Rifle Association as Glen Albyn). We follow the course of a stream which leads us down towards Stag Ride, opening out just north east of Putney Vale Cemetery.

In this valley we encounter the smooth light grey trunks of aged beech (*Fagus sylvatica*), the upright and grooved trunks of sturdy oaks (*Quercus robur*) and the light and dark streaked trunks of mature hornbeams (*Carpinus betulus*), gracefully spreading out and showing off their green summer glory, which later becomes a golden cascade of carpeting amber leaves. In the autumn we feel the childish joy of walking on these leaves and on the scrunchy beech mast, which provides a store of nuts for the woodland fauna. Acorns, in years of plenty, are quickly seized upon, particularly by squirrels and jays. All of a sudden the whistles of a nuthatch may break the tranquility, as we watch it walking up and down tree trunk and branches. Later, perhaps, we hear the chip calls of the great spotted woodpecker; and not infrequently does the woodland echo to the yaffle call of the green woodpecker, with its bright red cap and yellow rump.

Where the trees are younger and the canopy less dense, the various shades of green of the understorey trees and shrubs are highlighted in shafts of summer sunlight; revealing on the slippery clay slopes dense thickets of blackberry (*Rubus fruticosus*), scattered bracken (*Pteridium aquilinum*), and honeysuckle (*Lonicera periclymenum*) clambering up tree trunks in search of light. There are hornbeam saplings, large and small hawthorn bushes (*Crataegus monogyna*), some sapling beech and very dense holly bushes (*Ilex aquifolium*) – the two last mentioned species forming a shrub layer beneath the canopy trees. In addition, the occasional yew (*Taxus baccata*), sycamore (*Acer pseudoplatanus*), birch (*Betula pendula*), elder (*Sambucus nigra*), bird cherry (*Prunus padus*) and black-thorn (*Prunus spinosa*) may be seen. Holly is the principal shrub layer species, but along the bed of the stream where there is more light, there is a variety of ferns and herbs. These include male fern (*Dryopteris filix-mas*), broad buckler fern (*Dryopteris dilatata*), wood avens (*Geum urbanum*), hedge woundwort (*Stachys sylvatica*), pale willowherb (*Epilobium roseum*), spear-leaved willowherb (*Epilobium lanceolatum*), water pepper (*Polygonum hydropiper*) and wavy bittercress (*Cardamine flexuosa*). Where there is even more light, three woodland grasses can be found, the shining leaved giant fescue (*Festuca gigantea*), the delicate slender false brome (*Brachypodium sylvatica*) and the tall hairy brome (*Bromus ramosus*). Toad rush (*Juncus bufonius*) and wood dock (*Rumex sanguineus*) are also growing here.

Arriving at the wide path known as Stag Ride, and walking in a southerly direction, with the Cemetery on our right, we come across wild cherry (*Prunus avium*), field rose (*Rosa arvensis*), and an interesting field flora, including greater stitchwort (*Stellaria holostea*), lords and ladies (*Arum maculatum*), enchanter's nightshade (*Circaea lutetiana*), fat hen (*Chenopodium album*) and, not surprising along this well used path, the common nettle (*Urtica dioica*), a plant indicative of disturbance. The rising woodland to the left has mature oak as the principal canopy tree, with hazel (*Corylus avellana*) and holly forming the shrub layer and blackberry in the field layer below. Other trees spotted near the path are the large-leaved lime (*Tilia platyphyllos*), red oak (*Quercus borealis*) and sweet chestnut (*Castanea sativa*), which is fairly abundant on the Commons. Close to the Cemetery wall there are stands of aspen (*Populus tremula*) which shimmer endlessly all summer, surrounded by their many offspring seedlings, with leaves deceptively large and pointed.

It is worth making a small diversion into the woodland south of Queensmere to visit some old rifle butts, a relic from the days when the National Rifle Association dominated the Commons, between 1860 and 1889 (see Chapter 4). Here you find a series of mounds and trenches surrounding a massive and gnarled hornbeam, hung with its delicate 'lanterns' of developing nutlets which go black when ripe. In late summer the ground is strewn with the fallen and disintegrating 'lanterns' (fruit catkins), which in the past have successfully generated many nearby sapling trees. All around, green light shows up the dark trunks of great oaks, with their branches reaching sideways to the sun. Also, with their orange/red berries glinting in the sun, some fine rowan trees (*Sorbus aucuparia*) can be seen along the woodland edge.

A few of the trees encountered on this walk may have been planted in the distant past, but most of the woodland on the slope appears to have developed by natural regeneration to its climax state. Although there has probably always been woodland here, managed to a greater or lesser extent by Man, there are no obvious indicators of ancient woodland. Plants often found in ancient woods, such as wood anemone (*Anemone nemorosa*), wood sorrel (*Oxalis acetosella*), dog's mercury (*Mercurialis perennis*), or even primrose (*Primula vulgaris*) do not appear to be present here, nor were they in Walter Johnson's day. However, it would seem that bluebells (*Hyacinthoides non-scripta*) were more abundant on the Commons in 1912 than they are today, although they are still common in the adjacent Fishpond Wood. Common dog-violet (*Viola

Figure 6.19 Dead trees left standing are valuable to wildlife.
Photo: Una Sutcliffe.

riviniana) and the showy foxglove (*Digitalis purpurea*) are now found in only a few places.

Throughout the woodland dead trees have been left standing or, when fallen, have been left to decay. This is a valuable part of any woodland habitat, as there is a host of invertebrates and fungi associated with decaying wood; it is all part of the recycling process.

Walk 2

From the Brook Cottage Car Park we enter the woodland by crossing over the Beverley Brook Bridge to Robin Hood Ride and walk past an area of disturbed ground on the left, 'the Acropolis' (one of the now overgrown heaps of spoil brought to the Commons, and mentioned earlier in this Chapter). As the path begins to ascend, the tree assemblages to north and south of the track take on a fairly uniform appearance. Here, on the London Clay, oak is very much the dominant tree, but birch and hazel are also well represented and holly forms a thick understorey . Although there is no current regime of coppicing in the woodland, there are some hazels that were obviously cut many years ago and now form part of the understorey .

Striking off southwards along a main path that crosses Farm Ravine, there is more dead wood to be seen here, and also attractive glades that allow light to penetrate, giving a richer flora and fauna at the woodland edges. Beside the stream (sometimes dry in summer) which runs from above Farm Bog to the

Figure 6.20 Fresh spring leaves make Robin Hood Ride sparkle.
Photo: Tony Drakeford.

Figure 6.21 Speckled Wood butterflies are often seen in woodland glades.
Photo: Tony Drakeford.

Figure 6.22 Rowan berries
are attractive to birds.
Photo: Antony Sutcliffe.

Figure 6.23 Beech and
hornbeam woodland in
autumn.
Photo: Antony Sutcliffe.

Beverley Brook, there is interesting bank vegetation of mosses and liverworts; and wavy bittercress and gipsywort (*Lycopus europaeus*) grow in these damp areas near the stream.

With the stream on our left, we follow an attractive narrow path for a short distance uphill, then take a path that re-crosses the stream and meets Robin Hood Ride opposite the site of former Brickfield Cottage. The larger hazels in glade areas, with their pollen covered male catkins and feathery crimson stigmas, are heralds of spring. In April, the magical appearance of the bright yellow Brimstone butterfly may be glimpsed as it flutters in the sunlight across the open glades, and later, throughout the summer, the Speckled Wood butterfly endlessly haunts these same glades and woodland paths. We frequently find the bright coloured fruits of the rowan, providing food for young thrushes in late summer and for migrant redwings and fieldfare in late autumn. The understorey here is enriched with elder, hawthorn, abundant holly, and ivy (*Hedera helix*) growing on pollarded oaks. Ivy provides insects with late autumn pollen, luscious black berries for thrushes in the winter and shelter for birds and small mammals throughout the seasons. Brambles and bracken grow in scattered profusion, providing vital ground cover and protection for wildlife.

A short distance down Robin Hood Ride we turn off northwards where there is a beautiful area of predominantly beech and hornbeam woodland. This appears to be a plantation, as the trees are of fairly uniform age. Some have a magnificent grandeur. Little light penetrates through the dense canopy of mature beeches, so there is no shrub or field layer to be found beneath them. In winter a warmth radiates from the gold and amber carpet of the woodland floor, and where there are hornbeams, their 'lanterns' make green carpeting in late summer. Unfortunately, any younger beeches tend to suffer from squirrel predation, which creates gaps in their bark where fungal spores can enter, thereby diminishing their chances of survival.

We approach Gravelly Hill (a major track) and proceed uphill in an easterly direction for a short distance. Here there is a community of oak, beech, large specimens of sweet chestnut, sycamore and an understorey of holly and bramble. We turn left into a wonderful winding woodland path (one of the joys of the Commons), which leads us to the horse ring; but as we ascend towards the more sandy Claygate Beds and the soliflucted gravel from the Plateau above, the woodland changes character. The ground becomes notice-ably drier, with birch the dominant tree. Birch can exist on poor soil where, along with some other forest trees, it is dependent for its nutrient uptake upon a symbiosis with certain fungi which form a mycorrhizal association with its roots (see Chapter 7). In this part of the wood there is a much more open canopy, with an understorey of birch saplings, quite dense bracken, holly and, unfortunately, the invasive rhododendron (*Rhododendron ponticum*). On the whole we are fortunate that vigorous non-native plants such as rhododendron and sycamore have not taken a strong hold in the woodland, although there is an increasing amount of Norway maple (*Acer platanoides*) which is recognised as being invasive.

Figure 6.24 Caesar's Well, and part of the circle of Austrian pines planted in the 1870s to commemorate the 1871 Wimbledon and Putney Commons Act.
Photo: James Reader.

Figure 6.25 Bryophytes (mosses and liverworts) adorn the banks of this stream, below Caesar's Well.
Photo: Antony Sutcliffe.

From the horse ring at the top of Gravelly Hill it is but a short distance (though one must be wary of golfers) to the well-known landmark 'Caesar's Well'. A ring of large granite blocks marks the site of the well, which was long ago filled in, and this is surrounded by a circle of Austrian pines (*Pinus nigra*), planted in the 1870s to mark the passing of the Wimbledon and Putney Commons Act of 1871. The banks of the stream running from the springs around 'Caesar's Well' abound with the emerald green moss (*Mnium hornum*) and the thalloid liverwort (*Pellia epiphylla*), both found in similar habitats on other parts of the Commons. In late spring the symmetry of the unfolding fronds of male and broad buckler fern is a sight to behold.

Of course, all woodland goes through the seasonal transitions. In winter the stark dark trunks and branches are portrayed against a sky ever changing in colour and mood. In spring it plays host to many excited singing and nesting birds and their young, searching for food and shelter amongst the fresh greenery that season provides. Here is an area of cool tranquil beauty in the summer heat and a feast of bright fruits and golden colours in the autumn. Mature woodland, such as we have on the western slopes of the Commons, is a habitat of outstanding importance for the diversity of wildlife it supports.

Chapter 7

Fungi and Lichens

Pete Guest and Frank Dobson

The Fungi of Wimbledon Common and Putney Heath

Pete Guest

Fungi are similar to plants in some ways, but do not possess the capability to photosynthesise, so gain their energy from living or dead plants and animals. In doing this they perform an essential function in the ecosystem, as in feeding on dead and decaying matter they recycle the basic nutrients essential to new plant growth. In this activity they are joined by bacteria and many soil animals such as earthworms, without whom the natural growth and death systems of the earth would fail; so it is no exaggeration to say that we depend on fungi as much as on any other part of the earth's living systems.

There is no real difference between the terms mushroom and toadstool, except in perhaps implying edibility, but, for simplicity, we shall use the term mushroom here. A mushroom is the fruiting body of a normally much larger organism which is usually hidden in the ground as a mass of minute, hair-like filaments called hyphae. The hyphae develop into a network called the mycelium, which grows through the material from which the fungus feeds. Often the mycelium is so fine that it can only be seen through a microscope, but can be visible in some species when it binds together into a mat. The fruiting body is formed when conditions are right, usually by two mycelia joining together, and in most species this occurs in autumn. There are two distinct groups of fungi, the Basidiomycetes where the spores are developed on specialised cells on the fruiting body and then fall off to be distributed by wind, and the Ascomycetes which form spores in small sacs from which the spores are shot out. Most of the species discussed in this text are of the former group as this includes all of the gilled fungi which most people recognise as fungi, having an obvious cap and stem. The second group includes a variety of forms such as candle-snuff fungus (*Xylaria hypoxylon*) and coral spot fungus (*Nectaria cinnabarina*), which are found frequently on the Commons and are as easily recognisable as their names imply.

Only a minority of species found in Britain have common English names, reflecting perhaps the traditional British disinterest in this diverse group of lower plants. Several thousand species of fungi can be found in the U.K., but a large number of these are very rare or only recognisable by experts. Of these at least 150 have been positively identified on the Commons, and it seems highly likely that many more remain to be discovered, especially those that need specialised skills to identify. Every autumn in past years a number of people have descended on the Commons with the purpose of collecting large numbers of edible fungi, mainly for sale. Sadly, some collectors have even been seen to destroy any fungi they do not want. The Conservators have decided to act on this and now do not permit any person to collect more than would be reasonable for personal use. It is not the purpose of this text to try to identify the edible species. If you want to try these out then it is your responsibility to

Figure 7.1

Figure 7.2

Figure 7.3

Figure 7.4

Figure 7.5

Figure 7.6

Figure 7.7

Figure 7.8

Examples of fungi to be seen on the Commons.

Figure 7.1 Fly agaric *Amanita muscaria*
Photo: Tony Drakeford.

Figure 7.2 The blusher *Amanita rubescens*
Photo: Dave Haldane.

Figure 7.3 Shaggy ink-cap *Coprinus comatus*
Photo: Tony Drakeford.

Figure 7.4 Bay bolete *Boletus badius*
Photo: Dave Haldane.

Figure 7.5 Birch polypore *Piptoporus betulinus*
Photo: Antony Sutcliffe.

Figure 7.6 Common earth-ball *Scleroderma citrinum*
Photo: Dave Haldane.

Figure 7.7 Stinkhorn *Phallus impudicans*
Photo: Tony Drakeford.

Figure 7.8 Sulphur polypore *Laetiporus sulphureus*
Photo: Antony Sutcliffe.

ensure that your identification is accurate. Some people also have quite severe allergic reactions to mushrooms that others thoroughly enjoy. If you think you have eaten a poisonous mushroom, you should go immediately to a hospital casualty department, taking a sample of what you have eaten if possible.

Perhaps the most familiar mushroom to most people, even if they have never actually seen one, is the fly agaric (*Amanita muscaria*). This is a common red capped mushroom, often with white flecks, which grows around the base of birch trees in autumn, and is often depicted in fairy stories. Like most species of this genus it is toxic, and its name comes from the medieval practice of using it to stupefy flies. Almost as common, and also with a cap of 5 to 15 cm across, is the blusher (*Amanita rubescens*), which has a brownish stem and cap and which grows in woodland or near trees. These, and many other mushrooms, are examples of mycorrhizal fungi that live in a mutually beneficial relationship with the trees, by supplying the trees roots with nutrients in exchange for the sugars created by the tree. Other fungi, such as the honey fungus (*Armillaria mellea*), are perhaps less welcome, especially by foresters, as they parasitise the tree and can destroy it. However, many trees do live long lives despite being infected with honey fungus and in natural woodland it plays a vital part in the ecosystem. In the great storm of 1987 a large number of trees were blown over, but interestingly not many of those already hollowed out by the actions of fungi, as a hollow tube is mechanically stronger than a solid rod.

A second group of fungi quite commonly found on the Commons in autumn are the Russulas. These have mostly bright red, purple, yellow or greenish caps that are flat or slightly convex. Key features are that the flesh is granular and crumbles easily, and the gills are very neat and geometric. Red capped russulas include the fragile russula (*Russula fragilis*) and the blackish-purple russula (*Russula atropurpurea*); the common yellow russula (*Russula ochroleuca*) has, as its name suggests, a yellow cap, and the geranium-scented russula (*Russula fellea*) has a straw coloured cap. Another group is the milk-cap fungi that exude droplets of a liquid that looks like milk when damaged, and which feature clearly identifies the group. Those most commonly found are the oak milk-cap (*Lactarius quietus*) and the ugly milk-cap (*Lactarius turpis*).

The shaggy ink-cap, or lawyers wig (*Coprinus comatus*), is quite often found in grassy areas on the Commons, and is distinguished by the black inky fluid that drips from the edge of the cap from which the group is named. These can grow quite large with a cap size from 5 to 15cm and stems from 10 to 37cm and can be easily seen when so large. A smaller cousin, the glistening ink-cap (*Coprinus micaceus*) is usually only up to 10cm high and grows on the stumps of broad-leaved trees or buried wood. Two even smaller ink-caps can also be found, (*Coprinus plicatilis*) and fairies' bonnets (*Coprinus disseminatus*), which are often found in large groups on or near to tree stumps. Also found on grassy areas near the Windmill are two of the wax caps, (*Hygrocybe miniata*) and the conical wax cap (*Hygrocybe conica*) and, of course, the fairy-ring champignon (*Marasmius oreades*).

The Boletes are distinguished by having tubular gills and the one most frequently found on the Commons is the red-cracked boletus (*Boletus chrysenteron*), which has a 4 to 11cm reddish cap which cracks to show coral coloured flesh. Others of this type include the bay bolete (*Boletus badius*), the orange birch bolete (*Leccinum versipelle*) and brown birch bolete (*Leccinum scabrum*). In some years the much sought after cep (*Boletus edulis*) can be found in abundance. The Commons do have rarer species and in 1992 a *Boletus pruinatus* was found on a fungi foray led by Brian Spooner from Kew Gardens.

Different species of fungi show a wide range of colours; from the bluish purples of the amethyst deceiver (*Laccaria amethystea*) and wood blewit (*Lepista nuda*), the yellow of the chanterelle (*Cantharellus cibarius*) and the reds of the Russulas. Some are almost pure white, such as the false death cap (*Amanita citrina*), or *Mycena pura*, or very dark, such as the ugly milk-cap. By far the majority tend to be fawn, greyish or brownish, and typical of this are such species as the oyster mushroom (*Pleurotus ostreatus*), which has a bluish-grey colour and can be found growing on stumps and fallen or standing tree trunks, in particular beech. The Clitocybe group often have funnel shaped caps and range from the cloudy grey, tinged with buff, of the clouded agaric (*Clitocybe nebularis*), to the pale yellow buff of the tawny funnel cap (*Clitocybe flaccida*).

Finally, we must not forget the fungi that do not have caps and stems. In addition to those mentioned earlier you can see the large birch polypore (*Piptoporus betulinus*) all year round. This is one of the bracket fungi. It grows out of the side of birch and it can reach up to 20cm across and 6cm thick. Many smaller brackets are also frequent on the Commons, including the hairy stereum (*Stereum hirsutum*) and many-zoned polypore (*Coriolus versicolor*). The common earth-ball (*Scleroderma citrinum*) is frequent from late summer to autumn in woodland, and when ripe emits clouds of millions of spores if touched even quite gently. Sometimes the first indication of there being a stinkhorn (*Phallus impudicans*) nearby is the offensive smell from the slime on its tip. This attracts flies which are fooled into landing on the fungus and having its spores stuck to them, which is how this species achieves dispersal.

There are several excellent books that can help in identifying fungi but a good start is to attend one of the fungi forays that are often arranged on sites like Wimbledon Common and Putney Heath, where you can learn about the characteristics used by mycologists to identify the different species.

Air Pollution and the Lichens of Wimbledon Common and Putney Heath

Frank Dobson

The close proximity to London, and the air pollution associated with this city, has meant that, over the last two hundred years, the lichen communities of Wimbledon Common and Putney Heath had been reduced to a very impoverished state. Fortunately this situation is now changing and an increasing number of species is being re-found on the Commons. This contrasts with the situation in those parts of England, such as Devon and Cornwall, which have the lowest levels of the pollutant sulphur dioxide (SO_2). Until recently the air in these regions was almost completely clean but now the world wide background level of pollution is increasing and this is affecting some of the most sensitive lichens found in these regions.

It is probably several centuries since the air was clean enough on the Commons to support such species as lungwort (*Lobaria pulmonaria*) or the sausage lichen (*Usnea articulata*). During the long period of industrial development, as the air pollution over the Commons increased, more and more species were lost until a low point was reached in the nineteen fifties and sixties. By this time almost all the tree-living lichens had disappeared. The ecological niche left vacant by their loss was largely filled by the 'pollution lichen' (*Lecanora conizaeoides*). It was first recorded in Britain from Leicestershire about 1860 and then rapidly spread across polluted areas of England. It may have been introduced on wood imported from near sulphurous springs in Iceland. On the Commons its grey-green crust covered many of the trees, filling the areas left vacant by the loss of the other lichens. This species has now diminished but is still found mainly on the rougher areas of bark of the birch trees (*Betula pendula*) that are common on the acid soils of the Plateau, including the golf course. It is also found on the fence posts and old seats with white areas of dead lichen due to the attack of a fungal parasite *Athelia arachnoidea*.

This recent reduction in *Lecanora conizaeoides* and other of the most pollution tolerant species has been noted from many formerly polluted areas of Britain. *Parmeliopsis ambigua* is another species that has spread from central and eastern Scotland in a manner similar to *Lecanora conizaeoides*. This species became common on the acidified bark of oak trees (*Quercus* sp.) throughout polluted areas of Britain. In Surrey, on Ranmore Common for example, it could be found on very many of the oak trees. It is now very much rarer there and is only currently recorded from about six trees. It has not yet been recorded from the Commons and it is possible that, with the improved air conditions, it may never be.

This reduction in the level of SO_2 in the air is due to a number of causes; the Clean Air Act, the pressure of environmental awareness on the main polluters and in SW London, the closure of power stations such as Fulham, Battersea and Kingston have greatly aided this process. Though the close proximity to the Commons of the very busy A3 gives rise to high levels of nitrous oxides, as long as these do not fall on the lichens as a concentrated acid solution in rainwater, they appear to have little affect, and indeed there is some evidence that this extra nitrogen may provide a nutrient for more growth.

It is noticeable that many of the sites on the Commons which have the most prolific growth of leafy lichens are those where the pollution is filtered out by a dense growth of surrounding trees, and where there is a track or clearing, allowing the sunlight to illuminate a particular branch or tree. It may frequently be just a single, suitably positioned branch that has this luxuriant lichen growth. The trunk of such a tree may often bear few, if any, lichens. This may be due perhaps to lower light levels, an older and therefore different type of bark or, possibly, from the high acid concentrations on the bark which are dissolved in the rain making it steadily more acid as it trickles down the trunk from the canopy. Some of the oak trees, especially those near Beverley Brook, have orange to rusty red patches of *Chaenotheca ferruginea*, another species that is tolerant of fairly high levels of air pollution which is becoming less common as pollution levels fall.

Many of the wooded areas found on the Commons are dense with a thick undergrowth of brambles (*Rubus* sp.), hawthorn (*Crataegus monogyna*) and holly (*Ilex aquifolium*), see Chapter 6. These dark conditions are only suitable for a limited number of lichen species. Many of these are sensitive to air pollution as well and still seem to be missing. Ivy (*Hedera helix*) is also frequently a problem in many Surrey woods as it smothers and kills any lichens growing on the trees. Fortunately it is not very prolific on the Commons and so does not seem to be too great a threat.

Much of the woodland is fairly young, there being only a limited number of really old trees still surviving. In clean air regions, it is these old trees that usually have the greatest range of lichen species. Unfortunately, due to pollution, these ancient trees on the Commons have very few lichens. Often the only lichen present is the glaucous-green, powdery *Lepraria incana* growing near the base. A number also support *Cladonia coniocraea*, with its small leaf-like squamules and finger-shaped fruiting bodies.

Any mature elms (*Ulmus* sp.) that were present on the Commons have now been killed by Dutch Elm Disease Fungus (*Ophiostoma ulmi*), its spores carried by the beetle *Scolytus scolytus*. Elms can have a very good lichen flora including some species that are almost entirely restricted to them. Unfortunately, due to this loss, it is not now possible to know if any of these interesting species were ever growing on the local elms.

There is normally a succession in the species growing on a tree, with the first lichens appearing on twigs after only approximately two years. These are small species often living largely under the new thin bark with only the dot-like fruiting bodies visible. These species are normally followed by crustose, and then leafy lichens as the twigs mature and grow. As twigs protrude from a tree they are therefore very exposed to any air pollution present. Due to the pollution levels still occurring, the whole of the early part of this succession does not occur on the Commons.

An important lichen as part of this succession is *Physcia aipolia*, a small grey leafy lichen with black centred jam-tart like fruits. It is found on the more mature twigs, frequently at a fork, or on rougher parts such as leaf scars. It is a species that only grows in relatively clean air and its recent return to a number of sites in Surrey such as Ashstead Common and Nonsuch Park indicate an improvement in local air quality. This improvement has now reached Wimbledon Common, where a single small specimen has recently been found in a sheltered site near Beverley Brook, where the presence of the nearby stream raises the humidity.

The lichen flora in a semi-polluted region is frequently at its best on willows (*Salix* sp.), growing in the more humid air near water. On the Commons this is true of a number of areas such as the small pond near Warren Farm where *Parmelia* species, *Evernia prunastri* and *Ramalina farinacea* are abundant. The reappearance here of the leafy grey lichen *Parmelia perlata* is a sure sign of improved air quality. Small specimens up to 2 cm across have been found in nearby areas, but in 1996, one was located on an oak tree on the bank of Beverley Brook that measured nearly 6 cm across. This is the largest specimen yet found in this part of the country.

The return of *Parmelia caperata* also shows improved air conditions. It has slowly become re-established closer to central London and in 1996 was even found in the grounds of Buckingham Palace. Small specimens of this species have now been found on the Commons. It is usually an apple green colour with very small wrinkles across its lobes. The specimens located on the Commons are mainly in shaded areas protected from the worst of the pollution. In sites such as these, where the light levels are fairly low, it does not produce the usual greenish pigment. This allows the maximum amount of light to reach the algal cells inside the lichen, enabling them to produce more of the sugars needed by both the alga and the fungus. The lack of coloured pigments in lichens growing in shaded conditions is even more noticeable in the normally bright orange *Xanthoria parietina*. When found in shade, only the centres of the fruits and the lobe tips are orange. The remainder of the lichen is light grey.

As lichens consist of a combination of a fungus and an alga, dispersal and reproduction have added complications. Any fruiting bodies formed are produced by the fungus alone and therefore contain only the fungal spores. When these spores germinate they will die unless they can rapidly obtain the appropriate alga and so grow into a mature lichen. Like many lichens, *Parmelia caperata* seldom produces fruiting bodies and relies on vegetative means of dispersal. Small pieces become detached and if they then land on a suitable site, as they contain both the fungus and the alga, they can develop into complete lichens. These small outgrowths take several forms and if the surface of mature lobes of *Parmelia caperata* is examined under a hand-lens, small areas can be seen where the outer layers have split open to reveal a powdery mass (soredia) that consists of mixed algal cells and fungal hyphae. It is these soredia that enable this species to spread to new sites.

The orange *Xanthoria parietina* is frequently common on bushes and trees where bird droppings have given nutrient enrichment. On these bushes it is found with a number of other species that also like nutrient enrichment such as *Buellia punctata* and *Physconia grisea*. These species almost cover the elders (*Sambucus nigra*) beside the path leading from Barham Road to Beverley Meads. The bushes are very exposed and are used as perching and lookout sites by birds, which provide the nutrient enrichment. The absorbent bark of the elder retains moisture and nutrients, providing an ideal site for lichens and mosses to grow. The isolation of these bushes also means that they are exposed to high levels of light. When it is in such a well lit situation, *Xanthoria parietina* is bright orange. This orange pigment protects the algal cells from being damaged by excessive ultraviolet light and, being acidic, is rather unpalatable so reducing browsing by insects. *Xanthoria parietina* is a species that produces abundant fruits and these will be seen as orange button-like structures raised up from the surface of the lichen. On nearby concrete fence posts a closely related species *Xanthoria calcicola* may be found. This species differs from *Xanthoria parietina* in having very few fruits and a rather knobbly surface.

There are few habitats available on the Commons for the lichens that grow on rocks. Almost the only natural 'rocks' are the pebbles of the plateau gravels. Pebbles in sites such as Ashtead Common, have a good lichen flora but, to date, no lichens have been recorded from them on Wimbledon Common and Putney Heath. The reason for this is not clear but it may be due to the disturbance from horses and walkers, which keep the gravels on the move. It is, therefore, the man-made substrates that form the important habitats for

Figure 7.9

Figure 7.10

Figure 7.11

Figure 7.12

Figure 7.13

Figure 7.14

Figure 7.15

Figure 7.16

saxicolous species. There are several markers, boundary posts and memorials made from limestone and these support a typical range of species for this substrate such as *Caloplaca citrina, Phaeophyscia orbicularis* and *Lecanora dispersa. Lecanora muralis* is another species that appears to have profited from man-made structures. Its natural habitat is on bird perching sites in hard limestone areas. In such regions it is a rare species but, over the last few years, it has become common on paths and roofs in most towns and cities. Its arrival on the pavements of Chiswick in the nineteen eighties caused great speculation as to its origin and before it was identified, it was even suggested that it might have come from outer space!

Examples of lichens to be seen on the Commons.

Figure 7.9 *Lepraria incana.*

Figure 7.10 *Cladonia coniocraea* (on oak).

Figure 7.11 *Physcia aipolia.*

Figure 7.12 *Evernia prunastri* (yellowy green lichen).

Figure 7.13 Xanthoria parietina.

Figure 7.14 *Parmelia caperata* (on oak; return shows improved air quality).

Figure 7.15 *Caloplaca citrina* (on concrete).

Figure 7.16 *Lecanora muralis* (on concrete).

Photos: Frank Dobson.

Table 7.1 List of lichens recorded on Wimbledon Common and Putney Heath with their most frequent habitat

On acid heathland:
  Cladonia diversa
         fimbriata
         furcata
         subulata
  Cetraria aculeata
  Peltigera rufescens

On Oak:
  Chaenotheca ferruginea
  Cladonia coniocraea
  Evernia prunastri
  Hypogymnia physodes
  Lepraria incana
          lobificans
  Parmelia caperata
          perlata
          subaurifera
          subrudecta
          sulcata
  Physcia aipolia
          adscendens
          tenella
  Usnea subfloridana
  Xanthoria polycarpa

On Elder:
  Buellia punctata
  Physconia grisea
  Xanthoria parietina

On Willow:
  Candelariella reflexa
  Parmelia revoluta
  Ramalina farinacea

On concrete posts and limestone:
  Caloplaca citrina
  Candelariella aurella
  Lecanora albescens
          campestris
          dispersa
          muralis
  Phaeophyscia orbicularis
  Physcia caesia
  Rinodina genarii
  Verrucaria nigrescens
          viridula

On wooden fences and benches:
  Cyphelium notarissi
  Lecanora conizaeoides
  Micarea denigrata
  Mycoblastus sterilis
  Placynthiella icmalea
  Lecanora albescens
  Thelocarpon laureri
  Trapeliopsis flexuosa
  Xanthoria candelaria

On other Substrates:
Dustbin lid
  Candelariella vitellina
Copper run-off
  Psilolechia leprosa

In the copper run-off from a plate on the memorial near the Windmill is found one of the most interesting species on the Commons. This is *Psilolechia leprosa*, a small nondescript grey crust, sometimes with pale pink, globose fruits up to 0.5 mm across. Copper salts are used as a powerful fungicide in horticulture but here is a lichen, the major part of which is a fungus, that actually thrives where the majority of other fungal species could not become established on such a lethal site.

There are a number of other man-made habitats on the Commons such as concrete posts, brick walls and bridges. These sites have not yet been examined in great detail and should, no doubt, produce more species to add to the list of lichens found. Good sites are often old fences and benches. Where these have not been treated with preservative a distinctive range of species can usually be found. Wimbledon Common and Putney Heath is no exception and possibly the two most interesting lichens found were on benches behind the Windmill. *Cyphelium notarisii* is a beautiful small yellowish green crust with black fruits. It is rare in Britain where it has a very strong easterly distribution and is mainly found near the sea. The other rare lichen on these benches is *Thelocarpon laureri* which consists of clusters of minute yellow warts. These are the only records for these two species in Surrey. A rubber dustbin lid is another man-made substrate that has been found on the Commons, with the granular, yellow *Candelariella vitillina* growing on it. Even the large number of dogs that are exercised on the Commons have probably helped another small yellow lichen, *Candelariella aurella,* to become established on the lower part of concrete posts.

The Golf Course is mainly man-made and is largely restricted to the plateau gravels. This site does not appear to be very suitable for lichens and few are found in this habitat. The Golf Course was originally an area of impoverished acid heathland. This habitat is favoured by a number of lichen species which cannot easily compete with the fast growing flowering plants. It is fortunate that small areas of this habitat still remain. The best of them can be seen east of the Windmill. This is a very important site as little heathland still remains in south west London this close to the centre of the capital. When the trees in this area shed their leaves in autumn these can form drifts on the ground cutting off the light and killing any lichens which grow underneath. Nevertheless, there are still some open patches of bare soil and it is in these areas, and under the fringing heather (*Calluna vulgaris*) that a range of *Cladonia* species is found. Although rare on the Commons, the spiky, glossy, chestnut coloured clumps of *Cetraria aculeata* are sometimes found in this habitat.

It is pleasant to be able to report an ecological improvement in the environment, and the return of a number of lichen species to Wimbledon Common and Putney Heath and the nearby Richmond Park has been noticeable over the past few years. As it has in parts of South West Surrey, the pollution sensitive *Usnea subfloridana* returned as a small, rare species to Wimbledon Common. Following its return, this bushy lichen only grew to about 5 mm high before the pollution killed it. For the first time in 1995 a specimen over 1 cm high was found on an oak tree and this specimen is still growing; an encouraging sign of improved air conditions.

There is still much work to be done to record all the lichens that are now growing on the Commons. If air conditions continue to improve, many more lichen species should return. It may be hoped that one day the Commons will appear as they did several hundred years ago, with the trees once again covered in luxuriant lichens.

Chapter 8

Aquatic Habitats of Wimbledon Common and Putney Heath

Una Sutcliffe, Tony Drakeford, Dave Haldane

The unique geology, topography and drainage patterns of Wimbledon Common and 'the hand of man' have all contributed to the formation of wetland areas (see Chapter 2). Spring-fed bogs supply several streams flowing either directly into the Beverley Brook or via artificially created ponds. Shallow ponds, some seasonally dry, have also developed in some of the old gravel excavations. All these habitats contribute to the diversity of plant and animal life found on the Commons.

Bogs
Una Sutcliffe

One of the special features of the Commons is the occurrence of bogs, containing a rich assemblage of wetland plants and associated fauna. The wet areas on the Plateau, resulting from localised water-logging, discussed in Chapter 6, differ from bogs, in that they are not permanently wet.

Natural bogs, some large, some quite small, are to be found where there are springs at the junction of the plateau gravel and Claygate Beds, or sometimes from impervious layers within the Claygates themselves (Chapter 2). These springs occur mainly on the steep western slopes of the Commons. They carry acid ground water; and bog vegetation, typically with an abundance of bog moss (*Sphagnum* sp.) develops around them. Excess spring water, together with surface drainage water, forms streams, which flow into the Beverley Brook.

Comparing the bogs today with those described by Walter Johnson in 1912, it would appear that, in general, the flora is less species rich now than in those days. The changes and losses must reflect human disturbance and management neglect during the turbulent intervening years.

There are three bogs worthy of special mention: – Those of the Ravine (a deep cut valley, with a stream leading into the new Ravine Pond and then finally into Queensmere); Stag Bog; and Farm Bog; the two last mentioned supplying streams that flow directly into the Beverley Brook. The flora of the first two will be described only briefly, but more space must be given to the largest and most spectacular bog on the Commons – Farm Bog; which has been extensively studied, particularly for the relationship of hydrology to its floral distribution. An understanding of this should help future management, for these bogs are dynamic ecosystems. Curbing scrub development and artificially maintaining a high water table is sometimes necessary to maintain the quality of these important habitats.

The bogs of the Ravine

First let us take a look at 'The Ravine'. Walter Johnson mistakenly named this valley Glen Albyn, a lovely romantic name for what must be one of the prettiest parts of the Common. Recently, however, it was discovered that the National Rifle Association had previously named the valley north of the Windmill, Glen Albyn, so henceforth the long valley that traverses the golf course south of the Windmill has had its name changed to 'The Ravine'. The head water is both surface run-off from the Plateau and spring-fed, so that parts of the valley are moist, even in times of severe drought, and there are additional wet flushes and boggy areas which feed the stream further down the valley.

The banks of the stream, like many of the other streams on the Commons, are clothed with the attractive thallose liverwort (*Pellia epiphylla*), and the graceful broad buckler-fern (*Dryopteris dilatata*) is commonly seen nearby. Hazel (*Corylus avellana*), rowan (*Sorbus aucuparia*), holly (*Ilex aquifolium*) and bramble (*Rubus fruticosus*) are all abundant, and the woodland on either side is mainly of oak (*Quercus robur*) with some willow (*Salix* sp.). Following the stream towards Queensmere, one encounters boggy areas with attractive wetland species, such as lesser spearwort (*Ranunculus flammula*), water mint (*Mentha aquatica*) and great willowherb (*Epilobium hirsutum*). It is in one such boggy area that a dam has been made, so creating a new pond, aptly named Ravine Pond. The creation of this pond is described in Chapter 16.

The principal bog, however, is to be found further down the valley. Here, on the east bank of the stream, is one of the remaining strongholds for a most beautiful aquatic herb, the bogbean (*Menyanthes trifoliata*). As the name suggests, it has large trifoliate leaves with oval green leaflets. The flowers, by contrast, have a delicate appearance, with five petals which are pink outside and white within, conspicuously fringed with white hairs. This is a true native of the Commons, recorded 150 years ago at the same sites as today. Growing near the bogbean is water mint, a huge clump of greater tussock sedge (*Carex paniculata*) and eared willow (*Salix aurita*) – a species that is rare on the Commons. More common plants indicative of wettish woodland include hazel, bramble, nettle (*Urtica dioica*) and water-pepper (*Polygonum hydropiper*) – an annual quick to colonise this type of habitat. Bog moss (*Sphagnum* sp.) was seen in 1991, but five years later it was no longer there. Undisturbed peat, more than one metre thick, is visible in the bank of the stream.

Stag Bog

We move on now to Stag Bog (Fig. 2.17), which lies west of the Golf Course. Two valleys, some distance apart, join together as one stream leading to the Beverley Brook. The southern stream is very overgrown and, in the dry summer of 1996, there was no sign of any water. The main bog, which unfortunately suffers trampling, especially by dogs, lies at the head of the northern stream. Nevertheless, the showy yellow flag iris (*Iris pseudacorus*) is spreading and there is a good patch of marsh pennywort (*Hydrocotyle vulgaris*), with its attractive round leaves, borne on erect stalks and looking like miniature parasols. The principal grass is purple moor grass (*Molinia caerulea*) and the rushes (*Juncus effusus*) and (*Juncus bulbosus*) are also fairly abundant. All this is interspersed with much bramble and bracken (*Pteridium aquilinum*) under an open canopy of young birch (*Betula pendula*) and oak, with also the occasional willow and alder buckthorn (*Frangula alnus*).

Dappled sunlight, close to the woodland edge, provides a good habitat for butterflies. A Red Admiral, Comma and two Speckled Woods, were seen together on a sunny August afternoon.

This has undoubtedly been a better bog in the past. The evidence to support this is an extensive area of oxidised dry peat, suggesting that it has been partly drained by deepening of the stream. Recently remedial action has been taken to reverse this trend by positioning three dams across the stream to hold back the water, thus raising the water table. An increase in the amount of *Sphagnum* present here and also along the stream banks below the dams, has resulted from this operation.

Farm Bog

Farm Bog (Chapter 2, Fig. 2.25) is situated close to the southern boundary of Wimbledon Common, north of Caesar's Camp. It is the largest bog on the Commons and carries the most interesting plant communities. Like the other bogs, it is spring and rain fed. There is a gradient of about twelve metres from its main source to where it feeds its stream and the direction of drainage is from north east to south west.

Farm Bog is for me a magical place. Its uneven terrain, with *Molinia* hummocks alternating with various species of *Sphagnum*, makes it difficult to traverse. In places there are *Sphagnum* pools, a haven for dragonflies and damselflies. Even at times of drought, most of the bog remains wet, and the shallow pools stand out, adorned with lush bright green or yellow *Sphagnum*. This plant has the unique capacity to draw up water through its leaves and absorb it like blotting paper in its empty (hyaline) cells, which make up most of the plant. These cells, which are enclosed between green chlorophyllous cells, are pierced by large pores and are supported by spiral wall-thickenings. The spongy nature of this plant helps to keep the water table high.

Figure 8.1 Map showing zonation of plants on Farm Bog in 1991.
Drawn by Una Sutcliffe.

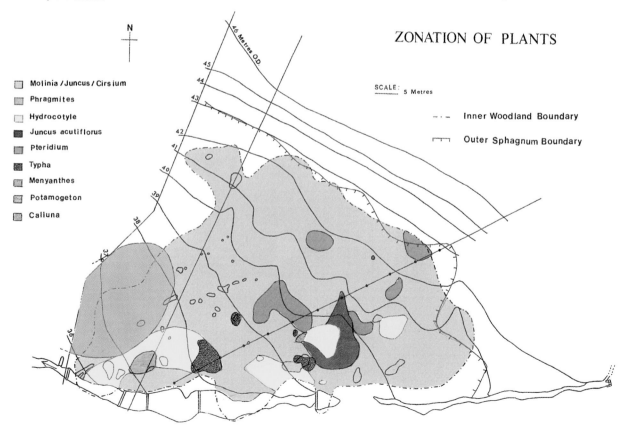

ZONATION OF PLANTS

Molinia / Juncus / Cirsium
Phragmites
Hydrocotyle
Juncus acutiflorus
Pteridium
Typha
Menyanthes
Potamogeton
Calluna

SCALE: 5 Metres

--- Inner Woodland Boundary

Outer Sphagnum Boundary

Figure 8.2 General view of
Farm Bog in May, with
Molinia hummocks.
Photo: Antony Sutcliffe.

Figure 8.3 Pools occur on
Farm Bog where the water
table is near the surface.
Photo: Antony Sutcliffe.

Figure 8.4 A carpet of
Sphagnum recurvum on
Farm Bog.
Photo: Antony Sutcliffe.

Figure 8.5 (below) *Typha* grows abundantly alongside *Phragmites,* where the Farm Bog water table is high.

Figure 8.6 (top right) Abundant marsh pennywort is a feature of Farm Bog in its wettest areas.

Figure 8.7 (bottom right) Bogbean growing on Farm Bog.

Photos: Antony Sutcliffe.

Although a large part of Farm Bog has a fairly homogeneous assemblage of plant species, some distinct zonation is also present. Even to the casual observer there is an orderliness in the plant distribution.

In the south western part of the bog is a very large (and getting larger) stand of common reed (*Phragmites australis*) and adjacent to this reed mace (*Typha latifolia*), often wrongly named bulrush. In 1990 this was confined to just a few places, but now, like the *Phragmites*, it is spreading. These two species are both robust fen plants that thrive in these conditions. They have stout rhizomes which enable them to spread rapidly. *Typha* also colonises from its fluffy windblown seeds. Obviously, these plants take up an enormous amount of water, so some management is needed to curb their advance. Yellow-flag iris, another rhizome plant growing by the stream, also does well. One of the very abundant and showy species in the summer is marsh thistle (*Cirsium palustre*). This grows throughout the bog and is a great nectar source for insects, particularly butterflies and bees. Marsh pennywort, with its distinctive round leaves, is abundant in pools and in the wettest regions adjacent to the stream, but is absent from the drier parts of the bog. Fortunately, bogbean is still thriving in its one patch.

At least four species of rush grow on Farm Bog. A large stand of sharp-flowered rush (*Juncus acutiflorus*), which likes wet acidic soils, is growing in a gully on the eastern side of the bog. On nearby higher ground bracken dominates.

Farm Bog has long attracted the attention of botanists, whose written record provides a valuable basis for the study of floral changes, resulting from both natural succession and human interference. Johnson (1912) described Farm Bog as "a small dark bog, formed by water oozing out below the gravel near Robin Hood Road. The water falls suddenly into Farm Bog ... good botanical ground. A little lower down the valley narrows to form the birch-clad Farm Ravine". He stated that Farm Bog was pre-eminently the haunt of the bogbean, indicating that it was probably then in greater profusion than it is today. Marsh Pennywort was abundant, and he described *Phragmites* as "the most interesting grass".

Johnson recorded many species that are not found on the bog today. These include the acid bog species cotton grass; and several species more typical of fen, including marsh marigold, water mint, cuckoo flower, ragged robin, and several sedges. In 1937, following ill-advised drainage operations on the bog, he reported that there had been several losses and that sundew was becoming very scarce. However, it must have clung on, because it was still there, together with bog asphodel, in a report made by the then Nature Conservancy Council in 1969. The reintroduction of sundew is under consideration.

What happened since is not entirely clear. Some slight hydrological change affecting the soil water regime and soil chemistry, human disturbance, or natural competition, may be responsible for the changing communities. But I suspect it is a combination of all these factors. Nevertheless, Farm Bog is still a very rich, but fragile, habitat.

Some substantial conservation work took place in the early 1980s to raise the water table by placing a number of dams in Farm Ravine stream, into which the bog drains. This achieved the desired effect by making the southern part of the bog much wetter. Also, at that time, the bog was made more open by the removal of some quite large birch and willow trees.

Before the start of regular management on Farm Bog, I conducted a study over a period of a year, August 1990 – July 1991, of the soil hydrology and its effect on the distribution of plant species. Since the results have formed a basis for future management, extracts from this study will be described briefly here.

In order to assess the environmental factors most influencing plant distribution, twelve dip wells, made of perforated gutter downflow piping, were installed at six metre intervals along a transect following as close as was practically possible to the main line of drainage (see Chapter 2, Fig. 2.25). These wells were to form the basis for collecting environmental data and linking this with plant distribution.

Water table fluctuations were monitored by taking well measurements on thirty five occasions during the study period. These readings provided information on:

(a) The response of the bog to rainfall episodes. This was very rapid. The bog acted like the overflow of a bath, pouring out excess water, which was channelled to cascade over the most westerly dam into the stream, allowing measurements to be taken of the rate of discharge.

(b) The average water table height for each well. These were found to vary considerably.

In addition to water table height, several other environmental variables were monitored at each well:

- Hydraulic conductivity (water movement through the ground).
- pH (measurement of acidity). This ranged from 4.6 to 5.8.
- Total Conductivity (the ionic content).
- Oxygen Saturation.

Twenty-four 1/4-metre quadrats were placed around each well (a total of 288 quadrats) and the plants identified. The percentage distribution for each plant at each well (site) was calculated. With this data it was possible, using a Computer programme called Discriminant Analysis, to calculate a score for each site which reflected the level of similarity, or otherwise between the twelve sites.

The environmental variables were then each plotted against the plant assemblage scores. The results were interesting. Water table height was the only variable that had a statistically significant bearing on the distribution of plants.

To summarise, most drainage collects in the south-west corner of the bog, where there is a concentration of swamp and fen species, tolerant of waterlogging. Where the water table is less close to the surface, there is a uniform assemblage of other bog species. Minor topographical variations can reflect changes in vegetation.

The plan of the zonation of plants (Fig. 8.1) was made during my survey in 1991. Even in one year's study it was possible to observe changes in flora. Today, at the end of the 1990s, with natural succession, and subsequent conservation work, there are inevitably changes in plant distribution. Unlike woodlands, which are climax communities and fairly stable, Farm Bog is an unstable dynamic community, dependent upon its soil hydrology, with a tendency to revert to wet acid woodland, with consequent drying out, if given the chance.

During the course of my study I was able to observe Farm Bog in all seasons. The winter of 1990-91 was cold and for several days, only the tall stems of *Phragmites*, *Typha* and *Juncus* rose above the snow cover. The *Molinia* hummocks were completely covered with pristine white snow, looking like waves on the ocean. The pools were mainly ice covered, except for those where there was seepage, and here the temperature of the water was above zero. There must be many more secrets yet to be revealed!

Plants noted on Farm Bog in 1991

Sycamore	*Acer pseudoplatanus*
Marsh Bent	*Agrostis stolonifera var. palustris*
Silver Birch	*Betula pendula*
Downy Birch	*Betula pubescens*
Ling (Heather)	*Calluna vulgaris*
Shepherd's Purse	*Capsella bursa-pastoris*
Star Sedge	*Carex echinata*
Oval Sedge	*Carex ovalis*
Marsh Thistle	*Cirsium palustre*
Lichen	*Cladonia coniocraea*
Common Spotted-Orchid	*Dactylorhiza fuchsii*
Broad Buckler-Fern	*Dryopteris dilatata*
Rosebay Willowherb	*Chamaenerion angustifolium*
Greater Willowherb	*Epilobium hirsutum*
Water Horsetail	*Equisetum fluviatile*
Moss	*Eurhynchium praelongum*
Alder Buckthorn	*Frangula alnus*
Yorkshire Fog	*Holcus lanatus*
Marsh Pennywort	*Hydrocotyle vulgaris*
Holly	*Ilex aquifolium*
Yellow Flag	*Iris pseudacorus*
Sharp-flowered Rush	*Juncus acutiflorus*
Bulbous Rush	*Juncus bulbosus*
Compact Rush	*Juncus conglomerata*
Soft Rush	*Juncus effusus*
Honeysuckle	*Lonicera periclymenum*
Common Bird's-foot-Trefoil	*Lotus corniculatus*
Gipsywort	*Lycopus europaeus*
Purple Loosestrife	*Lythrum salicaria*
Bogbean	*Menyanthes trifoliata*
Moss	*Mnium hornum*
Purple Moor-grass	*Molinia caerulea*
Liverwort	*Pellia epiphylla*
Common Reed	*Phragmites australis*
Moss	*Pohlia nutans*
Moss	*Polytrichum commune*
Tormentil	*Potentilla erecta*
Bog Pondweed	*Potamogeton polygonifolius*
Bracken	*Pteridium aquilinum*
Pedunculate Oak	*Quercus robur*
Buttercup	*Ranunculus sp.*
Bramble	*Rubus fruticosus*
Eared Willow	*Salix aurita*
Grey Willow	*Salix cinerea*
Crack Willow	*Salix fragilis*
Lesser Skullcap	*Scutellaria minor*
Bittersweet	*Solanum dulcamara*
Bog Moss	*Sphagnum palustre*
Bog Moss	*Sphagnum recurvum*
Bog Moss	*Sphagnum squarrosum*
Great Reedmace	*Typha latifolia*

Ponds and Meres

Tony Drakeford

Today, there are nine ponds and meres on the Commons, including Ravine Pond, created in 1998 (see Chapter 16). An additional major wetland area, lying just outside the Commons' boundary is Fishpond Wood. Its restoration is discussed in Chapter 16.

In addition to the present day water bodies, a map dated 1911 reveals sites of others which have long since disappeared. Two of these were situated at the northern limits of Putney Heath, one named Grantham Pond, lying just west of the Green Man Tavern and the other, smaller pond, west of Telegraph Road. The location of this pond, created as a result of gravel diggings, can be clearly defined by the surface topography. Other former ponds of the Commons are the sinister named Black Ponds (now known as the Silent Pools). These are situated west of Stag Bog and were apparently very rich 'hunting grounds' for entomologists. Now they are barely visible, being heavily overgrown and filled with leaf litter from the surrounding woodland. They only hold water during periods of excessive rainfall. An earlier map of 1865 includes a further pond, situated opposite North View, which was used for the sport of curling.

Our ponds are very important for the diversity of wildlife they attract. All are man-made, created either from wet areas on the clay that have been dammed (Kingsmere, Queensmere and Scio Pond), or old gravel pits that have flooded. Each pond has a characteristic flora based on its size, depth, water chemistry and possibly other factors such as shade or exposure, which gives it a unique attraction and value. Whilst some support the complete range of aquatic, marginal and marsh vegetation, others display a very impoverished and sparse selection.

Rushmere

Situated in the centre of Rushmere Green (Fig.2.20), referred to by many as the village green, this is by far the most ancient pond on the Commons. Its origin is probably Medieval.

Known as Rushmore in Tudor times, this pond, which even in severe drought conditions does not completely dry up, was a convenient and valuable source of rushes for thatching, and a place where villagers could keep their domestic ducks. It was always an amenity pond around which Victorian and Edwardian nannies would perambulate their charges and in the winter it would be used for skating. Today it is a magnet for walkers, model boat enthusiasts and dogs intent on retrieving sticks thrown by their owners, and on the rare occasions of thick ice it is still used for skating. As a result of these numerous activities, coupled with its acidity, wildlife is comparatively limited. Amphibians shun the acid water. Dragonflies and damselflies (Odonata) pay increasingly frequent visits but, in the absence of emergent vegetation and aquatic plants, they do not linger long.

Surprisingly, however, Rushmere has for several years supported a shoal of Japanese koi carp, at some stage in the past released into the shallow water, probably by an aquarist grown tired of his prize fish. The best time to view the carp is early on a calm, still summer morning, when their golden torpedo shapes can sometimes be glimpsed as the fish slowly cruise beneath the ripple-free surface.

Trampling around the margins of the pond until recently limited the rushes to a few small clumps, but happily the last few years have seen a revival, particularly along its west and north western banks.

The delightful summer visiting birds, swifts and house-martins, love to skim low over the water snapping up emerging insects, taking full advantage of the wide open spaces surrounding Rushmere to indulge in their aerial manoeuvres. In winter, flocks of mainly black-headed gulls rest on the water or scream aerobatically around the margins, catching bread thrown by equally excited children.

Travelling north along Parkside for a short distance we come to Bluegate Gravel Pit.

Bluegate Gravel Pit

This is an old gravel pit, basically divided into two sections connected by a narrow channel. Lightly wooded on all but its roadside fringes, Bluegate is one of the most attractive of all the aquatic habitats.

Throughout the year, but especially in spring, Bluegate offers some stunning visual effects, enhanced by a variety of subtle and quite dramatic lighting conditions, notably early in the morning and again late in the evening, as the setting sun shines 'lattice-like' through the screen of silver birches along the western shore.

Being so shallow, the lake tends to dry up completely in hot summers, so no fish can survive there in the long term. Around the marshy and muddy margins grow, amongst others, a profusion of marsh pennywort, *Sphagnum*, soft rush, willow, silver birch and oak, but yellow flag iris is scarce. The water is acidic (pH 5.3) and although a few frogs spawn from time to time, very few tadpoles hatch. However, dragonflies thrive; the main species present include the Common, Ruddy and Black Darters. It is only at Bluegate that migrant species from the Continent, namely the Yellow-winged and Red-veined Darters, have been recorded spasmodically in late summer over the years.

Figure 8.8 Bluegate Gravel Pit.
Photo: Tony Drakeford.

Moorhens and coots breed both on the small island in the larger half of Bluegate, and along the well sheltered margins. For several years now, a pair of Canada geese has also nested on the island, raising an annual brood of fluffy yellow goslings, much loved by local children.

A few hundred yards due west of Bluegate lies Hookhamslade Pond.

Hookhamslade Pond

Perhaps the least known of all the ponds, it is nevertheless quite unique because of an extraordinary event which took place in 1911. It was here, in May of that year, much to the dismay of the local botanists who greatly valued the site, that a trench was dug and the pond temporarily drained in order to obtain a clear area of heathland on which to lay a great bonfire to celebrate the coronation of King George V.

Nestling nowadays within a birch spinney, it lies partly hidden from view behind a screen of trees closely skirting its perimeter. Because of this it can appear rather gloomy on dull days, especially in winter.

Although tending to dry up in hot summers, Hookhamslade still yields a reasonable range of wildlife species. It is the regular haunt of our most magnificent and largest dragonfly, the Emperor. The Black Darter and Migrant Hawker dragonflies and Emerald damselfly can all be found there too. An attractive day-flying moth, the Orange Underwing, is a common sight in April, taking full advantage of the dense stand of young birch woodland bordering the adjacent swathe of heathland. Fish life is absent, but two amphibians, the frog and newt, breed there occasionally.

Lying rather off the beaten track and consequently quite peaceful,

Figure 8.9 Hookhamslade Pond.
Photo: Tony Drakeford.

Hookhamslade and its surrounds are worthwhile places for keen bird watchers to sit quietly scanning the trees. Surrounding bankside vegetation is sparse, with just a few brighter spots when small clumps of yellow-flag iris flower there in summer.

Continuing in a northerly direction along Parkside and opposite Inner Park Road is 7 Post Pond.

7 Post Pond

This pond has been selected for a detailed study as a prime example of the treasures to be discovered in one of the Commons' most accessible ponds (see Chapter 9).

Kingsmere

Lying approximately midway between Tibbet's Corner and the junction of the A3 with Roehampton Lane, is yet another roadside mere. This is the largest of the Commons' ponds and is extremely rich in wildlife. Situated just yards from the busy A3 trunk road, Kingsmere is screened from the highway by a thick belt of oak, willow and birch trees which, whilst acting as a visual barrier, do not shield the mere from the constant roar of speeding traffic. Nevertheless, the wildlife appears quite tolerant of the noise and consequent pollution, and the human ear can somehow, with practice, accept and obliterate the intrusion when absorbed in studying the flora and fauna.

Being very shallow throughout, a series of hot dry summers in the 1990s caused evaporation, resulting in extensive areas of the bed becoming exposed and dry. The local herons took full advantage of the situation and on some days, eight or nine birds could be seen standing motionless around the few remaining puddles containing stranded fish, spearing them almost at will. To ease the problem, the eastern half of the mere was dredged and deepened, the spoil obtained being used to create an island in the centre. This has enhanced the pond aesthetically and provides safer nesting sites for birds. Rushes and reedmace, surplus to requirements, were initially lifted from 7 Post Pond and planted around the perimeter of the island, after which nature rapidly took over, colonising the new area with grasses, alder, willow scrub and reeds.

The island now attracts a variety of birds, including coot, moorhen, mallard and Canada goose, all of which regularly nest. A pair of mute swans has on occasions visited for a while, but at the time of writing, they have not been

Figure 8.10 Kingsmere.
Photo: Antony Sutcliffe.

known to breed. With luck the keen observer may be rewarded in summer with a fleeting glimpse of a hobby hawking above the water for dragonflies.

The northern margins of Kingsmere are very marshy. Rushes and yellow flag iris predominate. Water-lilies are well established not far from the bank and the invasive introduced water milfoil, also known as Parrot's feather (*Myriophyllum aquaticum*), is abundant over large areas of the mere.

The shallow, open waters attract a wide range of Odonata species, with the majority of those listed for the Commons breeding here. Particularly common is the Emerald damselfly, with Ruddy and Common Darter, Black-tailed Skimmer, Broad-bodied and Four-spotted Chaser and Emperor dragonflies also abundant. In a good year, it is possible to have within clear view up to thirty pairs of Common and Ruddy Darters ovipositing at the same time.

The alderfly is frequently seen laying its raft-like batch of eggs on iris leaves, whilst caddis and the slim-bodied water measurer lurk in the rushes. Here too can be found the colourful larvae of the Knot Grass moth feeding on iris, the blooms of which also attract the long-tongued Large Skipper butterfly in June.

South-west of Kingsmere is Curling Pond.

Curling Pond

Of the two purpose-built 'curling ponds' originally sited on the Commons only one now remains. Sometimes referred to as Jerry's Pond, it lies west of the hills and very close to the A3. The game of 'curling', a kind of Scottish 'bowls on ice', was played both here and on the other rink, formerly situated close to the Wimbledon Common Golf Club in Camp Road, but filled in many years ago and now serving as a small Car Park.

Curling Pond is the smallest of the Commons' ponds. It is very shallow and is apt to dry out during all but the wettest of summers. Surrounded by mature trees, mainly birch, falling leaves add to the problem each autumn but, nevertheless, the pond supports the highest population of smooth newts on the Commons. Frogs also spawn there in large numbers, although tadpoles are liable to perish if water levels drop. The pond is also known to have an abundance of water snails.

With the exception of the Black Darter dragonfly and Emerald damselfly, most species of Odonata make an appearance during the summer months. A notable invertebrate, the whirligig beetle, can be seen circling the shallows on the water surface. Its eyes are in two parts, enabling it to see both above and below the water at the same time.

Scio Pond

A few hundred yards west of Kingsmere, and close to Roehampton Lane, lies Scio Pond. Many years ago the water was regularly stocked with a variety of fish, including, as an experiment, trout. Not surprisingly these were unsuited to the acidic water and did not survive. Although the practice of official stocking has long since ceased, fish are regularly placed there by anglers and as a result Scio is the richest water for shoaling roach, perch, carp and associated hybrids. Large pike swim there and in 1999 the pond was electro-fished to remove troublesome predators which were beginning to create problems among the nesting water fowl.

Despite what must be widespread predation by resident fish on dragonfly and damselfly nymphs, both insects are common, with an abundance of Azure and Common Blue damselflies. Broad-bodied and Four-spotted Chasers, Ruddy and Common Darters, all breed there, helped by adequate stands of yellow-flag iris and soft rush growing around the northern perimeter.

Scio Pond has been used for dumping unwanted terrapins, which on

Figure 8.11 Scio Pond.
Photo: Tony Drakeford.

summer days can occasionally be seen cruising with head angled above the surface. The pond suffers from considerable disturbance by local dogs, but during quiet periods a heron can be expected to drop in and try its luck among the fish population.

Queensmere

Walking due west of the Windmill, down a well-wooded incline, Queensmere can be glimpsed through the trees.

Thought by some to be a rather gloomy stretch of water, when compared with the more open aspects of both Kingsmere and Bluegate, Queensmere is by far the deepest lake on the Commons, shrouded on all sides by a variety of mature trees. Created to commemorate the Diamond Jubilee of Queen Victoria, it was excavated on an area of previously flat marshy grassland, crossed by a stream. Prior to the formation of the mere by damming, the location was said to be very fashionable and described as being "rather trippy", attracting large numbers of local visitors on bank holidays. In the 1830s the meadow acted as the focal point on the Commons for a number of famous duels until, in 1838, a man was shot dead and thereafter duelling was prohibited.

Very little in the way of marginal vegetation exists in Queensmere, but a superb stand of yellow water-lily graces the water in the summer. This species boasts the largest leaves of any British plant. Close by is a sizeable patch of white water-lily.

Rich in fish life, the water supports perch, and on a warm summer's day huge shoals of yearling fish can sometimes be seen swimming just below the surface. Large tench cruise near the bottom and pike of up to 22 lb have been recorded. In the mid 1990s it was noted that much wildlife, including coot,

moorhen and amphibians were mysteriously disappearing (see also Chapters 5 and 12). Suspicions were aroused when, standing above the lake on still sunny mornings, it was possible to observe sizeable pike moving slowly among the submerged vegetation. A team of specialists was employed to electro-fish the Mere and some large pike were netted and removed. During the course of this operation a 22 pounder was pulled out. At an Investigation Centre it regurgitated a black-headed gull, whilst another yielded up a 4 lb tench!

Both frogs and toads breed in Queensmere. Daubenton's bats skim the surface, homing in on the rich insect population. A colony of Brown Long-eared bats roost in a group of trees around the perimeter. Both moorhen and coot raise families and occasionally a pair of mute swans will stay for a few weeks. At dusk, tawny owls hoot in the surrounding woods. Dragonflies and damselflies are a very common sight, with most of the Commons' species recorded here. It is the main location for the Brown Hawker dragonfly, the only British species sporting brownish-tinted wings.

Ravine Pond

This new pond has been created in a valley upstream of Queensmere and is described in Chapter 16.

Beverley Brook

Dave Haldane

As we have seen in Chapter 2 (Fig.2.17) there is only one water course of any size on the Commons – the Beverley Brook. Entering Wimbledon Common at Mill Corner (TQ 21727065) it flows for approximately 1800 metres in a northerly direction before leaving the Common beneath the Beverley Bridge on the A3 Kingston By-pass. Beyond this it continues through Richmond Park and thence to the Thames at Barnes.

The Brook provides the only riverine habitat on the Commons, with potentially high biological diversity and amenity value, although unfortunately this is only partially achieved at the present time. To understand the problems causing this, we must look upstream to the catchment area that provides the headwaters of the Beverley Brook. Comparisons must also be made with neighbouring rivers, such as the Wandle, which flows into the Thames at Wandsworth, downstream from the Beverley Brook and the Hogsmill which enters upstream at Kingston. Both these rivers have their sources on the chalk of the North Downs where they receive some chalk water input.

In contrast, the Beverley Brook and its tributaries, the Pyl Brooks, beginning at Worcester Park, Sutton and Carshalton, rise on Tertiary deposits within the London Basin. David Stubbs, of the London Wildlife Trust, in his *Beverley Catchment Ecological Survey*, 1989, mentions a much lower diversity of freshwater invertebrates and aquatic flora in the Beverley Brook than the Wandle. The main cause of this biotic impoverishment is nevertheless largely man made rather than natural. Not only is the floodplain of the upper reaches of the Beverley Brook highly developed, with most run-off coming from the roofs and roads, but until 1999 the treated effluent from a large sewage plant at Worcester Park was discharged into it. This discharge contributed up to 90% of its flow during periods of drought. In that year the Worcester Park Works was decommissioned, its water being substituted with treated effluent continuously pumped through a conduit from a more modern plant on the Hogsmill. The replacement water should have a higher degree of purity, the biotic consequence of which is currently being investigated. On Wimbledon Common and in Richmond Park, streams issuing from bogs and other wet areas (Chapter 2) contribute cleaner water to the Brook although all of these tend to cease flowing at times of drought.

The densely populated higher reaches of the Beverley Brook above Wimbledon Common are extremely vulnerable to flooding. Although extensive engineering work including the construction of relief conduits has been carried out, existing channels still remain inadequate to carry away flash floods. It is important therefore that the part of the Brook that flows through Wimbledon Common, allows speedy passage of water. Past engineering works have provided the canalised channel, lacking morphological variety that we see today.

Prior to 1986 the Greater London Council (GLC) was responsible for all flood alleviation schemes in the metropolitan catchments. It was during their period of involvement that the wooden toe boarding and the occasional concrete embankments were installed. Unfortunately this form of channel engineering has had a marked effect on the ecology of the river. With no natural contours, the development of riffle and pools, which are an essential ingredient of a healthy marginal life, have been suppressed.

The responsibility for the Beverley Catchment is now in the hands of the Environment Agency (EA) the successor to the National Rivers Authority (NRA). They have a duty to further nature conservation and are undertaking a number of river enhancement schemes along the Brook, removing the toe-boarding and concrete banks to create more natural river corridors. It is

Figure 8.13 Beverley Brook,
showing steep banks and
wooden toe boarding.
Photo: Antony Sutcliffe.

Figure 8.13 Beverley Brook,
showing steep banks and
wooden toe boarding.
Photo: Antony Sutcliffe.

important also to conserve existing areas of green space adjacent to the Brook
to provide flood storage areas, so reducing the need for heavy engineering
works in the future.

Historically the Beverley Brook is poorly documented. The evidence available throws little light on the character of the river much before the latter part
of the nineteenth century. Walter Johnson in his book on 'Wimbledon
Common' gives us a possible clue to the origins of the Brook's name. Beverley
is derived either from Befer-Beaver and leah-meadow, (Beaver meadow) or
possibly from the Saxon name Beferithe, Befer-Beaver and rith-brook
(Beverley brook). From this Johnson concludes that Beavers could still be
found along the Brook during Saxon times.

During the late 19th century a marshy stretch of land skirted the Brook on
the Common's western edge. The older maps identify this area as the Beverley
Plain. Today this same stretch, which runs between Warren Farm and Brook
Cottage and lies at the lower end of the Farm Bog ravine, favours an oak
(*Quercus robur*) dominated woodland habitat. A tiny remnant of this marsh still
remains just north of Fishpond wood, with such plants as water figwort
(*Scrophularia aquatica*), gipsywort (*Lycopus europaeus*), purple loosestrife
(*Lythrum salicaria*), great willowherb (*Epilobium hirsutum*), marsh thistle
(*Cirsium palustre*) and soft rush (*Juncus effusus*).

Where disturbances have occurred, scrub woodland and the occasional
stands of hawthorn (*Crataegus monogyna*), elder (*Sambucus nigra*) and nettles
(*Urtica dioica*) are found. This is graphically illustrated by the artificial mound,
known as the 'Acropolis', to the east of the Brook Cottage bridge. Created with
the Conservators knowledge from masses of imported rubble, it altered the
character of this part of the Common (See Chapter 4).

The Brook itself has undergone several transformations. A brief reference
informs us of it being deepened during the 1880s. A fuller account informs us
that in 1936 it was widened and straightened and the banks built up using the
dredgings. Walter Johnson, in an article written for the *Journal of the
Wimbledon Natural History Society* in 1937, entitled Wimbledon Common – a
Retrospect 1888-1937, stated, "The reconstructed Beverley no longer
meanders, no eyots dot its course, no fish dart about in its waters, no voles
burrow in its banks". We also know with certainty that some years later,
during 1952, a section of the brook running parallel to the Richardson Evans
Memorial Playing Fields was widened and the bank side raised to reduce the
risk of flooding the playing fields.

Figure 8.14 Hawthorn in flower on banks of the Beverley Brook.
Photo: Tony Drakeford.

Figure 8.15 Colourful fruits of field rose alongside the Brook.
Photo: Antony Sutcliffe.

The average width of the Beverley Brook is six metres. The channel substrate along the river course is a mixture of clay and coarse gravel with considerable fine silt deposits. The water flows very slowly during dry spells, with depths ranging from 15cm to 30cm. An avenue of hawthorn, oak, ash (*Fraxinus excelsior*) and sycamore (*Acer pseudoplatanus*) casts a deep shade over large stretches of the Brook. Where this occurs, marginal and aquatic vegetation is sparse.

There is a noticeable contrast in the areas where light penetrates, even in dappled form. Here long strands of filamentous algae, Nuttall's pondweed (*Elodea nuttallii*) and broad-leaved pondweed (*Potamogeton natans*) flourish. Slightly less common are the several stands of curled pondweed (*Potamogeton crispus*). A native aquatic plant which appears in several parts of this reach but is considered scarce in Greater London is the small pondweed (*Potamogeton berchtoldii*). Two other aquatics occurring here, which are of interest because they are scarce or uncommon in the Greater London area, are the various-leaved water starwort (*Callitriche platycarpa*) and a single colony of the showy unbranched bur-reed (*Sparganium emersum*) with its two types of leaves, upright stem leaves and the floppy ribbon-like floating leaves.

The steep slopes of the banks, sometimes as much as 3.5 metres high, tend to be unstable with the lower portion periodically below the water level. Consequently only very resilient plants such as ivy (*Hedera helix*), stinging nettle and bramble (*Rubus fruticosus*) can tolerate this regime. The upper slopes are more productive, with plants such as common figwort (*Scrophularia nodosa*) and cuckoo pint (*Arum maculatum*) sheltering among the prolific cow parsley (*Anthriscus sylvestris*), mugwort (*Artemesia vulgaris*) and marsh thistle.

Animal life in the Brook has not been fully surveyed but reports from the NRA Fisheries Unit in 1992 indicate river fish as poor and macro-invertebrates limited. The only fish reported were eels, three spined sticklebacks and tench, the latter found in the stretch close to the Richardson Evans Memorial Playing Fields. It was thought the tench had entered the Brook from an overflow channel fed from Queensmere.

The following macro-invertebrate families were identified and considered abundant along the Commons' reaches. They are the water shrimps (Gammaridae), flatworms (Planariidae), pond snails (Lymnaeidae), bladder snails (Physidae), pea mussels (Sphaeriidae), leeches (Erpobdellidae), water lice (Asellidae), larval stage of non-biting midges (Chironomidae) and worms (Oligochaeta). More recent biological surveys have been undertaken on the Beverley Brook during 1998 and 1999.

Macro-invertebrates are often used as biological indicators to assess the water quality of a river. This method has been used first by the NRA and later the EA for monitoring the various reaches of the Beverley Brook, including Wimbledon Common at TQ 21507150. The Biological Monitoring Working Party (BMWP) score is calculated by assessing which families of invertebrates occur in a sample. Each family represented is allocated a biological score ranging from one to ten, (one being the most pollutant tolerant and ten being the least pollutant tolerant). The scores for the sample are then totalled and the results will give the site a biological quality class, ranging from A to E. In 1992 the Biotic Class for all the Beverley Brook samples including Wimbledon Common was D – poor. Recent samplings have shown no improvement but it is hoped that the water quality will improve with the change from Worcester Park to Hogsmill treated sewage effluent. The pH of the Brook averaged 6.1 and, not surprisingly, the conductivity was extremely high, as much as 975 μS cm at Brook Cottage Bridge (see Chapter 2).

Although the river corridor is rich in bird species it seems the Brook holds little attraction for those birds generally associated with flowing water. Mallards and coots are the most common residents, with both species recorded as breeding birds. Since 1986 they have been joined by the mandarin duck, an introduced species now naturalised in local waters. The only other water dwellers found here are the grey wagtail (feeding on the silt drifts along the water's edge) and, as an occasional visitor, the kingfisher.

There have been no confirmed sightings of water voles or water shrews during the past decade. Small holes occasionally found in the banks are the work of common shrews and wood mice. With the absence of suitable prey it is very unlikely that the mink, now well established in Surrey, will find the Beverley to its liking.

In 1988 a Beverley catchment ecological survey was carried out along the length of the river, by David Stubbs of the London Wildlife Trust. This was followed up in 1998 by a re-survey of the same area carried out by LWT, London Natural History Society and the Ecology & Conservation Studies Society for the purpose of establishing a yard-stick for the assessment of future ecological changes. The Environment Agency has just produced the *Beverley Brook Catchment Strategic River Corridor Survey*; so together, valuable ecological data is already at hand.

Today, the riverside paths are pleasant to walk along, especially when the hawthorn is in blossom, but how much nicer it would be if the river itself was more attractive.

With the Environment Agency currently working on schemes for flood alleviation of the Beverley Brook, what better time to address improvements. While we applaud the move to improve water quality, we must not ignore the Brook's intrinsic value as an aesthetically attractive river. Some enhancements could be achieved quite simply and effectively, such as the trimming back of overhanging trees along the river corridor to improve light penetration with a consequent increase of aquatic plants; and the removal of some of the toe-boarding to encourage a more natural flow. Perhaps slightly more ambitious, and requiring some degree of channel engineering, would be the creation of marshy bays to add character and diversity to this ancient waterway.

Chapter 9

Special Studies of Two Selected Habitats on the Commons

Una Sutcliffe and Tony Drakeford

7 Post Pond
Una Sutcliffe

It is remarkable that, of all the ponds on Wimbledon Common and Putney Heath, the one that has greatest biotic variety also seems to have the greatest number of factors working against it. This is 7 Post Pond, a special place for me.

7 Post is a perched water table pond (see Chapter 2), with an area of only 950 square metres, created during the nineteenth century by gravel extraction; and later used for a time as a 'water splash' by waggoners needing to expand the wooden wheels of their carts. It is situated at the boundary of the Common, immediately adjacent to Parkside, the principal highway between Putney and Wimbledon, which at busy times may carry as many as thirty vehicles a minute. A concrete wall, supporting the road, its lowest part below water level, forms one edge of the pond. Considerable pollution is caused by wind blown debris, possible run-off from the road and vehicular gasses. As the pond is so accessible it is occasionally used as an educational facility by parties of school children accompanied by their teachers.

Since the pond is small and shallow there is an on-going problem of natural

Figure 9.1 General view of 7 Post Pond, with busy Parkside beyond.
Photo: Antony Sutcliffe.

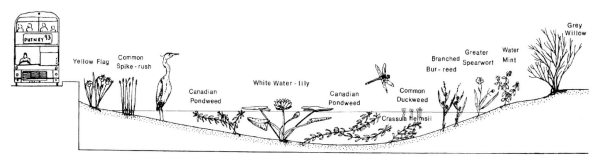

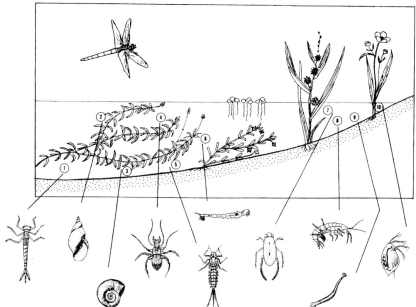

POND INVERTEBRATES

1.   Damselfly nymph
2.   Great Pond Snail
3.   Great Ramshorn
4.   Water Spider
5.   Mayfly nymph
6.   Ghost larva
7.   Lesser Water Boatman
8.   Freshwater Shrimp
9.   Leech
10.   Water Flea (*Daphnia*)

Figure 9.2 Schematic section through 7 Post Pond, illustrating representative flora and fauna.
Drawn by Una Sutcliffe.

succession, where marginal plants spread towards the centre, decreasing the water depth by increased silting, and eliminating the floating leaved and submerged plants growing there. Extensive disturbance, with potential loss of invertebrates, is therefore necessary from time to time when clearance is undertaken to arrest this vegetational succession. A few years ago a stand of reedmace (*Typha latifolia*), although attractive, was spreading too rapidly and so had to be removed to one of the larger ponds. Recently, one particularly invasive and unwelcome plant became established, the alien species, Australian stonecrop (*Crassula helmsii*). This soon covered most of the pond surface, and in an attempt to remove it, the pond was scraped over part of its area to the gravel base.

Water level in the pond fluctuates with the general level of the water table. It is rare for the pond to dry out completely, but conditions of biotic stress are likely to develop annually at times of drought. In spite of all these problems there is a rich and diverse aquatic flora and fauna, showing great resilience (Fig. 9.2).

During the early summer, with its stands of bur-reed, yellow flag iris and white water-lily, the pond is a sight of great beauty. Perhaps the showiest of the marginal plants in the spring are the clumps of yellow flag, with their beautiful flowers, conspicuous to motorists passing by on Parkside. Other

Some 7 Post Pond plants

Figure 9.3 (above)
Yellow Flag Iris.

Figure 9.4 (top right)
Branched Bur-reed.

Figure 9.5 (right) Water Mint.

Figure 9.6 (far right)
Greater Spearwort.

Photos: Antony Sutcliffe.

notable emergent plants are common spike rush, actually not a rush but a sedge, occupying the north-east corner and small sweet grass, spreading over much of the pond in the summer months. What was thought to be Hampshire purslane (*Ludwigia palustris*) was recorded here in 1995. This caused considerable interest as the plant is an extremely rare native species, thought to be restricted to south Hampshire. Its presence at 7 Post Pond was therefore regarded with some suspicion. However the species continued to flourish and in 1997 it received further scrutiny by an eminent field botanist Eric Clements, who has now re-identified the plant as *Ludwigia mullertii*, a species used in aquaria which equates to the hybrid *L. natans* x *L. palustris*. Although not the native species, our record of *L. mullertii* growing in a natural habitat is new to Britain, and so deserves some acclaim.

Canadian pondweed, a submerged plant, abounds in the pond. Although introduced to this Country in the nineteenth century, it is a valuable water plant, producing a large amount of oxygen, thus purifying the water and also providing shelter for the invertebrates. The slender and feathery alternate-flowered water-milfoil also grows beneath the surface of the water. Another spectacular plant, the white water-lily, is an example of a rooted plant with large floating leaves. Again, shelter for the pond fauna. The plants growing around the edge of the pond (marginals) and on the banks are equally important, as they provide a haven for insects, both aquatic and terrestrial. They include water mint, gipsywort, water forget-me-not, greater spearwort, trifid bur-marigold and a number of rush species. Hawthorn, birch and willow grow close to the water's edge on the western side.

Water pH measurements have been taken for all the Commons' ponds (Chapter 2), including 7 Post Pond and Kingsmere (its nearest neighbour, but a much larger body of water). The pH was found to be considerably higher at 7 Post (6.6) than at Kingsmere (6.0). The concrete wall on the pavement side of 7 Post Pond may be a contributory factor in this respect. In the 1980s the water of these two ponds was analysed for calcium and magnesium content. Surprisingly, Kingsmere was found to have a higher content of these two elements than 7 Post Pond, although the latter is known to be the best pond on the Commons for aquatic snails, which of course need calcium for their shells. Molluscs gain calcium from food and water and it has been shown that abundance of mollusca increases in sites with abundance of plants (Powell & South, 1978).

The habitat is favourable for several groups of molluscs. Gastropods found in fresh water can be sub-divided into operculates (gill breathers) and pulmonates (lung breathers). The operculates need water that is fairly well oxygenated. The pulmonates are less particular and are most densely concentrated on aquatic plants. These emergent and submerged plants are coated with epiphytic scum flora composed of microscopic organisms. Bivalve molluscs, by comparison, have respiratory siphons, with the gills not only acting as respiratory organs, but also as a feeding mechanism. Their food consists of microscopic algae and particles of detritus suspended in the water.

In surveys in June and November 1996, the following molluscs were recorded from 7 Post Pond:- great pond snail (*Lymnaea stagnalis*), wandering snail (*Lymnaea peregra*), great ramshorn (*Planorbarius corneus*), ramshorn (*Planorbis planorbis*), Lister's river snail (*Viviparus fasciatus*) and horny orb

Figure 9.7 Great Pond Snail on Canadian Pondweed.
Photo: Antony Sutcliffe.

mussel (*Sphaerium corneum*). The first four, which were abundant, are pulmonates and so are able to survive in very little water. The river snail is an operculate and the orb mussel a bivalve. These must find fluctuations in water level stressful.

In addition to the rich molluscan fauna for such a small pond, 7 Post Pond has another very interesting invertebrate which is often unnoticed, as out of water it appears a dull velvety black colour. This is the water spider (*Argyroneta aquatica*). When submerged, however, it is covered by a silvery layer of air. The spider's whole life is spent under water; but it is air breathing, so needs its own supply of oxygen. It does this by spinning a dome of silk amongst the vegetation, filled with bubbles of air brought from the surface. After mating, the female lays eggs in early summer inside this 'diving bell' nest. Soon after hatching, the spiderlings disperse and often take up temporary residence in empty snail shells, which they fill with air obtained from the surface. So there is an indirect association between a pond with snails and the water spider. A favoured food of the water spider is the water louse (*Asellus aquaticus*), also recorded in 1996 in this pond. It is good to know that in November 1996, even after two or three months of drought, when very little water was left in the pond, and after the added disturbance of conservation work to attempt to clear the *Crassula*, the snail population was still impressive and several water spiders were also recorded at that time. However, no dragonfly nymphs and considerably fewer damselfly and mayfly nymphs were recorded than had been present in the previous June. In a survey in late August 1997 small damselfly nymphs were again recorded in great numbers, demonstrating a flourishing population from that year's egg laying and showing the resilience of pond invertebrates. At this time also, small fiercely carnivorous Dytiscidae beetles were seen to be terrorising some of the slower moving fauna.

7 Post Pond is particularly good for amphibians, especially the common frog (*Rana temporaria*) and the smooth newt (*Triturus vulgaris*). In the June 1996 survey an abundance of tadpoles in advanced development was recorded, and just as many were seen the following year. The pond is also a suitable environment for the common toad (*Bufo bufo*) which lays spawn in

Figure 9.8 Tadpole of Smooth Newt: note the gills.
Photo: Antony Sutcliffe.

Figure 9.9 Frogs spawning in the pond.
Photo: Tony Drakeford.

Figure 9.10 Coot on nest at 7 Post Pond, only a few metres from the busy road.
Photo: Antony Sutcliffe.

long double strings, like an unwieldy necklace, twined around the abundant water plants. The amphibians fortunately do not suffer from late summer drought, because there is always sufficient water in this pond at the time they are breeding and the tadpoles developing. No doubt the adults will be back again to breed next spring and the spring after that. The bountiful flora and fauna must make this an ideal pond for amphibians.

Today the Commons supports two, or possibly three, native reptile species and it was beside 7 Post Pond in 1995 that the most recent sighting of grass snake (*Natrix natrix*) was recorded.

On sunny summer days I have seen a number of dragonflies and damselflies at different times, including the beautiful Ruddy Darter (*Sympetrum sanguineum*) resting on bankside plants, and the Brown Hawker (*Aeshna grandis*) laying her eggs in the water. Two of the most impressive of our dragonflies, the Emperor (*Anax imperator*) and Southern Hawker (*Aeshna cyanea*) can be seen patrolling their respective territories. Mating Common Blue damselflies (*Enallagma cyathigerum*), Azure (*Coenagrion puella*) and Blue-tailed (*Ischnura elegans*) flit around the willow trees, looking like jewels in the sunshine. The water mint is a nectar plant for a myriad of insects, including butterflies, bumble bees and honey bees, and the noisy rattle of Meadow Grasshoppers (*Chorthippus parallelus*) can be heard as they jump around on the grass.

Different bird species are to be seen at the pond through the seasons. The ubiquitous crows and black-headed gulls are common when the pond is partially dry, scavenging for tit-bits in the mud, but in the winter there are often families of mallards and sometimes coots and moorhens, and towards dusk a stealthy heron stalking for prey can occasionally be seen. It is incredible to think that this little pond, lying next to a busy main road, is home for so many plants and animals, thanks partly to the low-key management undertaken when deemed necessary.

Table 9.1 Plants recorded in and around 7 Post Pond

Submerged	Canadian Pondweed	*Elodea canadensis*
	Australian Stonecrop	*Crassula helmsii*
	Curly Water-thyme	*Lagarosiphon major*
	Alternate-flowered Water-milfoil	*Myriophyllum alterniflorum*

| **Floating leaves or stems** | White Water-lily | *Nymphaea alba* |
| | Common Duckweed | *Lemna minor* |

Emergent	Bulbous Rush	*Juncus bulbosus*
	Branched Bur-reed	*Sparganium erectum*
	Yellow Flag	*Iris pseudacorus*
	Hampshire Purslane (hybrid)	*Ludwigia x mullertii*
	Soft Rush	*Juncus effusus*
	Sharp-flowered Rush	*Juncus acutiflorus*
	Common Spike-rush	*Eleocharis palustris*
	Water Forget-me-not	*Myosotis scorpioides*
	Water Mint	*Mentha aquatica*
	Pennyroyal	*Mentha pulegium*
	Greater Spearwort	*Ranunculus lingua*
	Gipsywort	*Lycopus europaeus*
	Brooklime	*Veronica beccabunga*
	Trifid Bur Marigold	*Bidens tripartita*
	Small Sweet-Grass	*Glyceria declinata*

Surrounding Herbs and Grasses	Yellow-eyed Grass	*Sisyrinchium californicum*
	Redshank	*Persicaria persicaria*
	Nettle	*Urtica dioica*
	Bramble	*Rubus fruticosus*
	Hard Rush	*Juncus inflexus*
	Yorkshire Fog	*Holcus lanatus*
	Perennial Ryegrass	*Lolium perenne*
	Wall Barley	*Hordeum murinum*
	Creeping Thistle	*Cirsium arvense*
	Common Mallow	*Malva sylvestris*

Surrounding Trees and Shrubs	Hawthorn	*Crataegus monogyna*
	Sycamore	*Acer pseudoplatanus*
	Birch	*Betula pendula*
	Grey Willow	*Salix cinerea*

Life in an Oak Tree

Tony Drakeford

Standing on the eastern bank of Bluegate Gravel Pit Pond is a large oak tree. Gnarled and misshapen, its upper boughs twist and writhe in all directions like a demented octopus, roots partially submerged, whilst some lower branches brush the surface of the water. The age of the tree is difficult to estimate, but probably it has lived for about a hundred seasons, a mere youngster compared with a few older oaks scattered over the Commons, and far younger than some growing in neighbouring Richmond Park, which are thought to be at least 600 years of age.

There is an old adage which states that an oak spends the first three hundred years of its life growing, the next three hundred resting and the final three hundred in decline, so the Bluegate oak, although old in human terms, is still in its prime.

Recent technological advances, including the study of pollen from peat bog cores, give a wonderful insight into the sequence by which various tree species colonised Britain after the last ice age (see Chapter 3). The common, or pedunculate oak (*Quercus robur*) arrived on the scene about 7000 years ago and came to predominate in the 'wild wood' which thickly clothed much of the British Isles in prehistoric times.

The oak truly is a bountiful tree, an essential link in the ecosystem, directly or indirectly supporting a vast range of animals, birds, plants, fungi and lichens, all relying on their host for food or shelter. Much of the abundant wildlife is there because of the multitude of invertebrates, opportunists all, that have adapted so well to the tree throughout a lengthy evolutionary time span. In fact more wildlife, especially insects, derive sustenance from oaks than any other British arboreal species. The tree plays host to a myriad of bugs, beetles,

Figure 9.11 The Bluegate Oak in spring.
Photo: Tony Drakeford.

moth larvae, gall wasps, but, perhaps surprisingly, just one butterfly, the Purple Hairstreak (*Quercusia quercus*) can claim to be linked entirely with oak through its life-cycle.

Stand beneath the Bluegate oak, or any of its many fellows, on an early spring day, soon after the bright lemon-green tinted leaves have unfurled. Listen carefully, and if the day is bright and still, it is possible to hear what sounds rather like gentle steady rain pattering onto the leaf litter below. But these 'raindrops' are in reality the droppings of millions of tiny moth larvae of several species, busily feeding on the foliage, palatable at this tender age, prior to the flow of toxic 'tannins' flooding the leaf cells. The eggs were laid way back last summer on this year's dormant buds.

Most notable among the ravenous horde is the Green Oak Tortrix moth (*Tortrix viridana*), the caterpillars of which, using silk, will roll themselves up in the leaves and feed within. When disturbed, the larvae will drop from the leaf, suspended on gossamer threads, to be brushed from our faces as we stroll through the woods. So vast is this army of caterpillars that in some seasons they are capable of defoliating entire trees. But, over thousands of years, the oak has evolved to withstand such onslaughts so, undaunted, the tree produces a second set of leaves appropriately and seasonally named 'Lammas leaves'. Blue tits time the hatching of their broods to coincide with the wealth of succulent larvae, which are fed to their hungry fledglings.

The larvae of 160 moths, both macro and micro, feed on oak leaves. Other species, such as the family of Footman moths, choose lichens growing on the branches, whilst both Goat (*Cossus cossus*) and Leopard moth (*Zeuzera pyrina*) actually feed on the wood. The Yellow Legged Clearwing (*Synanthedon vespiformis*) uses the underside of bark.

In high summer, the Purple Hairstreak butterfly lays eggs on next year's terminal buds, and larvae hatch the following spring. This hairstreak, belonging to the Lycaenidae family, is generally very abundant, with Wimbledon Common and Putney Heath a major London site. However, the insect is often overlooked because, although most oak trees support their own colony, the adults spend much of their time high up in the canopy imbibing honeydew. Occasionally, two or three will suddenly leave the tree to indulge in territorial skirmishes, resembling dull silver coins in flight. In certain weather conditions, such as hot humid days, the butterflies descend to sip nectar from thistles, where they can be studied at leisure as they crawl slowly over the flowers, with antennae inclined downwards and proboscis uncurled.

Figure 9.12 Green Oak Tortrix Moth.
Photo: Tony Drakeford.

Figure 9.13 (below) Purple Hairstreak Butterfly.
Photo: Tony Drakeford.

Figure 9.14 (right) Stag Beetle larva.
Photo: Tony Drakeford.

Over forty species of beetle, including ladybirds, are associated with oaks, some living subterranean existences within the root system. Britain's largest, the magnificent stag beetle (*Lucanus cervus*), ferocious in appearance perhaps but perfectly harmless, can be grouped with numerous other 'little rotters' in that eggs are deposited within dead timber. Finger-sized creamy-white larvae feed on decaying wood for up to five years prior to pupating, special enzymes enabling them to digest tough cellulose. Man's preoccupation with tidying up the countryside in former years led to a decline in the population of stag beetles and indeed many other creatures, but nowadays more enlightened sensible management accepts the desirability of leaving fallen timber for a range of wildlife to feed on and recycle. The cockchafer or maybug (*Melolontha melolontha*) emerges in large numbers in May, often swarming at dusk to fly and feed on oak leaves. Coloured pinkish-brown, the males sport curious antennae which resemble miniature outstretched human hands. Another notable beetle, one of the family of longhorns (*Prionus coriarius*), feeds as a larva on stumps and pupates beneath bark. Larvae of tiny oak bark beetles (*Scolytus intricatus*) feed between bark and timber, channelling distinctive radiating galleries.

Ladybirds, being carnivorous, consume vast numbers of sap-sucking aphids, of which over forty species have been recorded on oak. True bugs (Hemiptera), possessing long needle-shaped mouth parts, suck juices from plants. The aptly named shield bugs are handsome bugs which derive their name from their conspicuous triangular dorsal plate. Frequently seen on oaks, one of the most familiar must be the green shield bug (*Palomena prasina*).

One of the most distinctive features of oak 'infestations', causing much comment, is the huge number of Galls, with over forty species recorded. Most are the work of tiny ant-sized wasps belonging to the Cynipidae family. Their life cycle is extremely complex, with alternating generations of the same species, one sexual (both male and female), the other asexual (females only), the two generations producing different types of galls. The galls themselves come in many shapes and sizes. They are formed in response to the hatching of the wasp's eggs which triggers development of abnormal tissues in the tree wherein the wasp grubs can feed and shelter. The galls may sometimes contain uninvited guests in the form of parasites, or even hyper-parasites, so that what emerges may not be the original occupant.

Figure 9.16 Previous year's Marble Gall on winter twig.
Photo: Tony Drakeford.

Marble (*Andricus kollari*), cherry (*Cynips quercusfolii*), spangle (*Neuroterus albipes*) and silk-button galls (*Neuroterus numismalis*) will be familiar, whereas the larger, rather spongy oak apple (*Biorhiza pallida*) resembles a small russet apple, numerous enough in a good season to appear as if the trees have produced a marketable crop! The knopper gall (*Andricus quercuscalicis*) only arrived in Britain in the 1970s. Acorns become deformed and for some years scientists voiced concern about future generations of oaks, but fortunately enough acorns escape the attention of the wasps to ensure continuation of our noble trees.

To the formidable list of invertebrates can be added sawflies, spiders, earwigs, lacewings, springtails and the delicate green coloured Oak and Speckled bush-crickets.

Some of the most familiar birds of oak woods include long-tailed, blue and great tits, chaffinch, green and great-spotted woodpeckers, tawny owl and treecreeper. Jay, nuthatch and woodpigeon all feed on acorns and the jay's habit of burying them ensures that any forgotten (and jays have long memories) may later germinate and thus assist the spread of oak woodland.

A great variety of mammals are abundant in oak woods. Wood mouse, bank vole, shrew and hedgehog are there and, of course, the alien grey squirrel consumes large quantities of acorns, as well as bird's eggs and even fledglings. Squirrels can also cause problems by stripping bark from saplings, causing their early death.

In autumn, the accumulation of dead leaves on the ground beneath the tree supports a complex decomposer food chain, consisting of micro-organisms and soil invertebrates which combine to break down the leaf litter so that the nutrients can be recycled back into the tree through its root system.

So, as we contemplate our Bluegate oak, reflected in calm waters and subjected to attack from so many quarters, not least the complex condition known as die-back, thought to be caused by a combination of oak mildew (*Microsphaera alphitoides*) and Tortrix moth damage; we can appreciate that each individual tree, and indeed the leaf litter below, is essentially a vibrant teeming city in its own right.

Figure 9.17 Silk Button Galls on oak leaves.
Photo: Dave Haldane.

Figure 9.18 Crop of 'Oak Apples' on young spring growth.
Photo: Tony Drakeford.

Chapter 10

Butterflies, Grasshoppers, Bush-Crickets and Dragonflies

Tony Drakeford

Insects comprise the most successful and numerous group of creatures the world has known. Up to the present day, over one million different species have been scientifically classified worldwide and there are many more awaiting discovery.

Whatever people feel about 'creepy crawlies', they form an essential part of the ecosystem, and without them, life as we know it could not continue. As a result of habitat losses, however, large numbers will probably become extinct even before we have an opportunity to study them.

Insects carry out so many vital functions, including pollination (vital also to crops); they occupy an important role in the food chain where they play a part in recycling organic matter. In fact, they constitute one of the major food sources for vast numbers of invertebrates and also fish, amphibians, reptiles, birds and mammals. Throughout our lives we are surrounded by insects exploiting every conceivable niche and habitat; they come in many different shapes and sizes, visible and practically invisible, from winged beauties, such as the butterflies, to more lowly forms, such as springtails, dwelling within the soil.

The Commons have their fair share of species; far too many to attempt to name and describe here. Therefore, in this and the following chapter, we have concentrated on the larger more familiar showy groups: butterflies and moths; grasshoppers and bush-crickets; dragonflies and damselflies; beetles and bumble bees. All these can be watched without too much difficulty when out walking.

The tide of insects begins to rise rapidly in March as days lengthen and become warmer and, although naturally most abundant in summertime, there are some species whose life-cycles are timed to coincide with the colder months, so there is usually something to see, even in winter.

Butterflies and Moths
(Order Lepidoptera)

Butterflies

Of all the insect groups butterflies are the most visible, spectacular and the best loved; their bright colours having influenced romantic poets for many centuries.

Unlike beetles and dragonflies, the delicate soft structure of butterflies does not lend itself to long-term preservation in ancient rock formations. Evidence suggests, however, that they first appeared upon earth approximately 150 million years ago, evolving in conjunction with flowering plants.

In Walter Johnson's book (1912), reference is made to butterflies at that time, but no species are named and any lists compiled then have not survived. Records relating to the butterflies of the Commons were published by the

Wimbledon Natural History Society in the 1930s, when twenty-four species had been observed, but unfortunately the actual species list cannot be traced.

We have to wait until the 1950s for the first positive records, when A.W. Jones revealed his findings to the London Natural History Society. Most of the more common species he saw are still with us today, but one of them, the Grayling, a butterfly of open sandy heaths, which was listed as scarce between 1947 and 1954, has suffered a dramatic countrywide decline during the past forty years and disappeared from the Commons. The Wall Brown was described as 'abundant' in those days, but our last positive sighting occurred in 1986 and it is also declining nationally. Other species recorded during those years include the Dingy Skipper (small numbers) and the Grizzled Skipper (rare). A single specimen of the Pearl-bordered Fritillary was spotted in 1945, with other unidentified Fritillaries occasionally observed. A single Brown Argus was sighted in 1950, as was the White Admiral and a High-brown Fritillary, a butterfly now extremely rare in Britain.

Norman Riley, writing in the booklet entitled *Walks on Wimbledon Common*, 1970, mentions the recent disappearance of the Grizzled Skipper, and of "how the lovely and elusive White Admiral had not been seen of recent years". Strangely, the Green Hairstreak was said to be the only Hairstreak flying on the Common at that time, but two others were almost certainly there, notably the Purple Hairstreak and the White-letter Hairstreak, both admittedly secretive in their habits and therefore easily overlooked. Sadly, the Green Hairstreak has not been sighted since the mid-seventies. The reasons for its demise are probably linked to the reduction in its larval food plant, gorse, which suffered badly as a result of widespread fire damage during the 1976 drought.

There is always a chance that some of the previous resident species will make a comeback and could possibly still be surviving at low densities in much the same way as the White-letter Hairstreak did, following the ravages of Dutch elm disease in the 1970s, but more of that later. I always feel that 'anything' could turn up on the Commons, such is its rich diversity of habitats.

To bring the picture up-to-date, a survey conducted between 1982 and 1999 listed twenty-eight species. Of these, twenty-two can be classed as long-term established residents, whilst the remainder are made up of annual or occasional migrants or vagrants. This total, approximately one third of the species regarded as British, compares favourably with older records.

It must be said that 'made ground' on the Commons, particularly the two artificial hills, which have developed a more neutral soil than the surrounding heath, provide valuable additional food plants for butterflies.

The emphasis, however, has shifted away from grassland and heathland butterflies, to those found in woodlands, which is consistent with increased tree coverage, evident over the last thirty years, and a national decline of some species. Bearing this in mind and also taking into account the fact that earlier surveys omitted two Hairstreaks, together with the Essex Skipper, which was not recognised as a separate species until early in this century, then the overall situation is encouraging.

At present the butterflies on the Commons are flourishing so, if management policies remain as they are, we should expect little change in the foreseeable future.

🦋 Systematic list of butterflies of Wimbledon Common and Putney Heath

SKIPPERS
(Hesperiidae)
[3 species]

A primitive worldwide group which could possibly be the evolutionary link between butter-flies and moths. Although classed loosely as butterflies, their structure really warrants a separate category. Skippers certainly possess more of the characteristics of moths, having plump furry bodies, large heads with eyes set wide apart, antennae widely separated at base and swept-back wings. Indeed, their life-cycle is more akin to moths, with caterpillars living and pupating within a loose cocoon, unlike true butterflies.

Skippers are aptly named from their habit of delicately 'skipping' from flower to flower and from one grass stem to another. Being fast flyers, I think of them as the 'Red arrows' of the insect world, as they can frequently be seen in groups flashing past, only a few feet above the herbage, with whirring wing beats clearly audible.

Small Skipper
Thymelicus sylvestris

A small gingery-brown species with rapid darting flight. Wings are held either roof-wise above the body, or in 'by-plane' fashion, fore-wings raised, hind-wings flat.
Flight period: Late June to mid-August
Status: Very common
Habitat: Rough coarse grassland, woodland rides and verges.

Essex Skipper
Thymelicus lineola

Almost identical to the Small Skipper except that undersides of antennae tips are black (brownish in Small Skipper), also black scent scales of male are less well defined.
Flight period: July to late August
Status: Very common
Habitat: Rough coarse grassland, woodland rides and verges.

Large Skipper
Ochlodes venatus

Noticeably larger and darker than the two previous species, the first Skipper on the wing. Flies rapidly but also loves basking with wings in 'by-plane' position, on thistle heads and brambles. Very territorial, darting off to intercept any intruder.
Flight period: Mid-June to late August
Status: Common
Habitat: Rough tall grassland, woodland verges and rides.

WHITES AND YELLOWS
(Pieridae) [6 species]

Medium to large butterflies, having white or yellow wings,.some with bold black markings and spots.

Brimstone
Gonepteryx rhamni

Often the first butterfly to awake from hibernation, as early as February if weather is mild. Males are a lovely sulphur yellow, females pale greenish-white. Wings are always held closed when at rest. Our longest-lived species.
Flight period: February to September. Hibernates as adult
Status: Quite common most years
Habitat: Woodland clearings, rides and margins, scrubland.

Large White
Pieris brassicae

A large creamy-white butterfly, upper surfaces of wings have black markings and spots. It is our only 'pest' species, but much less common nowadays as a result of agricultural pesti-cides and herbicides. A viral infection in the 1950s also affected populations. A powerful flyer, large numbers often migrate to our shores from abroad.
Flight period: May to September, in two broods
Status: Common some years, quite scarce in others
Habitat: Free-flying in all areas, especially flower-rich meadows.

Small White
Pieris rapae

A similar, smaller relative of the Large White, but less of a pest, as eggs are laid singly. Also a strong migrant.
Flight period: March to September, in two or three broods
Status: Common most years
Habitat: Grasslands and flowery meadows.

Green-Veined White
Pieris napi

A dainty species, similar to Small White when seen in flight, but wings are heavily veined in grey above, greenish-yellow on under-side of hind-wings. Flies with gentle dipping, fluttering motion around flowers, often in dull humid weather.

Flight period: April to September, in two broods
Status: Common
Habitat: Damp grasslands, shaded woodlands and along Beverley Brook.

Orange Tip
Anthocharis cardamines

The male is distinctive in having the greater part of the fore-wing orange, whereas the female lacks the orange patches and can be mistaken for a Small White, except that Orange Tips have a more delicate, lace-like appearance. Hind-wing undersides of both sexes are mottled in greenish-white.

Flight period: April to May
Status: Common
Habitat: Damp woodland rides, especially along Beverley Brook.

Clouded Yellow
Colias croceus

A medium sized species with deep yellow wings. These have black margins above, a series of small feint spots and a pinkish figure-of-eight in the centre of the hind-wings. Resembles a golden coin in flight. A restless free-flying butterfly, migrating to these shores only occasionally, but a few individuals could arrive any summer. The last notable influx occurred in 1983, when it bred here.

Flight period: June to October
Status: Very scarce. Absent most years
Habitat: Clover-rich flowery pastures. Most likely to be seen on the hills, north-west of the Windmill.

HAIRSTREAKS
(Lycaenidae)
[2 species]

Small dark coloured secretive butterflies, often overlooked as they spend most of their time in the woodland canopy.

Purple Hairstreak
Quercusia quercus

The most widespread and gregarious species on the Commons, virtually every oak tree plays host to a colony. Imbibes aphid-honeydew, but sometimes descends to feed on creeping thistle and bramble flowers, especially during very hot weather. Male has purple sheen all over upper surface, but purple restricted to patch on fore-wing in female.

Flight period: July to August
Status: Abundant
Habitat: Oak woodlands and even lone oak trees.

White-Letter Hairstreak
Strymonidia w-album

This dark velvety-brown species virtually disappeared following Dutch elm disease in the 1970s. However, from 1990 the butterfly recovered very well as the younger wych elms matured. Unfortunately, elms become prone to renewed bark-beetle attack once they reach a certain stage of maturity, so the butterfly population could be subjected to a series of peak and trough situations long-term (see Chapter 11). Even more secretive than the previous species, it lives in the tree canopy and feeds on aphid-honeydew secretions, only very rarely descending to feed, mainly on thistle and always with wings closed.

Flight period: Mid-June to end July
Status: Declining again since 1995 as elms die
Habitat: Wych elm woodlands and copse.

COPPERS
(Lycaenidae) [1 species]

Small Copper
Lycaena phlaeas

A brilliant little butterfly with glowing coppery-red, black spotted wings. Flight is so fast that its path is difficult to follow. Very territorial, chasing everything that enters its chosen patch.

Flight period: April to October, in successive broods
Status: Variable, increasing in numbers as summer progresses
Habitat: Rough flower-rich grassland and hillsides, especially where ragwort grows.

BLUES
(Lycaenidae) [2 species]
Common Blue
Polyommatus icarus

The bright blue wings of the male reflect sunlight as it dashes frantically 'to and fro' at ground level above the short grass, protecting its territory and searching for the dull brownish females, which are less often seen. Visits to low-growing plants and flowers by both sexes are frequent.

Flight period: Mid-May to June; July to August, in two broods
Status: Relatively common some years
Habitat: Flower-rich meadows and hillsides with short grasses.

Holly Blue
Celastrina argiolus

Sometimes mistaken for the Common Blue, but flies higher around bushes rather than at ground level. The Blue most likely to be seen in shrubby gardens.

Flight period: April to May; July to August, in two broods
Status: Very common some years, hardly seen in others
Habitat: Woodland rides and scrub with an abundance of holly and ivy. Often seen in gardens.

ARISTOCRATS
(Nymphalidae)
[5 species]
Red Admiral
Vanessa atalanta

Although this strikingly coloured migrant species occasionally over-winters in Britain, we are really dependent upon arrivals from the Mediterranean in May for our summer stock. In a good year the population gradually builds as the season progresses. The name 'Red Admiral' is often applied to other members of this family mistakenly, as all are rather similarly brightly coloured.

Flight period: May to October in successive broods
Status: Common some years, especially in late summer, scarce in others
Habitat: All over the Commons, particularly fond of buddleia and creeping thistle.

Painted Lady
Cynthia cardui

A migrant which does not survive our winters in hibernation, first arrivals normally reach our shores from North Africa and the Mediterranean in May and breed here through the summer.

Flight period: Early May to September
Status: Common some years, almost absent in others
Habitat: Woodland margins, scrub, hillsides.

Small Tortoiseshell
Aglais urticae

The most familiar and abundant brightly coloured butterfly of the family. First seen out of hibernation on warm early spring days. Frequently hibernates in houses and sheds. Found basking in sunshine, with wings opening and closing, wherever nettles grow.

Flight period: March to October in two broods
Status: Abundant
Habitat: All over the Commons, especially in rough pastures which have an abundance of nettles and thistles.

Peacock
Inachis io

Hibernates as adult, a large dark coloured species with beautiful eye-spots on upper surfaces of wings and blackish-brown undersides. First seen in late March or early April, dependent upon weather conditions.

Flight period: March to October, in a single brood
Status: Very common
Habitat: All over the Commons, especially in rough scrubby areas with an abundance of nettles and thistles, also alongside hedges and in woodland clearings.

Comma
Polygonia c-album

A medium sized bright orange-brown species with very distinctive ragged wing margins. Hibernates as adult. Patrols woodland rides and spends much time perching on a prominent leaf or twig with wings open.

Flight period: March to October in two broods
Status: Quite common and increasing
Habitat: Woodland margins and clearings.

Butterflies photographed on Wimbledon Common and Putney Heath. Photos: Tony Drakeford.

Figure 10.1 Large Skipper, Putney Heath.

Figure 10.2 Brimstone butterflies being attacked by a crab spider while mating.

Figure 10.3 Orange Tip butterfly, 'Acropolis'.

Figure 10.4 White-Letter Hairstreak, Putney Heath.

Figure 10.5 Small Copper, Hills.

Figure 10.6 Common Blue butterfly, Hills.

Figure 10.7 Small Tortoiseshell, Beverley Meads.

Figure 10.8 Peacock butterfly.

Figure 10.9 Comma on a fox scat, Acropolis.

Figure 10.10 Meadow Brown, Putney Heath.

Figure 10.11 Ringlets mating, Beverley Meads.

Figure 10.12 Small Heath, Hills.

BROWNS
(Satyridae) [6 species]

A group of sombre brown or dull orange-brown butterflies, having a prominent round eye-spot on the fore-wings. Six species currently occur on the Commons, whilst a seventh, the Wall Brown, has not been recorded since 1986 and is in decline throughout England.

Gatekeeper or Hedge Brown
Pyronia tithonus

A medium sized orange-brown butterfly of high summer. Resembles, but is smaller than the Meadow Brown. Eye spots on apex of fore-wings have two tiny white pupils.
Flight period: July to September
Status: Steadily on the increase
Habitat: Sheltered grassland with brambles and scrub.

Meadow Brown
Maniola jurtina

A large mainly brown species, upper side of male almost totally brown, female has orange markings. Prominent eye-spots on fore-wings. By far the commonest 'Brown', with a very weak fluttering flight, often on dull humid days.
Flight period: Mid-June to late September
Status: Super-abundant
Habitat: All grassy areas, hillsides and woodland clearings.

Ringlet
Aphantopus hyperantus

The upperside of the male's wings are a deep bitter-chocolate colour, almost black, with pale yellow-ringed black circles, whilst the slightly larger female is paler, and when fresh the wings of both sexes are edged with white. A series of distinctive yellow circled black eye-spots adorn the underside of the wings. This butterfly 'arrived' on Beverley Meads in 1997 and has spread to form discrete pockets of population. Females scatter eggs whilst in flight.
Flight period: Late June to mid-August
Status: Scarce but on the increase
Habitat: Areas of mixed grassland and sheltered scrub, especially Beverley Meads.

Small Heath
Coenonympha pamphilus

The smallest of the 'Browns', a light orange-brown, almost like a mini Meadow Brown. Flies close to ground and perches **always** with wings tightly closed.
Flight period: May to September, in two broods
Status: Common
Habitat: Rough grassy areas, especially common on the hills.

Speckled Wood
Pararge aegeria

A dark chocolate-brown butterfly with yellow patches and spots on all wings. Flies slowly and spends much time basking in dappled sunlight. Often two males can be seen in open woodland spiralling upwards in a territorial skirmish.
Flight period: Late March to October, in several broods
Status: Very common
Habitat: Woodland margins, rides and alongside hedgerows.

Marbled White
Melanargia galathea

The title Marbled White is rather a misnomer as the butterfly belongs to the family of 'browns'. An unmistakable species, wings of both sexes similar and patterned in a dark brown and white chequer board effect. Renowned for being a sedentary butterfly, rarely straying from its chalk downland habitat, the Marbled White seems suddenly to be on the move, turning up in unexpected places, including the hills on the Commons.
Flight period: Late June to mid-August
Status: Very scarce
Habitat: Grassland, especially the hills.

Confirmed or occasional 'one off' sightings

During our most recent ongoing survey, other non-resident species have been recorded from time to time. The most notable sighting took place in 1991 when a Large Tortoiseshell (*Nymphalis polychloros*) was seen in a Wimbledon village garden. Although it is just possible that the insect in question was a migrant, it was more likely to have been a home-bred release, as this species is currently Britain's rarest. In 1985 two Dark Green Fritillaries (*Argynnis aglaja*) were recorded, a year in which the insect was unusually abundant, but no further sightings have occurred since. White Admirals (*Limenitis camilla*) have been reported on occasions, as have Silver-Washed Fritillaries (*Argynnis paphia*) in Beverley Meads, but neither species can be classed as a true resident.

Breeding butterflies for pleasure has always been a popular hobby so sightings of non-endemic species should be treated with caution before classing them as positive records.

Day-flying Moths

It is sometimes assumed that any brightly coloured insect seen fluttering among the wild flowers on a sunny day must be a butterfly, as surely all moths fly at night! Most of them do, but in Britain there are in fact more species of day-flying moths than butterflies, and several can readily be seen on the Commons. Those most likely to be encountered are described below.

Systematic List of Day-flying Moths of Wimbledon Common and Putney Heath

THE 'BURNETS'
(Zygaenidae,)
[3 species]

These blue-black crimson spotted moths arouse much favourable comment as they lazily crawl over thistles or, with rapidly whirring wings, manoeuvre slowly in 'bumbling' flight from flower to flower. Almost as familiar as the moths themselves are their streamlined buff coloured papery cocoons festooning long grass stems in late June/early July.

5-Spot Burnet
Zygaena trifolii

Distinguished from the similar 6 Spot Burnet by having five crimson spots or blotches on the upper surface of each fore-wing. The colour of the moth apparently changes, dependent upon how light strikes the wing surfaces, from blue to green or black.
Flight period: July to August
Status: Very common
Habitat: Mainly on flower-rich hills and the Acropolis (i.e. 'Made Ground').

Narrow-Bordered 5-Spot Burnet
Zygaena lonicerae

Very similar to the 5-Spot, but with slightly longer fore-wings and more pointed hind-wings.

6-Spot Burnet
Zygaena filipendulae

Much like the other Burnets in general appearance, but with six spots or blotches on each fore-wing.
Flight period, status and habitat requirements match those of the two former species.

(Saturniidae)
[1 species]
Emperor Moth
Saturnia pavonia

The only British member of the silk-moth family, the Emperor is a large striking insect with prominent 'ring of Saturn' eye-spots. Only the male flies by day, rapidly dashing about over the heath searching for females, which it can detect from up to two miles away, resting in heather or long grass.
Flight period: Late April to May
Status: Quite common but not often seen
Habitat: Heathland and extensive grassy areas.

(Arctiidae) [2 species]
Cinnabar
Tyria jacobaeae

Blackish wings, having two red spots and a red stripe on each fore-wing, which distinguishes this species from the Burnets. Although the Cinnabar can be seen during daytime, fluttering weakly about, it is really a nocturnal species. The caterpillars are conspicuous, their alternate black and orange ringed bodies feeding in groups on ragwort.

Flight period: May to July
Status: Common
Habitat: Rough grassy areas with an abundance of ragwort.

Vapourer
Orgyia antiqua

A small brownish moth with a white black-ringed tiny eye-spot. Only the male possesses wings, the female being flightless. Males can sometimes be seen fluttering busily among woodland searching for mates which remain on their cocoons after hatching.

Flight period: July to October
Status: Common but secretive
Habitat: Woodland margins.

**(Geometridae)
[2 species]**
Orange Underwing
Archiearis parthenias

An early species found on heathland where there is birch, the moth flying around the tree tops.

Flight period: March to April
Status: Common, but easily overlooked
Habitat: Heathland and light birch woodland.

Latticed Heath
Semiothisa clathrata

Very 'butterfly-like' with fast flight low over heath and grassland. Easily disturbed, it will quickly move and alight some distance away.

Flight period: Common in April and May. Population tailing off as summer progresses
Status: Quite common most years
Habitat: Heath and grassland, especially on the hills.

(Noctuidae) [3 species]
Burnet Companion
Euclidia glyphica

A mottled brownish, fast-flying restless species. Resembles a butterfly from a distance, especially the 'Skippers'.

Flight period: May to July
Status: Quite common most years
Habitat: Rough grassland, especially the hills.

Mother Shipton
Callistege mi

A greyish-brown moth, the markings on each fore-wing resemble the profile of an old Yorkshire witch, hence its name.

Flight period: May to July
Status: Quite common most years
Habitat: Rough grassland, especially the hills.

Silver-Y
Autographa gamma

A rapid flyer, the species is a strong migrant, arriving in Britain in large numbers some years in late summer, where it can be seen feeding on wild flowers including heather, wings rapidly whirring, with the 'Y' marking clearly visible on the fore-wings.

Flight period: May to October
Status: Abundant some years, common in most
Habitat: Rough scrubby grassland and heath.

**(Incurvariidae)
[2 species]**
Nemophora degeerella
(no common name)

A small greenish yellow-banded moth, with long thread-like antennae, the longest of any British species, can be seen in small swarms around light woodland.

Flight period: April to June
Status: Quite common but, because of its small size, often mistaken for a fly
Habitat: Light woodland, especially where hawthorn grows.

Green Longhorn
Adela reaumurella

A beautiful tiny iridescent green species, which swarms, rather like midges around wych elms and hawthorn. Males possess long thread-like antennae.

Flight period: April to May
Status: Super abundant
Habitat: Light woodland and copse.

Moths photographed on Wimbledon Common and Putney Heath. Photos: Tony Drakeford.

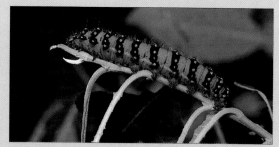

Figure 10.14 Emperor Moth larva.

Figure 10.13 6-Spot Burnet and cocoon on a grass stem, Hills.

Figure 10.15 Emperor Moth on heather.

Figure 10.17 Cinnabar Moth, near Windmill.

Figure 10.16 Cinnabar Moth larvae on ragwort, a plant poisonous to horses.

Figure 10.18 Latticed Heath Moth, Hills.

Nocturnal Moths

Even by employing modern light traps, or old fashioned 'sugaring' methods on tree trunks, it is still virtually impossible to list every night-flying moth present, due to the sheer number of species likely to frequent a given area. Thanks mainly to excellent fieldwork undertaken on the Commons during the 1980s by the Wandsworth Nature Conservation Unit, headed by Dr James Whitelaw, around two hundred species have been found. However, this total probably represents only a fraction of all resident and migratory moths. Described below are just a few of the most spectacular species, together with some others, which warrant special mention.

Hawkmoths (Sphingidae) command much attention, which is hardly surprising, being mainly large, fast-flying colourful insects. One which can sometimes be seen late on a June evening, hovering around rose bay willowherb and depositing eggs, is the Elephant Hawkmoth (*Deilephila elpenor*). Later in the year its caterpillar is more frequently encountered than the moth itself, being large, brownish-grey, with enormous false eyes, giving the impression of a small snake as it rears its head and extends its 'trunk' – hence Elephant Hawkmoth.

Another equally impressive hawkmoth, the Eyed Hawk (*Smerinthus ocellata*) has life-like false eyes located on the upper surfaces of the hind-wings, which are 'flashed' when threatened. It is quite common, the larvae feeding mainly on willow and poplar.

The Buff Tip (*Phalera bucephala*), perfectly camouflaged to mimic a broken-off twig, is very common. The yellow and black downy-covered larvae feed gregariously on oak and can be found quite readily in late summer.

One of our prettiest residents is the Peach Blossom (*Thyatira batis*). Wings are light brown, decorated with pink blotches within white circles which convey an impression of spring petals or blossom. What a shame this moth hides its delicate beauty at night! The larvae feed on bramble in early summer and again in autumn.

The Burnished Brass (*Diachrisia chrysitis*), so called because patches on the fore-wings shine exactly like highly polished brass plates, can sometimes be found resting in long grass early in the morning in mid-summer.

The Large Emerald (*Geometra papilionaria*) is a strikingly beautiful insect, with wings of delicate light green. At its best when freshly emerged, the colours fade to white as the moth ages.

Double Line (*Mythimna turca*) a Biodiversity Action Plan species, has recently been discovered in a moth trap operated at a woodland edge. This is a species of grasslands and open woodland with only one other site in London.

The Winter Moth (*Operophtera brumata*) flies between autumn and spring. The males will often flutter into car headlight beams. It is one of several similar winter species; the female is wingless, thus saving energy for egg-laying activities.

One final moth, which must be mentioned, is the Green Oak Tortrix (*Tortrix viridana*). This tiny pale green insect flies from June until August. Prior to emergence, its millions of larvae feed on oak leaves and are capable of completely defoliating trees. Blue tits time their breeding cycle to coincide with the vast number of larvae present. On windless days it is possible to actually hear a pitter-patter of droppings falling to the ground, so great are their numbers in the oak canopy (see Chapter 9).

Grasshoppers and Bush-Crickets
(Order Orthoptera)

The scientific term Orthoptera is derived from the Greek word 'Orthos', referring to the straight or rigid nature of their wings. Another name sometimes used to describe these insects is 'Saltatoria', from the Latin 'Saltare', to leap. In all but the adult stages, they have the ability to partially regenerate lost limbs.

The only records available from the past are those mentioned in Walter Johnson's book of 1912. Just three species of grasshopper were listed then, namely, the Common Green, Meadow and Mottled. The sole Bush-Cricket identified was the Speckled. Thereafter records are non-existent until the mid-1980s. We now compile species lists on an annual basis.

In theory it would seem that the Commons support a greater number of species now compared with earlier times, but a more likely explanation is that these insects probably commanded less attention than more colourful groups and many were no doubt overlooked or not recognised.

Grasshoppers (Acrididae) [5 species]

These greenish-brown insects with short antennae are very well known and can be seen jumping in all directions as we walk through long grass, their chirping chorus evocative of warm sunny days. The 'singing', or to be more precise 'stridulation', is usually made by males in courtship, rubbing a file on their hind legs against a scraper situated on the fore-wings, thus producing a wide ranging resonance. With practice, each species can be recognised and identified by its own very individual 'song'. The hearing organs of grasshoppers are situated in openings on either side of the first abdominal segment. All species seem able to ventriloquise and 'throw their voices', making it hard to detect them in the grass.

After hatching in early summer, grasshoppers undergo a four-stage metamorphosis, the nymphs shedding their skins at each stage. Tiny white nymphs, perfect but smaller images of the adults, can sometimes be seen springing about in the grass, but they cannot 'sing' until adulthood. Diet consists entirely of grasses and some herbage. Eggs, which overwinter, are laid in batches of up to fifteen, contained in pods inserted into or in some cases on the surface of the soil.

🌿 Systematic list of Grasshoppers of Wimbledon Common and Putney Heath

Mottled Grasshopper
Myrmeleotettix maculatus

A comparatively small species; colour varieties of brown, green, or almost black are encountered; always with mottled markings. A distinguishing feature is the antennae, which are swollen at the tips.
Stridulation: June to October
Status: Uncommon
Song: A series of chirps, sounding like the winding of a clock
Habitat: Dry grassland and heath.

Common Green Grasshopper
Omocestus viridulus

Distinguished from other species by having a short 'keel' on the top of its head. Colours vary from mainly light green, through greyish to brown.
Stridulation: Mid-June to September (usually the first to be heard)
Status: Quite common
Song: Resembles the sound of a free wheeling bicycle, i.e. a steady 'ticking'
Habitat: Lush soft grasses.

Meadow Grasshopper
Chorthippus parallelus

The only flightless species; it can of course jump long distances. Easily distinguished from other species by its short fore-wings and lack of hind-wings. The wings of the male are comparatively longer than those of the female. Mainly seen as a green form, but brown varieties also occur.

Stridulation: Late June to late September
Status: Very common
Song: An undulating rattle in short bursts, likened to a sewing machine
Habitat: Rough grassy areas and damp pastures.

Common Field Grasshopper
Chorthippus brunneus

A species with many colour varieties, which can be heard right through the summer into late autumn, often in great numbers.

Stridulation: July to November
Status: Abundant
Song: A series of very short 'chirps', seemingly groups holding conversations with each other!
Habitat: Dry grassland and bare patches, e.g. asphalt car parks or edges of concrete regions.

Stripe-winged Grasshopper
Stenobothrus lineatus

Mainly green, the species is distinguished by a comma-shaped white stripe two thirds of the way along the fore-wings, and by its very conspicuous stridulation, unlike any other grasshopper. The male moves his legs very slowly when stridulating, almost as though he is riding a bicycle.

Stridulation: Mid-July to September
Status: Scarce
Song: A distinctive loud swish – swish – swish – swish, increasing in strength with each 'swish'
Habitat: Dry grassland, especially the hills, heathland between the hills and Kingsmere.

Bush-Crickets (Tettigoniidae) [6 species]

Bush-Crickets are generally more secretive than their grasshopper relatives. In contrast to the latter, they possess very long hair-like antennae. Furthermore, stridulation mechanisms are confined to the wings which rub together to produce their 'songs', with the exception of the Oak Bush-Cricket, which drums its hind legs onto a leaf surface. Hearing organs are on the fore legs.

Their life-cycle is basically similar to that of grasshoppers. The nymphs shed skins at regular intervals as they grow, but instead of four moults, there are, dependent upon species, from five to nine moults prior to attaining adulthood. In common with grasshoppers, each nymphal stage resembles a miniature version of the adult. Diet consists of small insects and caterpillars in addition to vegetable matter. Again, in contrast to grasshoppers, the eggs of bush-crickets are laid singly.

🦗 Systematic List of Bush-Crickets of Wimbledon Common and Putney Heath

Oak Bush-Cricket
Meconema thalassinum

A secretive late summer species, mainly nocturnal, bright green and rather delicate looking. This cricket often enters houses, with a weak fluttering flight, on warm evenings from high summer. The male possesses long curved 'claspers' at the end of his abdomen, whereas the female has a gently up-curving ovipositor. Normal stridulation does not take place, instead, the male drums his hind feet rapidly on leaves or other vegetation, but the sound is almost inaudible to the human ear.
Stridulation: Mid-July to November
Song: None, apart from rapid drumming
Status: Very common but not often seen
Habitat: Lives in canopy of not only oak but all deciduous trees in wooded areas.

Speckled Bush-Cricket
Leptophytes punctatissima

A bright green almost wingless insect with numerous dark brown spots, its long legs give the creature a rather spidery look. Rarely seen until dusk.
Stridulation: August to October
Status: Abundant
Song: A weak scratchy chirp, virtually inaudible to the human ear
Habitat: Dense vegetation, especially brambles, a range of shrubs and low-growing trees.

Dark Bush-Cricket
Pholidoptera griseoaptera

Colour varies from light brown to almost black on upper surface, bright green below. The wings of the male are short, but almost absent on the female. Most active at night but sometimes stridulates on warm afternoons.
Stridulation: June to October
Status: Very scarce
Song: A short high-pitched chirp repeated at intervals
Habitat: Brambles, low shrubbery and scrub.

Roesel's Bush-Cricket
Metrioptera roeselii

A large handsome species, glossy dark brown tinged with green and a beautiful yellowish band around the pronotum behind the head. Quite easy to observe when eventually located, but in common with other species, and grasshoppers, it has the ability to 'throw' its 'song' and defy the listener to find it. If disturbed it will drop to the ground. First recorded on the Commons in 1985 and now well established, Roesel's is gradually increasing its range nationwide. Its loud continuous rattling hiss is a feature of late summer days on the hills and meadow near the Windmill; when stridulating, its wings can be seen vibrating with a rapid blur. Increasingly, a long-winged version is produced which has the ability to fly and colonise new areas.
Stridulation: July to October
Status: Common
Song: A continuous high-pitched hiss, heard both day and night in warm weather
Habitat: The hills and meadows with long grasses.

Long-Winged Conehead
Conocephalus discolor

A very recent addition to our list of species, first recorded on the Commons in 1995, following a succession of hot dry summers. A long, slim, graceful insect; light green in colour, somewhat resembling a pea pod in shape, with very long wings, hence its name. Its 'song' is similar to, but a more staccato version of Roesel's Bush-Cricket.
Stridulation: July to October
Status: Spreading all over the Commons
Song: A high-pitched staccato hiss
Habitat: Lush and dry tall grasses; Farm Bog.

Short-Winged Conehead
Conocephalus dorsalis

Another recent addition, smaller than the previous species and less common, with shorter wings.
Stridulation: July to October
Status: Quite common
Song: High pitched, alternating periods of hissing and ticking
Habitat: Mainly on moist grassland.

138

Grasshoppers and Bush Crickets photographed on Wimbledon Common and Putney Heath. Photos: Tony Drakeford.

Figure 10.20 Meadow Grasshopper.

Figure 10.19 Empty grasshopper nymphal case.

Figure 10.21 Oak Bush-Cricket.

Figure 10.22 Speckled Bush-Cricket.

Figure 10.23 Courting pair of Roesel's Bush-Crickets, Hills.

Figure 10.24 Long-Winged Conehead.

Dragonflies and Damselflies
(Order Odonata)

Fossil evidence suggests that these beautiful and spectacular insects first appeared about three hundred million years ago in the Carboniferous period. Evolving long before the reign of the dinosaurs, they lived alongside such fearsome beasts as *Tyrannosaurus rex*, and continue to thrive today with few structural alterations or changes in life-style, except that the earliest specimens were very much larger. Those giant dragonflies of the Carboniferous period, known as Meganeuridae, have been discovered with wingspans exceeding fifty centimetres. Dragonflies are one of evolution's greatest success stories, as their original design was so well adapted to cope with climatic and other variations over millions of years that they have had no need to change much over such a lengthy time span.

Supreme masters of aerial manoeuvre, they have the ability to fly forwards, backwards, sideways, up, down and hover, and have been timed at speeds approaching twenty miles per hour. Enormous wide-angled eyes enable the insects to detect airborne prey from almost any direction and at considerable distances. After a short chase, the victim is scooped up in mid-air by bristly legs, which are thrust forward to form a kind of basket, and the prey is then devoured at leisure after the dragonfly has perched.

The life-cycle of dragonflies and damselflies is similar but, whereas most of the former spend two or more years under water as carnivorous nymphs, feeding on tadpoles, larvae and small fish, damselflies complete the watery phase in one year, eating smaller prey like *Daphnia*. Potential food is carefully stalked, then caught by a highly specialised mobile mouthpart called a mask, which can be shot out rapidly to grasp the victim.

Odonata can often be seen locked together, flying in 'tandem'. Following a barely token courtship, the male approaches the female in flight and grasps her neck, or prothorax, with his anal claspers. After settling on vegetation, mating takes place in a position known variously as the 'heart' or 'wheel'.

Both true dragonflies and their more delicate looking relatives, the dainty damselflies, are environmentally sensitive and so their presence in any given habitat is indicative of clean healthy conditions. Prior to the mid 1980s, before annual records were compiled, little attention was paid to Odonata of the Commons, beyond a few brief references. Our forefathers called dragonflies and damselflies 'Horse Stingers' and 'Devil's darning needles', respectively. At the turn of the century Walter Johnson captured the "rather repulsive looking larva" of *Libellula depressa* (the Broad-Bodied Chaser dragonfly), together with the "Azure blue devil's needle", presumably the Azure damselfly. At the same time he saw the Blue-tailed damselfly and Southern Hawker and Ruddy Darter dragonflies.

No further records are available until 1971, when Norman Riley, writing in *Walks on Wimbledon Common*, lists the Blue-tailed damselfly, the Four-spotted Chaser and Emperor dragonflies; plus the Common and Southern Hawkers. Both the Common and Ruddy Darters are also mentioned. The most interesting sightings of that time, however, were the Red-veined and Yellow-winged Darters. Both are strong migrants which occasionally fly from the Continent in hot summers. In fact, the Yellow-winged Darter was also recorded in 1995 at Bluegate Gravel Pit.

Odonata are divided into two sub-orders, namely ANISOPTERA (True Dragonflies) and ZYGOPTERA (Damselflies).

True Dragonflies
(Anisoptera)
[11 resident species
plus 1 vagrant]

These are chunkier, more robust and dashing than the slender damselflies. Anisoptera stems from the Latin 'unequal wings' as, unlike the damselflies, hind and fore-wings differ in configuration.

Dependent upon their habits, dragonflies are divided into self-explanatory groups, which include the 'Hawkers' (family Aeshnidae), 'Darters', 'Chasers' and 'Skimmers' (family Libellulidae). All are strong wide-ranging migrants, so it is not uncommon for non-resident species, such as the Yellow-winged Darter, to grace our waters from time to time.

Egg-laying can often be observed. Most Hawkers lay either directly into rotting wood, or in some cases above water level into wet mud on the bank, or on plants some distance away. Other species fly low over the water, constantly dipping their abdomens onto the surface to release eggs, one at a time. At the end of a lengthy aquatic nymph stage they will climb the stem of a convenient water plant, such as yellow iris or reed, and carefully extricate themselves from the old skin, leaving the empty shucks or exuviae attached to the stem. This remains a ghostly memento of a former existence.

❧ Systematic list of Dragonflies of Wimbledon Common and Putney Heath

The Southern Hawker
Aeshna cyanea

Both sexes are dark brownish-black with broad green stripes and patches on the abdomen. The female has green instead of blue markings at the rear end of her abdomen. A very inquisitive dragonfly, which will hover in front of the observer as if to study him in detail. It will not, of course, attack humans. Flies even in dull weather, hawking over water or along woodland rides.
Flight period: Late June to mid-November, if weather holds
Status: Quite common
Habitat: Especially fond of tree-fringed water such as Fishpond Wood, Curling Pond, Scio Pond and Queensmere.

The Common Hawker
Aeshna juncea

Similar to the Southern and Migrant Hawkers, with which it is readily confused. Male is brown with yellow markings on thorax and blue patches on abdomen. The female has a similar ground colour but with green markings on abdomen.
Flight period: Mid-June to late October
Status: Despite its name, it is generally much less common than the Southern Hawker
Habitat: Queensmere, Kingsmere and Scio preferred.

The Migrant Hawker
Aeshna mixta

Somewhat smaller, but similar to the Southern and Common Hawkers. Male has a dark brown abdomen, with blue spots and a distinctive yellow triangular mark on segment two of the abdomen, just behind the hind wing roots. Female is similar but duller. Fond of hovering and flying high up among tree canopies hunting for prey.
Flight period: July to October
Status: Common
Habitat: Most still water locations.

The Brown Hawker
Aeshna grandis

A large easily identified species, as this is the only dragonfly with brownish (not clear) wings. Males and females are similar. Coloured dark brown all over, with only a few yellow and blue markings. Female can often be seen laying eggs into damp logs or planks bordering pond sides.
Flight period: July to October
Status: Quite common
Habitat: Most favoured site is Queensmere, but can also be seen in good years at Kingsmere and Scio Pond.

The Emperor Dragonfly
Anax imperator

The largest and most majestic British species; very wary and alert, consequently difficult to approach and photograph. Male has green head, thorax and first segment of abdomen. The rest is a beautiful clear blue, with a wide black line running its whole length. The female is light green all over with a broad brownish line along the top of her abdomen. Fond of hawking rapidly over water taking insect prey.
Flight period May to late September
Status: Quite common most years
Habitat: Well sheltered sites, notably Hookhamslade Pond and Queensmere, but can appear anywhere.

The Broad-Bodied Chaser
Libellula depressa

A very plump looking territorial species, fond of perching by pond margins and suddenly dashing off to chase away rivals or snatch prey, before returning to perch on its favourite twig or sun-drenched bank. Mature male has brown thorax, bordered by two yellow stripes; a powder-blue abdomen, at the sides of which are yellowish patches. The female and also immature males have a brown thorax and light brownish-yellow abdomen, with larger yellow patches at the sides. Wings are virtually devoid of markings.
Flight period: Mid-May to September
Status: Common
Habitat: Prefers smaller sheltered ponds such as Scio, but also quite common at Kingsmere.

The Four-Spotted Chaser
Libellula quadrimaculata

An extremely active species, which can be confused with the Broad-Bodied Chaser, the main distinguishing feature is on the wings, which have triangular brown patches at their bases, and two prominent dark spots on leading edges. Both male and female are similar, with overall brownish colour, having yellow abdominal flashes and dark brown at rear of abdomen.
Flight period: May to August
Status: Much less common than the Broad-Bodied Chaser
Habitat: Large bodies of water such as Kingsmere, but also found at Scio Pond.

The Black-Tailed Skimmer
Orthetrum cancellatum

Superficially similar to the Broad-Bodied and Four-Spotted Chasers, but slimmer bodied. Mature male has brown thorax, with blue abdomen merging into black near the tip. Sides of abdomen have dull yellow patches. Female differs in being overall dull brownish yellow with dark markings on each abdominal segment.
Flight period: Late April to late August
Status: Hitherto scarce, but population increasing currently
Habitat: Large open water preferred. Kingsmere and Ravine Pond.

The Black Darter
Sympetrum danae

A small very active species, often seen away from water, flying low around vegetation. Male is virtually black overall, with a noticeable 'waist' at abdominal segments three to five. Female, yellowish-brown with black triangle on top of the thorax and yellow patches at sides of thorax and abdomen.
Flight period: June to October
Status: Common
Habitat: Sheltered sites such as Hookhamslade, Bluegate Gravel Pit and the new Ravine Pond.

The Ruddy Darter
Sympetrum sanguineum

A small species, the male has a reddish-brown thorax, a blood-red heavily 'waisted' abdomen and black legs. Female is dull brownish-yellow, with a line of dark stripes along each side of the abdomen. Legs also black.
Flight period: June to October
Status: Abundant
Habitat: Sheltered and heavily vegetated waters, such as Bluegate, Hookhamslade, Kingsmere and Queensmere.

The Common Darter
Sympetrum striolatum

Similar to the Ruddy Darter, but duller red, male an overall brownish-red and abdominal 'waist' less pronounced. Female similar, but more heavily marked with black lines along the abdomen.
Flight period: June to October
Status: Very common
Habitat: Sheltered vegetation-rich waters. Kingsmere and Hookhamslade preferred.

142

Dragonfly and Damselflies photographed on Wimbledon Common and Putney Heath.
Photos:Tony Drakeford, except Figure 10.33 by Ron Kettle.

Figure 10.25 Southern Hawker flying over Hookhamslade.

Figure 10.26 Migrant Hawker, Hookhamslade.

Figure 10.27 (left)
Brown Hawker
ovipositing at
Kingsmere.

Figure 10.28 (right)
Broad-Bodied Chaser,
Scio.

Figure 10.29 Black-Tailed Skimmer, Kingsmere.

Figure 10.30 Black Darter, Hookhamslade.

Figure 10.31 (left) Ruddy Darter

Figure 10.32 (above) Common Darter, Putney Heath.

Figure 10.33 (left) Yellow-Winged Darter, Bluegate Gravel Pit.

Figure 10.34 (above) Azure Damselflies mating, 7 Post Pond.

Figure 10.35 (left) Emerald Damselfly, Kingsmere.

Figure 10.36 (below) Banded Agrion, increasingly observed along the Beverley Brook.

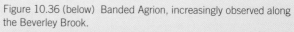

TheYellow-Winged Darter
Sympetrum flaveolum

Non-resident, essentially a migrant from the Continent, which periodically arrives in large numbers late in a hot summer. Male has a brown thorax and a bright red abdomen, somewhat similar to the Common and Ruddy Darters, but main identification feature is that all wings have large yellowish-amber patches emanating from their base. Female is pale yellowish-brown.

Flight period: July to October
Status: Very rare occasional migrant
Habitat: Recorded at Bluegate Gravil Pit only, a habitat admirably suited to its somewhat specialised requirements.

Damselflies
(Zygoptera) [7 species]

The Greek name translated is 'equal wings' indicating that fore and hind-wings are approximately similar in configuration. Damselflies are smaller, more delicate looking than true dragonflies, with a weaker fluttering flight, reminiscent of mini helicopters, as they flicker above reeds and pond surface.

Damselflies are endophytic; that is to say, they deposit single elongated eggs directly into plants, as opposed to scattering them on the surface as do some dragonflies. With some species, the male leaves his partner as she disappears below the water, but hovers above to guard her or ward off predators or rivals. With other species, the male also descends with the female.

After one year spent as an aquatic nymph, the damselfly, like the dragonfly, will find a convenient marginal plant to shed its skin and so transform into a graceful and colourful flying insect.

Systematic List of Damselflies of Wimbledon Common and Putney Heath

The Azure Damselfly
Coenagrion puella

One of two very similar species which are difficult to distinguish at a distance, males are a soft powder blue with black hoops at intervals along the abdomen, on segment two of which is a 'U' shaped mark, and a 'crown' on segment nine. Females are dark bluish-black above and yellowish-green below. The species can be seen in swarms by pond sides on a warm sunny day, being one of the most abundant on the Commons.

Flight period: Early May to September
Status: Super abundant
Habitat: Most favoured locations are Kingsmere and Queensmere. Also found at 7 Post Pond and Scio Pond.

Common Blue Damselfly
Enallagma cyathigerum

It so resembles the Azure that, unless viewed close-up, it is extremely difficult to tell the two species apart. The powder-blue colouration of the male is similar, with black abdominal hoops. Main distinguishing features are the black 'ace of spades' or 'stalked ball' configuration on segment two of the abdomen and lack of 'crown' at tip of the abdomen. The female is mainly black or dull green above and greenish below. The species tends to appear slightly later than the Azure.

Flight period: Mid-May to late September
Status: Super abundant; swarms frequently seen over water
Habitat: All still water, but Kingsmere, Queensmere, Scio and 7 Post Pond are favourite locations.

Blue-Tailed Damselfly
Ischnura elegans

Much less common, and should not be confused with the other two blue species. It is also less active and does not swarm. Male is blackish-blue, with a prominent powder-blue broad band on segment eight at rear of abdomen. Female similar, but blue band is duller.
Flight period: Mid-May to late September
Status: Quite common
Habitat: Mainly Kingsmere, 7 Post Pond, Scio Pond, plus most still water.

Large Red Damselfly
Pyrrhosoma nymphula

Usually the first species on the wing, male is red with narrow black abdominal hoops and black legs. Female is similar but more heavily marked with black.
Flight period: April to September
Status: Scarce
Habitat: Still water and bogs. Most favoured haunts are Fishpond Wood and Queensmere.

Emerald Damselfly
Lestes sponsa

A beautifully coloured damselfly, larger than the 'blues', with long slender abdomen, can possibly be confused with the Blue-tailed, but the male is a striking iridescent greenish-bronze, with light bluish-white patches on thorax, and a bluish-white broad hoop at each end of the abdomen. Bluish eyes are very prominent. Female similar but duller. Usually rests with wings half open, a useful identification feature. With age, colour tends to bleach out.
Flight period: June to October
Status: Common
Habitat: Vegetation-rich waters, notably Kingsmere and Hookhamslade.

The Banded Agrion
Calopteryx splendens

A magnificent large dark coloured species. Found in unpolluted slow moving rivers and streams, rarely breeding in still water. Increasingly the insect has been seen along the Beverley Brook, an indication that the quality of the water may be improving. Male has a metallic dark bluish-green abdomen and large dark patches on wings. Female and immature males are a bright metallic mid-green, with clear greenish wings.
Flight period: May to September
Status: Very scarce on the Commons
Habitat: Slow moving river margins. Increasingly sighted along the Beverley Brook.

Red-eyed Damselfly
Erythromma najas

Resembles the Blue-tailed damselfly, but is larger, with a blue-tipped abdomen and prominent red eyes.
Flight period: Mid-May to mid-August
Status: Very scarce
Habitat: Kingsmere and Queensmere.

Chapter 11   Beetles and Bumble Bees

Max Barclay and Shirley Goodwin

The Beetles of Wimbledon Common and Putney Heath
Max Barclay

There are more species of beetle (Order Coleoptera) than any other group of organism, and even in Britain we have almost 4,000 species. The Commons, because of their high diversity of soil types and habitats, ranging from wetland to sandy heath and gorse scrub, from herb rich hills to mature oak and beech woodland, support an extremely rich beetle fauna for an area of their size. Preliminary searches in 1995 and 1996 (MVL Barclay unpublished data) revealed more than 400 species, of which almost 10% were listed as 'nationally scarce'. It seems likely that the true number of beetle species occurring on the Commons is closer to 1,500.

Beetles are characterised by the front wings being hardened into protective 'wing cases' or elytra, which defend them from crushing and desiccation. The whole body of most species appears strongly 'armoured'. Like many 'higher' insects, most famously butterflies and moths (order Lepidoptera), beetles show 'complete metamorphosis'. This means that the eggs hatch into wingless larvae, or grubs, which, after a feeding stage, form a pupa from which the adult beetle emerges.

Many beetles are small and inconspicuous, living in leaf litter or dense foliage, but there are a number that are likely to be seen and relatively easily identified by the keen naturalist or the casual observer. A brief description of the most important families, along with examples taken from the fauna of the Commons, is given below. The species have been chosen for their large size, bright colours or conspicuous or interesting life histories. Illustrations of many of these can be found in popular field guides.

Family Carabidae, the Ground Beetles

Carabidae, which are quite easily recognised in the field, are second only to ladybirds in terms of their popularity with the general naturalist. The glossy black or metallic adults are voracious predators, and are often found under stones and logs, or running in sunlight on bare ground or by the margins of lakes such as Bluegate and Kingsmere. They are unusual amongst beetles because the adults of most species can be found all year round, often hibernating in large numbers in rotten logs or reed litter. When handled, carabids give off a pungent odour that clings to the skin. Almost 100 species have been recorded from the Commons, including one, *Harpalus griseus*, which has been found nowhere else in Britain.

Carabus violaceus, the violet ground beetle, is probably the largest species on the Commons. It is 20-30 mm long, matt black with a striking violet margin to the thorax and wing cases. *C.violaceus* is nocturnal, and can often be seen on paths at night hunting snails and earthworms. There are four other large species of *Carabus* known from Wimbledon. Carabid rarities include the primarily coastal *Polystichus connexus*, collected at light by Martin Henderson, and *Synuchus nivalis*, known from only seven localities in the London Region, collected in an underground trap by Richard Thompson. Other Carabidae of interest on Wimbledon Common include the delicate, arboreal *Dromius*, the tiny *Bembidion*, which swarm by the edges of the meres and gravel pits, and the familiar black *Pterostichus* and *Nebria*, usually found under stones and logs. Most of these are widespread all over the site.

Family Dytiscidae, the Diving Beetles

Wimbledon Common and Putney Heath support a large number of aquatic beetles, although there are much greater numbers of 'Water Bugs' (Order Hemiptera). These can be distinguished from most water beetles by the near-absence of antennae on the head, which in Dytiscidae are long and conspicuous. Dytiscidae are all predatory; they are unable to 'breathe water' and must return to the surface regularly for air. The impressive Great Diving Beetle (*Dytiscus marginalis*) occurs in the smaller ponds, such as 7 Post Pond and in Bluegate, though not in large numbers. It is a large insect, often over 30mm, black with an iridescent green sheen in the male, and yellow edges to the wing cases and thorax in both sexes. Adults and larvae, in particular the larvae, are formidable predators, often killing newts and small fish. Another common resident, particularly of Bluegate Gravel Pit, is the Screech Beetle (*Hygrobia hermanni*). This beetle is so strange that some authorities place it in its own family, the Hygrobiidae, but recent evidence from DNA suggests that this may be inaccurate. The beetle gets its English name from the loud and alarming squeaking noise it makes when handled. In Victorian times, these 'talking' beetles were sold in the streets as a novelty! They are weak swimmers, unlike the majority of diving beetles, which are extremely fast underwater. Diving beetles are also powerful fliers, and may be attracted to lights at night. Aquatic beetles of the families Hydrophilidae (Water scavenger beetles), Haliplidae (Crawling water beetles) and Gyrinidae (Whirligig Beetles) also occur on the Commons, though these are smaller and less obvious.

Family Staphylinidae, the Rove Beetles

This is the largest family of beetles in the UK, including about half of the British beetle fauna. However, most 'Staphs' are small (1-4mm), elusive and notoriously difficult to separate to species. They are ubiquitous in rotting material, such as decaying fungus, carrion, dung and dead wood, where they feed predominantly on fly larvae.

Staphylinids are characterised by very short wing cases, which leave the long articulated abdomen exposed. This makes them flexible and able to move quickly even in close-packed material. Their slender shape and short elytra has led to their being confused with earwigs, a quite unrelated group closer to crickets and cockroaches! One of our largest 'staphs', very common in Wimbledon, is the familiar Devil's Coach Horse Beetle (*Staphylinus olens*). This large (25–30mm) jet-black insect is parallel-sided with large, powerful jaws. It is most often seen on paths on autumn evenings. When threatened it arches its tail over its head, scorpion-like, and emits a strong, obnoxious odour. It can also bite if handled, but like the Carabidae it is beneficial to gardeners, as it destroys large numbers of damaging grubs and slugs. The several hundred other species of Staphylinidae found on the Commons are all very much smaller, and most will only be noticed by the specialist. An exception is the numerous tiny species that swarm on the wing on warm summer evenings, and can cause discomfort by flying into the eyes or mouth, where their defensive secretions sting painfully.

Superfamily Scarabaeoidea, the Stag Beetles, Dung Beetles and Chafers.

Three species of Stag Beetle (Family Lucanidae) are present in the British Isles, and all three are found on the Commons. The magnificent Greater Stag Beetle (*Lucanus cervus*), although much declined and protected by law in Britain and several other European countries, is still relatively abundant along Commonside and in areas of the Commons where old dead deciduous stumps have been left undisturbed. It is the largest British beetle, with big males reaching up to 75mm, although tiny males as small as 25mm have also been recorded. The males may be seen and heard slowly flying, due to their large and cumbersome 'antlers', somewhat above head height, on warm humid evenings in late May and June. The females lack the characteristic 'antlers', which are used for fighting between males. Their flight is much faster and more directed, and hence less likely to be noticed. The Lesser Stag Beetle (*Dorcus parallelipipedu*s) is also widespread on the Commons. In this much commoner species, neither sex has antlers, and at 20–30mm the average size is smaller. *Dorcus* is also uniform greyish-black in colour, while *Lucanus* usually has a black head and thorax with contrasting chestnut brown wing cases.

The third species of Lucanid, *Sinodendron cylindricum*, is smaller still at 12–16mm. The male has a small rhinoceros-like horn on its nose, hence the genus name *Sinodendron* (nose-finger). The species name *cylindricum* (cylindrical) is also very apt for this beetle. It is rarely seen, but occurs at low density in the beech woods leading down to Queensmere.

The Geotrupidae or 'Dor beetles' are represented on the Commons chiefly by the Minotaur Beetle (*Typhaeus typhoeus*). This heavy-bodied black dung beetle, up to 25mm long, builds tunnels up to 5 feet deep in sandy soil, for example near the Windmill Car Park (see also Chapter 13). Both sexes build and guard the tunnel, which is provisioned with dung, preferably rabbit, which the developing larvae feed on. The parents will remain in the tunnel with the larvae throughout the winter. Although the beetles themselves are seldom seen, their circular burrows, about 18mm in diameter, are a common sight where rabbits abound. The male is a striking insect with three long forward-pointing horns, resembling the prehistoric dinosaur *Triceratops*. He uses the structures to push debris, and probably intruders, out of the communal burrow.

The true Scarabaeidae includes a huge number of species of dung beetles and chafers, including the Sacred Scarab (*Scarabaeus sacer*) of the Ancient Egyptians. However, the British fauna is quite impoverished with a mere 85 species, of which I have recorded only sixteen on the Commons. Nine of these are small (3-12mm) seed-like dung beetles of the genus *Aphodius*, which can be found flying in sunshine or feeding in dog, horse or other dung on the rides. The 'chafers' include the well-known 'Maybug' or Cockchafer (*Melolontha melolontha*) which is most commonly found flying to lights on warm May evenings; it is extremely common in certain years, and scarce in others. The larvae, called 'Rook worms' develop on roots and can be an agricultural pest. Similar, but smaller, is the Summer Chafer (*Amphimallon solstitialis*) which can swarm in the late afternoon and early evening in June and July, often around a large deciduous tree; in flight they can easily be mistaken for bumble bees. The most attractive chafer on the Commons is the glorious iridescent green Rose Chafer (*Cetonia aurata*), a species that has much declined in recent years. Adults can be seen flying, very fast, in the hottest part of June and July days, or feeding on flowers such as roses, rhododendrons and *Pyracantha*. The large white grubs, which, curiously, move only backwards, develop in compost heaps or dead wood mould.

The most interesting Scarabaeid beetle on the Commons is the tiny

Saprosites mendax. This rust-red beetle is a native of Australia, but established itself in the early 1900s at Arundel Park. A single specimen I collected in Queensmere wood in 1996 made Wimbledon the third locality in Britain where it had ever been recorded.

Family Elateridae, the Click Beetles

Click beetles have a distinctive linear to long-oval shape. They are so named because when turned onto their back, they can right themselves by leaping into the air with an audible 'click'. Adult click beetles are usually seen from May to August in long grass, or flying slowly over hedgerows and woodland margins. One species of national importance, which breeds on the Commons, is the striking scarlet-red and black *Ampedus sanguinolentus*. Like so many rare beetles, it develops in dead wood, in this case birch or pine on acid soil. A number of specimens were found in 1995 in a huge dead birch tree near Bluegate Gravel Pit. One of our largest click beetles, the elusive *Stenagostus rhombeus*, is common in the woods near Queensmere. The huge, fierce looking black larvae occur in dead wood, but the nocturnal adult is rarely seen except by Lepidopterists with moth traps.

Family Buprestidae, the Jewel Beetles

Buprestidae is truly a family of the moist tropics, with those species reaching Britain but a pale shadow of their tropical relatives. All Buprestidae in Britain are uncommon, but the Commons boasts at least 3 species. The small *Agrilus laticornis* is the commonest. About 10mm long, it swarms around oak trees. The narrow-bodied adults, which fly extremely fast, look like tiny green chips of malachite.

Family Cantharidae, the Soldier Beetles

Soldier beetles are slender, soft bodied insects, often brightly coloured. Most noticeable is the Orange Soldier Beetle (*Rhagonycha fulva*) which is 8-10mm, bright orange with black tips to the elytra. It appears every year on about the 24th of June, and by mid-July is one of the commonest beetles in almost every habitat. Orange Soldiers are usually seen on the flowers of hogweed (*Heracleum*) or bramble (*Rubus*), sometimes in enormous numbers. Often they are mating, which may take many hours. The larger (14mm) black and red (*Cantharis rustica*), sometimes called the 'Sailor Beetle' is abundant in the grassy meadows of the Commons. Both species are predominantly predatory. The soft, velvety larvae of Cantharidae are voracious, active predators in the leaf-litter.

Family Tenebrionidae, the Darkling Beetles

Tenebrionidae is a very variable family which is most abundant in deserts and arid regions. On the Commons, most Tenebrionidae of interest are associated with man-altered environments. The large, ponderous Cellar or Churchyard Beetle (*Blaps mucronata*) is apparently still a relatively frequent sight around the stables and the Windmill. This sturdy beetle may live for a decade or more. Also around the stables, the two species of Mealworm Beetle *Tenebrio molitor* and *T.obscurus*, whose larvae are familiar as bait and pet food, live in the natural state, scavenging on meal and oats dropped by the horses.

Family Coccinellidae, the Ladybirds

Ladybirds are undoubtedly the most familiar and well-loved family of Coleoptera, and a good starting point for the beetle-beginner. The adults are abundant, colourful and conspicuous, and species can usually be identified in the field, without harming them. Like butterflies, most species have English names as well as Latin ones. However, there is more to their identification than just counting spots, and a reliable field guide should be obtained. Ladybirds are very active and widespread in summer; although adults can be found in winter as well. Some species hibernate communally in 'roosts' of thousands or even millions of individuals. Such a 'roost' is a sight never to be forgotten!

The Commons boast a rich fauna of at least eighteen species of ladybird, most of which are very abundant. The ubiquitous 7-spot (*Coccinella 7-punctata*), 2-spot (*Adalia 2-punctata*) and 10-spot (*Adalia 10-punctata*) are all common, as are the strangely named Pine Ladybird (*Exochomus 4-pustulatus*), which likes a wide range of trees and the 19-spot or 'Water Ladybird' (*Anisosticta 19-punctata*), found in reed beds, especially at Bluegate. The Orange Ladybird (*Halyzia 16-guttata*) is a beautiful insect which until recently was rather rare, but has spread incredibly in the last decade. It was first recorded on the Commons in 1995. Examination of the patches of heather, for example, near the Windmill, will be very rewarding for the ladybird enthusiast, and may reveal the Hieroglyphic Ladybird (*Coccinella hieroglyphica*), or the Kidney Spot Ladybird (*Chilocorus renipustulatus*), which is not restricted to heather. Better still, the Heather Ladybird (*Chilocorus 2-pustulatus*) might be found, which to my knowledge is still unknown from the Commons. Pine trees are also a rich source of ladybirds and many pine species (e.g. *Neomysia oblongoguttata*, *Myrrha 18-guttata*, *Halyzia 4-punctata*) are under-recorded, or even unknown from Wimbledon; so there is much scope for the amateur to add to our knowledge of the Commons' wildlife, even in this well studied group.

Family Cerambycidae, the Longhorn Beetles

The Cerambycidae include some of the most impressive beetles. The larvae mostly develop in dead wood, and because of the low nutrition content of this food development may take several years. The short-lived adults feed on flowers, tree resins, or in some cases, do not feed at all. Many of the commoner small species, such as the black *Grammoptera ruficornis* and the Wasp Beetle (*Clytus arietis*) may be found by examining hawthorn blossom in early May. *Strangalia maculata* (14-20mm) is a very elegant yellow and black beetle which feeds on hogweed and bramble flowers in late June and July, often alongside Orange Soldier Beetles. Another, smaller flower visitor *Leptura livida*, is unique among British longhorns in that the larvae develop not in wood but in the soil, on the mycelia of the 'Fairy Ring Toadstool' (*Marasmius* sp.). Adult *L. livida* are also common in all sorts of flowers in June, July and August. The Musk Beetle (*Aromia moschata*) is a very large (12-35mm) metallic malachite-green longhorn which is found rarely and usually singly, in July and August on umbellifer or bramble flowers growing near sickly willow trees (*Salix* sp.). The most recent records from SW London have been from Putney Heath in the late 1980s but the species undoubtedly still persists on the Commons in low density. The name 'Musk Beetle' derives from the pleasant musky odour emitted by the adults. The larvae develop in moribund or dying willow trees; the species is listed as 'nationally scarce'. Finally, there are a number of nocturnal species of longhorn which are seldom seen except by lepidopterists running light-traps, to which they are attracted. *Arhopalus rusticus* (10-30mm) is a parallel sided brown insect, with short antennae for a 'longhorn', which is strictly nocturnal; its abundance on the Commons is betrayed by the lozenge shaped emergence holes in the bark of dead pines, for example those logs used as boundaries on the Windmill Car Park. The holes are 5-8mm across, and there can be hundreds in a single log!

Family Chrysomelidae, the Leaf Beetles

Leaf beetles are a very abundant group of beetles, which as the name suggests feed on living plants. On young aspens and poplars in scrubby parts of the Commons, one might see adults and larvae of the Red Poplar Leaf Beetle (*Chrysomela populi*), which at 10-12mm is among the largest of this conservatively sized family. The adults, active from May to October, are bright red, with black head and thorax, while their larvae are black and shiny. Individual trees are often almost stripped of their leaves by these beetles, but the populations seldom grow large enough to do real harm. Handling the beetles causes them to emit a strong-smelling acid, sequestered from willow leaves. Also striking are the Tortoise Beetles, Genus *Cassida*. Several similar species occur on the Commons, and they are most often seen on thistles and water mints. The thorax and wing cases are expanded to form a 'shell' beneath which they can retract their appendages, hence their English name. The spiny larvae, which have no such defensive shell, disguise themselves with a coating of their own excrement. The tiny 'Flea Beetles', subfamily Alticinae, of which more than twenty species are known from the Commons, also belong to this family.

Superfamily Curculionoidea, the Weevils

Weevils are characterised by the 'rostrum', a nose-like extension of the front of the head. They are the largest beetle group of all, although their diversity is centred in the tropics, and in this country the Staphylinidae are more numerous. Nevertheless there are about 100 weevil species known from the Commons. In the spring beautiful vivid metallic silver green weevils of the genera *Phyllobius* and *Polydrusus* are found all over the Commons, feeding on fresh leaves of birch and oak. The acorn weevils, such as *Curculio glandium*, are also common. The female *Curculio* drills a hole in an acorn using her incredibly long rostrum, into which she lays an egg, and the larva develops inside the shell. The leaf rolling weevils of the family Attelabidae are well represented on the Commons, for example the Scarlet Hazel Weevil (*Apoderus coryli*), Oak Roller Weevil (*Attelabus nitens*) and the Birch Roller (*Deporaus betulae*). All three species lay their eggs, singly, on leaves which the female then rolls up to form a triangular or barrel-shaped roll, depending on the species. The larvae then develop in the comparative safety of the leaf-roll; by killing the leaf, this process also protects the larvae from secondary poisons produced by the tree in defence. Another weevil of interest is the 'Woodworm Weevil' (*Euophryum confine*) which exists in enormous numbers in the beech woods above Queensmere. This insect is an introduction from New Zealand which has spread all over the UK, and has become a pest of damp wood in houses, for example behind sinks. Another pest, the Grain Weevil (*Sitophilus granarius*), still exists in the Windmill itself from the days when it was functional! Finally, the most destructive (in the UK) of all weevil pests, the Elm Bark Beetles (*Scolytus scolytus*) and (*Scolytus multistriatus*), responsible for transmitting the fungus which killed an estimated 25 million elms in the 1960s and 1970s, are abundant still on the Commons. They attack the young growth of elm as soon as it reaches a certain size. Martin Henderson, a fellow worker on the beetles of the Commons, observed that "*in 1995 the wych elms along Wildcroft Road were clearly dying, showing yellow leaves and dead branches*". The characteristic patterns of the *Scolytus* galleries under the bark easily betray its involvement.

Of course, the beetles listed are only a fraction of the hundreds of species likely to occur on the Commons, but it is hoped that they give a good overall picture of the variety of Coleoptera, as well as allowing identification of some of the more striking species. Most of all I hope I have indicated how rewarding and exciting the study of Coleoptera can be, and how much of a contribution the amateur can make to biological recording, and to our understanding of beetles on the Commons and elsewhere. There are many useful identification books available and I will happily confirm identifications of Coleoptera from the Commons.

A selection of beetles found on the Commons

Figure 11.1 Mating Greater Stag Beetles (*Lucanus cervus*).
Photo: Tony Drakeford.

Figure 11.2 Cockchafer (*Melolontha melolontha*).
Photo: Tony Drakeford.

Figure 11.3 Rose Chafer (*Cetonia aurata*).
Photo: Tony Drakeford.

Figure 11.4 Longhorn Beetle (*Strangalia maculata*).
Photo: Charlie Wicker.

Figure 11.5 Musk Beetle (*Aromia moschata*).
Photo: Charlie Wicker.

Figure 11.6 Elm Bark Beetle (*Scolytus scolytus*).
Illustration: Tony Drakeford.

Bumble Bees and their Flowers on Wimbledon Common and Putney Heath

Shirley Goodwin

The first warm days of spring in late February or March bring forth large bumble bees from hibernation to feed on the nectar and pollen of early flowers. These bumble bees are fertile *Bombus* queens, the only survivors from the many bumble bee colonies of the previous summer. These furry bees will soon be seeking nest sites in dark inviting spaces in hummocks of grass, holes in ground, hedgerows, cavities in trees or sometimes in buildings. Each queen will establish her own nest, although this is often delayed by cold weather, a shortage of food, or even a lack of suitable nest sites.

Bumble bees are social insects and by the summer each nest may contain about fifty or two to three hundred bees. Some species are more prolific than others but environmental conditions and length of season are contributing factors. After emerging from hibernation, a few weeks may elapse before a queen lays her first batch of eggs. These are laid on a lump of pollen which she has gradually collected together during many foraging trips and placed within the nest. She incubates the eggs by placing her body across the pollen lump; occasionally leaving the nest briefly to feed on nectar and collect more pollen. When the eggs hatch the larvae eat their bed of pollen and when it is finished they each spin a cocoon and pupate.

Approximately five weeks after the eggs are laid the adult bumble bees emerge from their cocoons. These first few bees, about six to twelve, are infertile female workers which are smaller than their mother. They soon start caring for the next brood and the queen who, no longer working alone, continues laying eggs for successive broods. The first small worker bumble bees can often be seen busily foraging in the latter part of May. Pollen is taken back to the nest in even greater quantities as increasing numbers of workers emerge to swell the workforce. As food becomes more plentiful for the larvae, later emerging workers are usually larger. The size of an adult bee does not change and is determined by the amount of food it receives in the larval stage prior to pupation.

During the summer a new community of bumble bees will gradually appear from the many nests established in the spring. A colony matures and reaches its peak when the next reproductive generation has been reared. The timing of this varies between species, with some new queens and males emerging in June

Figure 11.7 *Bombus terrestris/ B. lucorum* foraging on thistle. Photo:TonyDrakeford.

and those from later maturing colonies emerging in July or August. Mating occurs soon afterwards, often while they are in flight. Shortly after this event the new queens go into hibernation, some as early as July, and will not reappear until the following spring.

In the British Isles there are sixteen true bumble bees, *Bombus* species, although some are now rare; and six cuckoo bumble bees, *Psithyrus* species. *Psithyrus* resemble *Bombus* in size and colour but are less furry and have a quieter buzz. *Psithyrus* females are not called queens: they are unable to collect pollen and therefore cannot rear their own offspring. There is no worker caste and only males and reproductive females are produced. Their numbers are never very high. As the name implies, this cuckoo bumble bee lays her eggs in a *Bombus* nest where the workers care for her brood. The *Psithyrus* female attempts, and often succeeds, to dominate the nest and at some stage is likely to kill the *Bombus* queen. However, not all are successful because, in a strong nest with many *Bombus* workers, the *Psithyrus* interloper may be stung to death and her body carried outside.

British bumble bees can be divided into three colour groups: browns; black-bodied white tails with yellow bands; and black-bodied red tails with or without yellow bands. The colour patterns of some species are similar although there are usually subtle differences in colour or in band width. With some species the coat pattern varies between male and female, which adds to the difficulties of identification.

On Wimbledon Common and Putney Heath, six common bumble bee species have been recorded. Unfortunately they do not have simple English names for easy reference. Of the six species, the queens of *Bombus lapidarius* and *Bombus terrestris* are relatively large and can be easily identified in spring, if they keep still long enough! *B. lapidarius* is velvety black with a red 'tail', as the end of the abdomen is called. Her workers are the same colour but smaller; the males, which do not appear until July, have two narrow yellow bands in addition to a red tail. *B. terrestris* queens have a dull yellow band behind the head, a brighter yellow band on the abdomen and a distinctive beige-pink tail. Her workers and males also have two yellow bands but their tails are white. This makes them difficult to distinguish from *Bombus lucorum* queens and workers which also have two yellow bands and a white tail. The *B. lucorum* male is a more colourful bee: he also has a white tail but has three wide, bright lemon-yellow bands and a noticeable yellow tuft on the top of his head. *Bombus hortorum* is another bee with a white tail, but both male and female have three yellow bands. *Bombus pascuorum* is an easy one to recognise as it is brown. The colour varies from light brown to dark red-brown on the thorax and the abdomen is banded in light browns and black. Male and female are the same colour. This bee has a long season and in mild autumns may still be seen as late as November, long after other bumble bees have disappeared.

Bumble bees need sunlit areas in undisturbed grassland and open woodland in which to safely nest and find sufficient forage. Unlike honey bees they do not hoard large amounts of food and can only survive a few days on their meagre stores. So they need an unbroken succession of flowers providing nectar and pollen throughout their colony cycle, which for some species continues into late summer or autumn. The long tongues of these relatively large bees enable them to forage on an extremely wide range of flowers. Together with many shorter tongued insects they can feed on shallow, disc-shaped flowers. But, with their long tongues, they can also reach nectar in long tubular flowers, such as bluebell, honeysuckle or the deep, narrow florets of some clovers and thistles.

Figure 11.9 *Bombus lapidarius* on cat's ear.

Figure 11.8
Bombus pascuorum on blackberry, a favoured food plant.

Artist: Shirley Goodwin.

Many plants are dependent upon bees for pollination and the large size of bumble bees, and thick fluffy coats which get covered in pollen, make them particularly good pollinators. The continuous activity of bees on flowers, either feeding or collecting pollen for their larvae, ensures pollination. The seeds and berries which then develop, not only renew plant life, but also feed a host of other creatures in the wild. As pollinators, bees have a key role in the ecosystem.

On the Commons a valuable source of early spring nectar and pollen for bees and many other insects are the willows, which flower in late February and March. Other early sources are coltsfoot, dandelion and red dead-nettle. These are closely followed by bluebells and Spanish broom. Bumble bees are attracted to the rich forage provided by large clumps of massed flowers; and during the summer there are two such plants readily found on the Commons, particularly to the north of the Windmill. In June, when the vast expanse of bramble is in flower, some clumps are often smothered in bumble bees. If you go at the right time, all six species recorded for the Commons can be found there. The other plant is the heather, abundant on the Plateau (see Chapter 6). Its main flowering occurs after bramble and when in bloom most bumble bee species can be observed foraging on it. The flowers of large colourful patches of bird's-foot trefoil are very attractive to the workers of *Bombus lapidarius* during June and July. Other plants on the Commons which have great appeal for bumble bees are the vetches, foxglove, hogweed and thistles. During dry summers, when flowers are scarce or non-existent in open grassland, pond margins, ditches, or low-lying damp areas may still support some flowers for bees and other insects. In late summer 1996 at 7 Post Pond, three species of bumble bee were foraging on water mint, which was the only plant in flower in the vicinity.

By late summer in Britain any remaining bumble bee colonies are in decline. All workers, males and old queens will die by the end of the season. The only ones to live on until the following year are the new queens who are now in their winter quarters. Typical hibernation sites are under thick leaf litter or at shallow depths in the soil in the shelter of trees, shrubs or rocks. The continuation of bumble bees in the locality depends upon the survival of these fertile, over-wintering *Bombus* queens. Their hibernation sites need to remain undisturbed. These queens are the winter link from the bumble bee populations of one summer to the next.

Bumble Bees recorded on Wimbledon Common and Putney Heath, 1996

Bombus hortorum   *Bombus pratorum*
Bombus lapidarius   *Bombus terrestris*
Bombus lucorum   *Psithyrus* sp.
Bombus pascuorum

Table 11.1 Major sources of forage on the Commons for bumble bees, providing a continuous succession of flowers throughout the season

Plant Family	Species	
Pea	Common Gorse	*Ulex europaeus*
	Spanish Broom	*Spartium junceum*
	Red Clover	*Trifolium pratense*
	White Clover	*Trifolium repens*
	Everlasting Pea	*Lathyrus latifolius*
	Tufted Vetch	*Vicia cracca*
	Common Vetch	*Vicia sativa*
	Goat's Rue	*Galega officinalis*
	Bird's –foot-Trefoil	*Lotus corniculatus*
Daisy	Coltsfoot	*Tussilago farfara*
	Dandelion	*Taraxacum officinale*
	Cat's Ear	*Hypochoeris radicata*
	Creeping Thistle	*Circium arvense*
	Marsh Thistle	*Circium palustre*
	Black Knapweed	*Centaurea nigra*
Dead-nettle	White Dead-nettle	*Lamium album*
	Red Dead-nettle	*Lamium purpureum*
	Bugle	*Ajuga reptans*
	Water Mint	*Mentha aquatica*
	Spear Mint	*Mentha spicata*
Rose	Hawthorn	*Crataegus monogyna*
	Blackberry	*Rubus fruticosus*
	Dog Rose	*Rosa canina*
Heather	Heather (Ling)	*Calluna vulgaris*
	Cross-leaved Heath	*Erica tetralix*
Willowherb	Rosebay Willowherb	*Chamaenerion angustifolium*
	Great Willowherb	*Epilobium hirsutum*
Willow	Willows	*Salix* spp.
Lily	Bluebell	*Hyacinthoides non-scripta*
Figwort	Foxglove	*Digitalis purpurea*
Honeysuckle	Honeysuckle	*Lonicera periclymenum*
Carrot	Hogweed	*Heracleum sphondylium*
Buttercup	Buttercups	*Ranunculus* sp.

Chapter 12

Fish, Amphibians and Reptiles

Tony Drakeford

FISH

[8 species at present time]

Only the Beverley Brook and five of the Commons' nine ponds regularly contain fish species. These are Queensmere, Scio Pond, Kingsmere, Rushmere and 7 Post Pond. Three, namely Bluegate Gravel Pit, Hookhamslade Pond and Curling Pond, are liable to dry out from time to time and as a result cannot support fish.

Pike
(*Esox lucius*)

A large and fierce predatory species which can exact a heavy toll, not only on other fish, but also water birds and their young and amphibians too. In the mid 1990s it was noted that coots, moorhens, mallard and frogs were disappearing from Queensmere. Pike were the principal suspects and a Company was called in to electro-fish the water. As a result, several large pike were lifted from the

Figure 12.1 Extract from the local *Guardian* newspaper, 28th December, 1993.

Monster from the blue lagoon

Diary

Maev Kennedy
••••••••••••••••••••••••••

FOR some years children in Wimbledon have been deprived of a true Family Values seasonal treat. That ritual after-Christmas black-mailing of the most vulnerable adult, into taking the whole brood out for a nice walk to feed the ducks, had to be abandoned. At Queensmere, on Wimbledon Common, there have been no ducks. No ducklings. No sticklebacks, frogs or newts. No gulls even. There was something ... well, almost sinister about the pond. The Wandsworth Borough News reports how the fisheries experts paddled to the rescue, with an assortment of electric stunning equipment and drift nets worthy of the good old days of the Cold War. First they pulled out, as they expected, 45 reasonable sized pike. Then they got a really vicious brute, weighing over 12 pounds. But gouged along it's side it had — could we have some sinister music please? — even bigger teeth marks. They kept dredging. Eventually up from the depths came — crescendo of sinister music, please — Priscilla, nearly four foot long, 22 pounds. I know you're sick of turkey, but there's no point in

rushing round with a fishing rod and some heavy duty line. Priscilla has been moved to a holding tank near Woolwich. On her second day there she turned an even more unpleasant green, and was violently sick. Regurgitating an entire black headed gull.

Figure 12.2 Artist's impression of the 22 lb Pike in Queensmere, about to consume the unfortunate Black Headed Gull.
Sketch: Tony Drakeford.

mere, one of which weighed 22 lbs and measured three feet in length. The next day the monster fish regurgitated an adult black-headed gull! (see also Chapter 8). A few weeks later, another pike was found in a distressed condition, thrashing about in the shallows. Although slightly smaller, the fish was found to be choking on a four pound tench!

Pike spawn in the shallows during March and April.
STATUS: Still present in some numbers.
HABITAT: Queensmere and Scio pond.

Perch
(*Perca fluviatilis*)

A strikingly handsome predator which can weigh up to four pounds. Notable features include two dorsal fins, the front one of which is spiny, and six to seven vertical bars on an olive-green ground colour. Small perch swim in large shoals and, on a hot summer's day, vast numbers can be seen swimming just below the surface.

Eggs are laid in springtime, in jelly-like strips entwined among water plants.
STATUS: Abundant.
HABITAT: Queensmere, Kingsmere and Scio pond.

Common Carp
(*Cyprinus carpio*)

Thought to have been introduced into Britain in Roman times, carp have been extensively bred for centuries and many varieties and hybrids occur. Carp grow slowly and are extremely long-lived, with thirty year old specimens not uncommon. If present in large numbers, their bottom feeding activities can cause turbidity of the water. They also consume large numbers of bottom living invertebrates such as dragonfly and damselfly nymphs.

Spawning takes place throughout the spring and summer.
STATUS: Quite common.
HABITAT: Kingsmere and Scio support sizeable specimens.

Figure 12.3 Carp in Scio Pond.
Photo: Dave Haldane.

Koi Carp
(*Cyprinus carpio*)

A small shoal, no doubt tipped into the water several years ago, now swim in Rushmere which is otherwise poor in aquatic life. The large orange-coloured torpedo-shaped fish are best observed early on a still summer morning as they lazily move about in the centre of the mere. They have successfully bred during the late 1990s.

STATUS: Few adults, but young fish now present.
HABITAT: Rushmere, Kingsmere

Goldfish
(*Carassius auratus gibelio*)

Originating in eastern Asia, this is the familiar goldfish with its distinctive gold and silver colouring. No doubt populations on the Commons have built up from discarded pet fish being dumped in the ponds. It is content with almost any quality of water and is not particular about diet.

STATUS: Currently in small numbers.
HABITAT: Scio Pond.

Rudd
(*Scardinius erythrophthalmus*)

Up to 30 cm long, it differs from roach in that the dorsal fin is placed further back, not opposite the pelvic fins. Furthermore, the lower lip of the rudd extends beyond the upper lip and the fins are a deeper red. It feeds on a variety of invertebrates. 200 small specimens were counted in Scio Pond in the autumn of 1999.

STATUS: Locally abundant.
HABITAT: Scio Pond, Kingsmere.

Roach
(*Rutilus rutilus*)

A medium sized silvery red-finned shoaling species, which feeds on a variety of invertebrates, worms and vegetable matter. Hybrids occur with other carp species.

Spawning occurs in late spring to early summer.
STATUS: Uncommon.
HABITAT: Scio Pond, Kingsmere.

Tench
(*Tinca tinca*)

A thick set deep-bodied fish, coloured deep brown or greenish-bronze, with large rounded fleshy fins. Tench are bottom-feeders and spawn in late summer. Weight can reach about seven pounds.

STATUS: Uncommon.
HABITAT: Scio Pond and Queensmere.

Three-spined Stickleback
(*Gasterosteus aculeatus*)

A ubiquitous small species, the well known 'tiddler' of childhood fishing forays is the only British freshwater species to construct a nest from vegetation. Males, which take on a rosy-red colour during springtime breeding activities, entice females into their nest where eggs are laid and fertilised. Hatching fry are guarded around the nest until old enough to fend for themselves. Sticklebacks have voracious appetites, devouring worms and aquatic insects.

STATUS: Abundant, but less so than in former times.
HABITAT: Beverley Brook and 7 Post Pond mainly, but can occur in Scio, Kingsmere and Queensmere.

AMPHIBIANS

Past records indicate that the great crested newt (*Triturus cristatus*) was present in some ponds years ago, but very few colonies now survive anywhere in London, where it is classed as the most protected yet most endangered amphibian. In just twenty years the species has declined by 42%.

Unsuccessful efforts have recently been made to locate the smallest British newt, the palmate newt (*Triturus helveticus*). Similar at first glance to the common or smooth newt, the hind feet of the male are fully webbed (hence palmate), the crest is unridged, the tail sports a short hair-like tip and the underside of the male has very few spots compared with the smooth newt. This species may still inhabit the Commons in small numbers, but the likelihood is slim. However, females of both the above species are very alike.

The common European tree frog (*Hyla arborea*), a small bright green species, introduced in the early nineteenth century, has colonised some isolated locations in South East London and surprisingly one was recorded by Bluegate Gravel Pit in 1988. However, it does not seem to have gained a foothold on the Commons. As its name implies, this agile frog climbs trees by means of adhesive pads on its toes.

Present day amphibians on the Commons [3 species]

Figure 12.4 Female Smooth Newt returning to one of the ponds to spawn.
Photo, taken in March: Tony Drakeford.

Smooth or Common Newt (*Triturus vulgaris*)

Catching newts has always featured high on the springtime priorities of every child. They will be familiar with the newt's attractive colours of olive brown with dark spots on the yellow underside. As the breeding season approaches, the male acquires a magnificent spotted and scalloped wavy crest along his back which extends along the whole of his tail; his colour intensifies and the underside takes on a lovely orange, black spotted hue. The female is quite drab and more lizard-like, without the splendid enlarged tail.

Bearing in mind that both are amphibians, considerable differences exist between the life-cycles of frogs and newts. For example, in complete contrast to frogs, there is virtually no physical contact between male and female newts when mating, but courtship for these amorous amphibians is quite an elaborate affair. The male approaches a female and, placing himself in front of her, bends his body into a bow, then commences a series of violent shivering and wriggling movements with his great flag of a tail to waft an aphrodisiac scent towards her. If receptive to his advances, the male drops a sperm package which is taken up by the female from the bed of the pond as she moves forward behind him. Deftly using her hind feet, which look remarkably like human hands, the female wraps up every sticky egg in a piece of water plant, taking time and exercising great care to ensure maximum protection and concealment. Tadpoles hatch after a week or so, breathing with the aid of branched antler-like feathery gills.

Newts are carnivorous from birth, feeding on *Daphnia* (water fleas) and similar minute organisms. Again, unlike frog tadpoles, the front legs appear before the hind limbs. The majority of newts are ready to leave their ponds at the end of the summer, but if eggs are laid late in the season the tadpoles remain in the water and complete their development the following year.

Once on dry land newts do not return to water to breed until they reach maturity at two or three years of age, living sometimes quite a distance from where they were born and emerging under cover of darkness to feed on worms and insects. Newts hibernate, often several coiled together under stones or in similar damp situations.

STATUS: Super abundant

Common Frog
(*Rana temporaria*)

With the exception of Rushmere and Bluegate, the majority of ponds and meres support this well known amphibian.

Basic colour of the smooth skin varies considerably from green through brown to light yellow, but always with a dark patch located behind the eyes.

Emerging out of hibernation in February, mating commences and soon the familiar spawn, composed of transparent jelly containing thousands of tiny black specks of life, can be seen piled up around the shallow margins of ponds. As the spawn matures, the round dots unfurl to form little comma-like shapes. Some time later, regular pulsating movements can be detected, and finally the time arrives for the tiny tadpoles to break out of their protecting glutinous

Figure 12.5 Common Frogs mating.
Photo: Tony Drakeford.

globes. Before moving on to solid food, they feed for a while on the remains of the jelly, hanging suspended on thin life-supporting strands. If those strands break, the tadpoles sink to the bottom of the pond and, denied access to food, will perish or be snapped up by newts or dragonfly nymphs. Because the mortality rate is so high, enough spawn is laid to ensure survival, and it only requires two individuals of opposite sex to reach adulthood to guarantee continuation of the species. Frogs reach maturity at three years of age.

A few years ago some populations were affected by a viral disease, causing spawn to disintegrate and dissolve, and adult frogs would suddenly die for no obvious reason. Fortunately, the frog populations are once again healthy.

STATUS: Abundant.

Common Toad
(*Bufo bufo*)

Unlike the frog, the toad does not leap, but walks or waddles, its hind legs being less well developed.

The colours of the very rough, dry, warty skin are basically dark blackish-brown, or occasionally grey to dark green, and the animal looks almost like a lump of earth, so well does it blend in with its surroundings.

A comparitively long-lived species, maturity is not reached until five years of age. The toad is active mainly after dark, spending the day hidden. Worms, slugs, snails and a variety of insects constitute its diet.

Spending winter in hibernation, the toad breeds somewhat later than the frog, in deeper water, where spawn is laid in long double strings wrapped around water plants, unlike the globular masses of frog spawn.

STATUS: Less common than the frog.

Figure 12.6 Common Toads mating.
Photo: Dave Haldane.

REPTILES

Past records refer to adders (or vipers) and sand lizards inhabiting the heathland, but sadly neither has been seen recently on the Commons. The sand lizard is one of the Country's rarest reptiles and now only occurs in a few locations in southern England. All six native species of reptile are fully protected by the Wildlife and Countryside Act of 1981. The same protection applies to our six native amphibians.

Present day reptiles of the Commons [2, possibly 3 species]

Adder
(*Vipera berus*)

The adder is our only poisonous snake and has a life-span of up to twenty years. A lover of open, extensive dry heathland, this snake has not been seen on the Commons for several years, but may possibly be surviving unrecorded. Certainly in the London area numbers have plummeted since the Second World War, and the adder remains in very few locations. Emerging out of hibernation in early spring, the snake spends much time basking in sunny spots but, being perfectly camouflaged, is difficult to observe. There should be few problems identifying this species as the greenish-grey brown ground colour bears a characteristic black zig-zag running almost the full length of the back, with a 'V' shaped marking at the base of the head.

Diet consists of mice, voles, frogs and possibly the young of ground-nesting birds. Up to fifteen fully-formed young are born in late summer.

STATUS: Very rare or absent on the Commons.

Grass Snake
(*Natrix natrix*)

A greenish body colour flanked with black patches, with a characteristic yellow and black partial 'collar'.

The grass snake usually prefers moist areas close to ponds. It is an accomplished swimmer and preys on frogs, tadpoles and similar small creatures.

A batch of as many as forty papery white eggs is laid on compost heaps or warm damp vegetation and they hatch after about eight weeks. Hibernation occurs in crevices, hedge banks or holes beneath tree roots.

STATUS: Less frequent than in former years, the species survives on the Commons in small numbers. The most recent sighting was in 1995 when clearing invasive weed from 7 Post Pond, along Parkside.

Common Lizard
(*Lacerta vivipara*)

Not often seen, but frequently heard as a rustle in the heather, is the agile and secretive common lizard. As its name implies, this is the most widespread of the three native lizards, which includes the slow-worm. It is at home on sandy heath, or dry grassland and scrub, but can equally well be found in boggy areas.

Coloured mainly brownish with green, yellow, white and dark stripes, the species grows to a length of six or seven inches.

Emerging from hibernation under rocks or crevices on the first warm days of spring, it spends much time basking in the sun to soak up heat; it is extremely wary and easily disturbed. Mating takes place in April or May and the young are born fully formed, each one of the batch, numbering from five to ten, a tiny blackish worm-like replica of the adults, which then take no further interest in their offspring.

Diet consists of insects, mainly flies, beetles, caterpillars, grasshoppers, and also spiders. As the lizard grows, it sheds its skin from time to time during a life-span of up to seven years. It has the ability to shed its tail in an instant as a

Figure 12.7 Common Lizard
sunning itself on a rotting tree
stump.
Photo: Dave Haldane.

means of escape when under attack by one of its many enemies, which include
kestrels, weasels and rats. However, the new tail will not be as splendid as the
original.

STATUS: Fairly abundant throughout the Commons, but a recent decline has been
noticed.

ALIENS AND INTRODUCTIONS

Deliberate release of unwanted pets without regard to the consequences is
both misguided and irresponsible. This applies especially to three species,
namely the European pond terrapin, red eared terrapin and, most undesirable
of all, the snapping turtle. The first two have appeared in Scio Pond,
Kingsmere and Queensmere, fortunately in small numbers, but evidence
suggests that they prey on many amphibians and even bird's eggs, or young
aquatic birds. The third and most obnoxious of all, the snapping turtle, can
inflict a serious bite if handled carelessly and children especially could be at
risk. For more about this vicious beast, see Chapter 15.

Figure 12.8 Red Eared
Terrapin amongst organic
debris in Queensmere.
Photo: Charlie Wicker.

Chapter 13 Birds

Tony Drakeford, Ron Kettle and Dave Haldane

Daybreak
Tony Drakeford

A few minutes before first light on a chilly morning in early May I am on Wimbledon Common for the dawn chorus, that glorious springtime phenomenon that never fails to enthrall and stimulate the senses of anyone fortunate enough to experience it at first hand.

With my back to the edge of a dark foreboding wood, I sit facing a meadow, as yet barely visible, from where I hope to hear the first heraldic notes of a Skylark. Instead, the silence is broken by the thrilling clarion call of a Song Thrush just above. The song increases in strength, and suddenly, as if waiting for a clear signal, other birds now fully awake join in, like the assorted musical instruments of a symphony orchestra in concert; each one lending its own very individual yet essential contribution, but all blending together as an integral part of the whole harmonious offering.

Nearby, a Tawny Owl murmurs his wavering hoo twit hoooo, and deeper in the wood another answers. All at once I am surrounded by a wonderful all-pervading sensation, drenched in quadraphonic sound. Now a Robin comes in, and on the woodland fringe two Chaffinches chatter away at one another with barely a pause between each rollicking delivery. I am almost deafened by a Wren so very close; what a big sound from such a tiny bird!

A flight of cackling Canada Geese swishes overhead, winging their way to a nearby lake as several Crows begin cawing on the meadow, the only strangely discordant, alien sounds in the morning's recital. Great Tits call, Wood Pigeons coo softly in the tree tops; the laughing cry of a Green Woodpecker echoes through the canopy and close by a Great Spotted Woodpecker chips in. Slowly I walk down into the wood, disturbing ghostly forms of grazing rabbits, causing them to scurry away nervously into the shadowy undergrowth.

Some birds are easy to identify and my ears strain to detect each newcomer as it adds its own distinctive voice to the chorus. A Nuthatch pipes up, while on either side Blackcaps sing their strident songs, perched high on hawthorns. Protesting harshly at my intrusion, a Starling flutters into his nest hole and I catch sight of the Nuthatch hanging stock still upside down on a gnarled bough. At the height of the sing-along I add to my list, Blue Tits, a Coal Tit, Dunnock and Chiffchaff.

Strolling quietly back towards the meadow, a Willow Warbler's sweet cadence issues from sallow scrub, in competition with two Whitethroats busy near their nest sites, hidden within an extensive bramble patch. Returning to the mist enshrouded field I sit down and wait. Not a breath of wind stirs the cool air.

Then, within seconds, to my left the sun breaks through a lattice work pattern of distant leafless oaks. Gently the golden orb rises above the ragged tree-line, transforming the scene before me. Beams of bright light flood horizontally across a narrow band of translucent mist hovering a few feet above the ground, base and top so sharply defined that it resembles a thick white ribbon stretched tautly for hundreds of metres in either direction. Below, the dew-laden grass glistens with a million points of reflected light, interlaced with countless spider's webs, gossamer cat's cradles shimmering with brilliant rainbow colours. Seemingly reluctant to ascend above the vapour, Skylarks begin to sing as they walk rapidly on the turf only yards away. I sit mesmerised, absorbing the wealth of visual and oral sensations surrounding me.

Beyond the Commons' northern perimeter, a jet-liner, Heathrow bound, whispers along an invisible flight path, throttled back engines unobtrusively muted in the windless atmosphere. Behind it, glinting like a chain of twinkling stars strung out in the morning sunshine, other aircraft form an orderly queue stretching far into the distance. Then, almost miraculously, as the sun's warmth gathers strength, the mist melts away. Simultaneously, three Skylarks lift heaven-wards into the palest of blue skies, their exuberant songs joyfully proclaiming the dawning of another day.

Of course the scientist will clinically explain that all this song, admittedly beautiful to the human ear, is really only a territorial statement, nature's way of ensuring that every bird declares his right to a particular patch of woodland or field, and woe betide any rival who attempts to trespass! Quite correct, but is there not a little more to it than that? Listening to this morning's choir in full song, it occurs to me that surely each songster must be enthusiastically greeting the dawn with an "it's great to be alive, spring is here" message to the world? That is what I like to believe anyway, whatever the wet blanket 'official' view.

The Bird Population
Ron Kettle

Since the last account of the bird life was published thirty years ago in the centenary booklet *Walks on Wimbledon Common* there have been considerable changes. Many species have disappeared or declined and only a few have been gained or have increased. Two major causes for this are likely to be: (a) national decline due to changes in and loss of habitat, and (b) increased disturbance due to more people, and particularly dogs, using the Commons. Nevertheless there is still much left to be enjoyed, and these pages look at the bird life as it is at the turn of the Millennium.

There is no doubt that the Commons occupy a unique place among wildlife areas in suburban London, as much for birds as other aspects of the flora and fauna. There is hardly anywhere else so close to Central London where the magical song of the Skylark can be heard, but in the 1990s there was only one pair, or rarely two, nesting on the meadow south of the Windmill. Here, too, the Meadow Pipit used to be a regular breeding species, but in only one or two years of the 1990s was one heard in summer, uttering its simple song in flight, to indicate probable breeding. The closely related migrant Tree Pipit, which performs a more elaborate song flight from scattered birches on open heathland, has been absent in recent years but might stage a comeback. Another species which breeds in few places so close to the city is the Reed Bunting. The distinctive black-headed, white-collared males used to utter their feeble song from many places around Hookhamslade and Kingsmere, but they disappeared, except on passage, after 1993; however, a pair returned to breed in 1998 and 1999 amongst the scrub at the southern edge of the Meadow.

One of the Commons' most welcome sounds of spring is the sweet cadence of Willow Warbler song when the birds return from Africa. The birch scrub came alive with the sound of scores of singing males until the start of the 1990s, when there was a sudden countrywide crash in numbers, leaving fewer than twenty on the Commons ever since. Soon after them come the Whitethroat and Lesser Whitethroat, the former with its hurried scratchy song, and the latter with a distinctive rattle on one note. Joining these in the bushy and thorny scrub areas, the related Garden Warbler has one of the richest of all songs, with its liquid notes tumbling over each other. The Blackcap, another of this group of warblers, has a short, clear, flute-like song of exquisite beauty and is now widespread all over the Commons in both scrub and woodland. Its population doubled in the 1980s to reach a remarkable figure of perhaps 100 pairs by the end of the century, replacing the Willow Warbler as the commonest warbler there.

In a walk across the Plateau one could be forgiven for thinking that the Commons were populated only by Carrion Crows, which dominate in the open areas, often in parties of up to fifty birds. This gregariousness may confuse people into thinking they are Rooks, which disappeared from London many years ago, while Carrion Crows have thrived. They benefit from bread thrown out around Rushmere by well-meaning but misguided people and from the faeces of the large number of dogs exercised on the Commons. The steady increase in these birds may be having a harmful impact on some other species. Hundreds of these crows come from miles around to roost in the woodland on the western slopes. Another crow which has increased greatly in recent years is the very conspicuous Magpie, the bird which most people love to hate because it raids the nests of thrushes and other species, but it is doubtful if it affects the total population of these birds. Its own nest is a large oval stick construction, that is often very obvious.

The open areas are the favourite hunting grounds for Kestrels, the long-

Figure 13.1 Heron on Kingsmere.

Photo: Antony Sutcliffe.

tailed, sharp-winged falcons, which hover uncannily stationary in search of small rodents, beetles, worms and small birds in the rough grass, but can often be seen perched on a tree or bush. The other raptor, the Sparrowhawk, has shorter broader wings and snatches small birds from the cover. Absent in the 1960s and 1970s due to the nationwide effect of toxic chemicals, this species returned in the 1980s and did so well that as many as nine nests were found in 1998. That attractive falcon, the Hobby, is sometimes seen flying across the Commons or feeding on dragonflies at Kingsmere. Similar to, but darker than the Kestrel, this species has swept-back wings and a wonderfully acrobatic flight and may become a regular visitor in the summer.

A feature of the Plateau areas in winter in the 1970s was the large flocks of Redpolls feeding on catkins in the birches, with some remaining to nest; but the numbers of these small streaky finches have declined everywhere and are now seen only occasionally, and in smaller winter flocks. A species worth looking for in the thorn scrub is the white-rumped Bullfinch, especially the handsome male, with its crimson breast, but this is another species which has become scarce. They are usually in pairs which keep in contact with soft piping sounds.

Some of the woodland birds, in contrast, have been flourishing, for example the Great Spotted Woodpecker, whose drumming resounds among the trees in spring. This black-and-white bird with its crimson patch under the tail has no doubt benefited from the grubs to be found in the trees blown down in the 1987 and subsequent gales, which were left on the ground to rot, and also from being able to make their nest holes in the many decaying birches. The staccato *chik* call gives its presence away. The much smaller Lesser Spotted Woodpecker is scarce and elusive; but the large brightly coloured Green Woodpecker, which can often be seen on the Golf Course feeding at ant's nests, is widespread. It is well camouflaged, apart from its red head, but it shows a conspicuous yellow rump as it flies off in switchback flight to land on a tree trunk. Its laughing song and strident calls are familiar but its drum is hardly ever heard.

The large branches of old oaks are favoured by the clean-cut, square-tailed Nuthatch, an active vocal bird with a repertoire of penetrating sounds, some like human whistles. It has an interesting habit of plastering up its nest-hole with mud, and it can even walk head-first down a trunk. Treecreepers, on the other hand, walk only up the trunk or sometimes upside down along the underside of a branch. Flush against the trunk, hiding their clean white under-parts, they are hard to see as they search the bark for tiny insects with their thin curved bill. They have a delightful fast, thin song,

Jays are strikingly handsome birds of the woods, which attract attention with their harsh screeches, displaying their white rumps and flash of blue as they fly through the trees on floppy wings. In autumn they are very obvious, going to and fro, collecting acorns to store for the winter.

Perhaps the most familiar hole-nesting birds are the tits. Blue Tits can be very active in the treetops on mild February days, and in March the woods are full of the two-note chiming songs of Great Tits, with their smart black, white and yellow plumage, as they court females. In May both species are busy collecting caterpillars from the oak leaves to feed their broods. Coal Tits, which are smaller and lack any blue or yellow but have a distinctive white patch on the back of the head, are scarcer and have a sweeter, thinner two-note song. They prefer conifers and can often be seen around Caesar's Well, where they will even nest in holes in the ground. In autumn the tits all join together to move through the trees in foraging flocks of up to fifty or more. Especially after the mild winters in the 1990s, those autumn flocks of tits have included many Long-tailed Tits, which have flourished. They build the most delicate of all our birds' nests, usually in a dense prickly bush, but often in a tree. A delightful sight is a family party of a dozen or so of these tiny-bodied birds, with their long streak of a tail, flitting across a gap one by one.

The smallest of all British birds, the Goldcrest, also favours conifers and suspends its fragile nest under a pine branch. It is a persistent singer of a thin, high-pitched churning song which ends with a flourish and is difficult for the elderly to hear. Few now breed, but in most autumns there is an influx of birds from northern Europe. They may then be widespread over the Commons, often mixing with foraging parties of tits, but readily distinguishable by their habit of hovering between branches as they look for tiny insects. Our earliest warbler to return in spring is the Chiffchaff, which repeatedly sings its name from the treetops from before the end of March. Unlike the similar looking Willow Warbler, this species is maintaining its numbers well.

In late May and early June, hordes of fledgling Starlings throng the oak woods to feast on the abundant caterpillars and fill the air with their whirring calls. Probably few of them come from nests on the Commons.

The Chaffinch, once the most numerous bird in Britain, is not at all common in winter in London, but many return in the spring to pair up and establish nesting territories. The cheerful, rollicking song of the brilliantly coloured males can often be heard around the Windmill, although their real home is the woodland. Especially in autumn, you may come across a charming flock of Goldfinches feeding on seeding thistles or other 'weeds', perhaps on the slopes of the Hills, and enjoy the light twitterings as they dance up, flashing their yellow wing bars.

When water levels are high the ponds attract a variety of waterfowl. The black Coot, with white bill and forehead was doing well in the 1990s, rearing its flame-headed chicks from large stick-nests out in the water on Queensmere, Bluegate Gravel Pit, Kingsmere, Scio Pond and even 7 Post Pond in some years (see Chapter 8). The handsome Moorhen, with its red and yellow bill, has nested in wet years on nearly all the ponds, except Rushmere and Queensmere, but its most regular sites are amongst the water-lilies on Kingsmere and along the Beverley Brook. Mallard can be seen with ducklings on any of the ponds, including Rushmere, and on the Brook. In winter moderate numbers of adults occur on many of them, together with smaller numbers of the dumpy, diving Tufted Ducks – the males in smart black and white and the females dark brown – on Queensmere and Kingsmere. The introduced alien Canada Geese unfortunately began to produce their engaging fluffy yellow goslings on Bluegate Gravel Pit in 1985 and on Kingsmere in the early 1990s. Mute Swans occasionally appear on the larger ponds, even on Rushmere, and in 1999 a pair remained on Queensmere for the first few months of the year but failed to find a safe nest site. One or two birds of other duck species, particularly Pochard, occasionally come to the ponds, but do not breed.

A Grey Heron or two have been regular visitors to Kingsmere, and one is often seen at Hookhamslade Pond, 7 Post Pond and at Fishpond Wood, particularly when frogs are available. Many Black-headed Gulls gather on Kingsmere, Queensmere and Rushmere in autumn and winter, when they do not boast their breeding season chocolate hoods but do have red bills and legs, whereas the few larger Common Gulls have yellow-green ones.

A selection of waterfowl and gulls photographed on the Commons.

Figure 13.2 Mute Swan, Kingsmere.
Photo: Tony Drakeford.

Figure 13.3 Canada Geese.
Photo: Tony Drakeford.

Figure 13.4 (below, left)
Mandarin Ducks.
Photo: Dave Haldane.

Figure 13.5 (below, right)
Mallard Duck.
Photo: Dave Haldane.

Figure 13.6 Coot chick, Queensmere.
Photo: Charlie Wicker.

Figure 13.7 Coot on nest, Queensmere.
Photo: Dave Haldane.

Figure 13.8 Black-headed Gulls above ice at Rushmere, January, 1996.
Photo: Antony Sutcliffe.

The Beverley Brook is favoured by families of Mallard, and the ducks can often be seen there followed by a scatter of chicks. Another duck to catch the attention here is the alien Mandarin Duck, introduced from the Far East and now breeding widely in Surrey. The drake has extravagantly decorated plumage, while the female is more soberly dressed and nests in holes in trees, from where she brings her young onto the Brook in most years. Moorhens also nest here. It is here too that the elegant Grey Wagtail may be noticed picking tiny creatures from patches of debris on the fast flowing water, constantly wagging its very long tail and showing the bright yellow underneath. At least one pair nests in most years. But, of course, the jewel one hopes to see is a Kingfisher, and when their population is high they can sometimes be glimpsed here as a flash of brilliant blue.

In winter the Richardson Evans playing fields are sometimes thronged with gulls and in summer with Wood Pigeons and Stock Doves feeding over the short grass. During hard weather the two wintering thrushes, the Redwing and Fieldfare, join resident Song and Mistle Thrushes and Blackbirds to search for worms when the ground is unfrozen, or strip the hawthorn berries from bushes along the Brook. The resident thrushes are widespread over the Commons, but a good way to see winter migrants is to stand on the larger hill early on a mid-October morning and watch flights of them passing overhead as they come into Britain from Scandinavia, accompanied perhaps by Chaffinches, Meadow Pipits and Skylarks.

Summering birds occasionally observed taking a break on the Commons at migration time are Ring Ouzel, Redstart and Pied Flycatcher, mainly in the spring; Whinchat and Common Sandpiper mainly in early autumn; and Wheatear at both times. Cuckoos are heard for a week or two in May but have not remained to breed since the 1980s. Swallows are sometimes seen flashing past low over the Plateau at these times, but they no longer nest nearby. White-rumped House Martins, however, may still have a few mud-cup nests under the eaves of the Richardson Evans pavilion and can also be seen swooping around the Rushmere area from nests on some of the large houses alongside Wimbledon Common. During the summer the unrelated, but similarly aerial feeding, sooty black Swifts often sweep the skies overhead in large numbers on scimitar wings.

Excitingly unusual species like the dapper Little Grebe, or Dabchick, the tiny Firecrest, the Brambling, the Jack Snipe, the cryptic Woodcock and even the brilliant Golden Oriole are sometimes discovered.

To observe bird life at its best, visits should be made as early in the morning as possible, especially on Sundays. Evening visits can also be rewarding, particularly in late spring when bird song is at its richest and the hoot of a Tawny Owl can sometimes be heard.

This account is based on the observations of many bird-watchers, but mainly those of a faithful team who have carried out annual surveys of the bird population of the Commons over many years. Particular credit must go to David Wills, who was coordinator of the surveys in the 1980s and again from 1998, on whose systematic list published in the *London Bird Report* (Wills, D.L. & Kettle, R.H.,1997) the species encountered on the Commons and their status is based. Wills' list of species observed on the Commons [or flying over (F)] in 1999 is shown in Table 13.1.

Table 13.1 Checklist of birds recorded on the common / heath during 1999

(From: *The Birds of Wimbledon Common and Putney Heath*, 1999)

Little Grebe	Wood Pigeon	Whitethroat
Cormorant (F)	Collared Dove	Garden Warbler
Grey Heron	Ring-necked Parakeet (F)	Blackcap
Mute Swan	Cuckoo	Chiffchaff
Greylag Goose	Tawny Owl	Willow Warbler
Canada Goose	Swift	Goldcrest
Shelduck (F)	Kingfisher	Spotted Flycatcher
Mandarin Duck	Green Woodpecker	Pied Flycatcher
Gadwall	Great Spotted Woodpecker	Long-tailed Tit
Mallard	Lesser Spotted Woodpecker	Coal Tit
Pintail	Skylark	Blue Tit
Pochard	Swallow (F)	Great Tit
Tufted Duck	House Martin	Nuthatch
Ruddy Duck	Tree Pipit	Treecreeper
Sparrowhawk	Meadow Pipit	Jay
Kestrel	Grey Wagtail	Magpie
Hobby	Pied Wagtail	Jackdaw
Moorhen	Wren	Carrion Crow
Coot	Dunnock	Starling
Lapwing (F)	Robin	House Sparrow
Snipe	Whinchat	Chaffinch
Black-headed Gull	Stonechat	Brambling
Common Gull	Wheatear	Greenfinch
Lesser Black-backed Gull (F)	Blackbird	Goldfinch
Herring Gull (F)	Fieldfare	Siskin
Great Black-backed Gull (F)	Song Thrush	Linnet
Common Tern	Redwing	Redpoll
Feral Rock Dove	Mistle Thrush	Bullfinch
Stock Dove	Lesser Whitethroat	Reed Bunting

❧ Status List of Birds of Wimbledon Common and Putney Heath

Little Grebe
Tachybaptus ruficollis

Often known as the Dabchick, it is seen on passage in most years in spring, or sometimes in autumn, on one of the ponds, usually Queensmere or Kingsmere. In 1999 a pair built a nest on Kingsmere but failed to breed successfully.

Grey Heron
Ardea cinerea

A regular visitor to several of the ponds, mainly Kingsmere and Fishpond Wood. In the late 1990s one was occasionally seen at several of the other ponds when undisturbed.

Mute Swan
Cygnus olor

An irregular visitor, usually in winter, to the more open ponds, normally staying only a few days; but a pair remained on Queensmere for a few weeks in January and February and the autumn of 1995, from March to July in 1998 and for the first five months of 1999. However, they have failed to find a safe nest-site there.

Canada Goose
Branta canadensis

An introduced species which has greatly increased and spread throughout most of Britain. A pair has bred on Bluegate Gravel Pit in most years since 1985, and since 1991 they have nested also on Kingsmere, where three pairs raised 22 young in 1999. Increasing numbers also occur in winter on Queensmere as well as Kingsmere, where as many as 60 have roosted.

Mandarin Duck
Aix galericulata

Another introduced species which started breeding in the wild this century, it first occurred on the Beverley Brook in 1984, since when it has become established, with one or two pairs present there each year. Occasionally seen on one of the ponds.

Mallard
Anas platyrhynchos

The most familiar and commonest duck, it occurs in varying numbers on most of the ponds and the Beverley Brook at times. Only a few pairs breed successfully however. Families of ducklings are often seen on the Brook, and one winter as many as 80 were recorded on Queensmere.

Pochard
Aythya ferina

A few visit Queensmere in most winters and Kingsmere and Rushmere occasionally.

Tufted Duck
Aythya fuligula

Occurs in small, but varying, numbers mainly in winter on Queensmere, where up to 30 have been seen. Bred for the first time on Kingsmere in 1998, but the brood of six chicks disappeared, probably taken by a predator.

Sparrowhawk
Accipiter nisus

Returned to the Commons in the 1980s after a long absence, and a few pairs nest each year. As many as nine nests were found in 1998.

Kestrel
Falco tinnunculus

Often seen hovering over the more open areas. About five pairs breed around the Commons.

Moorhen
Gallinula chloropus

Pairs nest on various ponds, and one or two are often seen on the Brook. With water levels high in 1999 a record total of 12 pairs nested on six ponds as well as the Brook.

Coot
Fulica atra

Pairs build their large nests out in the water on some of the larger ponds whenever there is enough water in them. An exceptional five pairs were present on Kingsmere in 1999 out of a record total of nine pairs on the Commons' ponds.

Woodcock
Scolopax rusticola

Occasionally sighted in winter.

Common Sandpiper
Actitis hypoleucos

A summer migrant seen on passage in some years at one of the open ponds, or occasionally along the Brook.

Black-headed Gull
Larus ridibundus

An abundant winter visitor to the playing fields and larger ponds.

Common Gull
Larus canus

Far less numerous than the Black-headed, but moderate numbers often occur in early autumn and late winter on the playing fields.

Common Tern
Sterna hirundo

A new species for the Commons. One was frequently seen fishing on Kingsmere in June 1999 for the first time ever.

Stock Dove
Columba oenas

An unfamiliar close relative of the Wood Pigeon, which it sometimes accompanies in quite large numbers to feed on the Richardson Evans playing fields in summer. A few can occasionally be seen feeding on the Meadow or on the grass by the Hills. A pair or two probably nest in tree holes in some years.

Wood Pigeon
Columba palumbus

A widespread breeding resident.

Cuckoo
Cuculus canorus

A few used to be present in the breeding season until about 1987, since when it has been heard only on passage during a few weeks in May.

Tawny Owl
Strix aluco

Probably about five pairs are resident around the Commons. October is a good time to hear their splendid hoots at dusk.

Swift
Apus apus

A common summer visitor, most frequently seen and heard overhead in June, when many birds often swoop low over the Meadow to catch flies rising from the rough grass. Almost certainly nests in buildings in the surrounding area.

Kingfisher
Alcedo atthis

Individuals occasionally seen along the Brook at any time of year and at Kingsmere in late summer or early autumn. In 1999 there was an exceptional number of sightings at some other ponds in the summer and two at Queensmere on 4 September.

Green Woodpecker
Picus viridis

A widespread resident which increased in the1980s and subsequently. Often seen on the Golf Course and the Meadow, where it feeds on ants' nests. Its penetrating, laughing cries are a familiar sound on the Commons.

Great Spotted Woodpecker
Dendrocopos major

A common resident which has also increased considerably since about 1980, it likes to make its nest-hole in the numerous moribund birches. Its loud drumming is frequently heard in the woodland in early spring and its alerting *chik* at any time.

Lesser Spotted Woodpecker
Dendrocopos minor

This much smaller black-and-white woodpecker is scarce and elusive, but one or two pairs certainly nest in most years. Its drum is longer and level, while the vocal *pee pee pee* sound is distinctive.

Skylark
Alauda arvensis

This celebrated bird has been the gem of the Commons' bird life, but sadly had declined to only one, or possibly two, nesting pairs in the 1990s. Its sublime song may still be heard from high over the Meadow. In October they can be seen flying north-west on migration from the Continent.

Swallow
Hirundo rustica

Another favourite bird, which no longer nests in any buildings around the Commons but is seen flying across during spring and autumn migration.

House Martin
Delichon urbica

A summer visitor which became scarce in the late 1990s. Distinguished by their white rumps, parties can be seen at Rushmere and possibly other ponds feeding in flight or collecting mud for their nests, which they build on surrounding houses; a few pairs may still use the gables of buildings on Putney Heath and the Richardson Evans pavilion.

Meadow Pipit
Anthus pratensis

This once common breeding species on the open areas of the Plateau has declined drastically and was absent in the early 1990s, although in 1994 and some following years one male could be seen uttering its sweet notes in display flight over the Meadow. Parties occur there and on the Hills during autumn migration and in winter.

Grey Wagtail
Motacilla cinerea

Often seen along the Brook, where it wags its long tail as it searches patches of debris for insects. Nests regularly at the north end and sometimes elsewhere along the stream.

Pied Wagtail
Motacilla alba

Absent as a breeding species for most of the 1990s, it is often seen at Rushmere when undisturbed in the early morning and around Manor Cottage.

Wren
Troglodytes troglodytes

An abundant and widespread breeding resident. Difficult to see as it mostly frequents the ground cover, but its shrill, elaborate song can be heard all through the year.

Dunnock
Prunella modularis

A widespread but less familiar bird which likes the scrub areas and has a short sweet song heard most often in early spring. One or two join House Sparrows under the open-air tables at the Windmill Café.

Robin
Erithacus rubecula

An abundant breeding resident and the dominant species in the woodland, with about two pairs to the hectare. Really does seem to like the plentiful holly understorey. Its clean, whistly song is heard most of the year.

Whinchat
Saxicola rubetra

A regular passage migrant, chiefly in early autumn, most often seen on the sapling willow stems on the southern part of the Meadow.

Wheatear
Oenanthe oenanthe

This smart white-rumped migrant is regularly seen in ones and twos on open areas on passage in spring and less often in early autumn.

Blackbird
Turdus merula

A widespread common breeding resident whose beautiful fluty song is a joy in the spring and early summer.

Fieldfare
Turdus pilaris

A winter visiting thrush which is plentiful in some years during severe weather, feeding on hawthorn berries along the Brook or on the playing fields when not frozen. Large flocks may be seen from the Hills, flying across as they migrate into Britain in mid- to late October. Distinguished by grey head and rump and chestnut upper parts.

Song Thrush
Turdus philomelos

A common breeding resident which was declining seriously in the country as a whole in the 1990s but recovered well on the Commons at the end of the decade. Its vigorous song of repeated short phrases can sometimes fill the evening air in late spring.

Redwing
Turdus iliacus

The other winter visiting thrush with a similar pattern of occurrence to the Fieldfare but nearly always more common, and widespread on the southern Plateau. Best distinguished by its prominent pale eye-stripe.

Mistle Thrush
Turdus viscivorus

This larger version of the Song Thrush is less numerous. Its wonderfully wild song rings out across the Commons in early spring from the top of a tall tree. Large parties are sometimes seen on the grass in autumn.

Lesser Whitethroat
Sylvia curruca

A regular breeding summer visitor in patches of scrub, but scarcer in the late 1990s with only a few pairs each year. Distinguished from the common Whitethroat by its rattling song.

Whitethroat
Sylvia communis

A regular breeding summer visitor, present every year in scrub areas in moderate but fluctuating numbers, increasing during the 1990s.

Garden Warbler
Sylvia borin

Another regular breeding summer visitor in small numbers, which was also increasing in the 1990s.

Blackcap
Sylvia atricapilla

A common and widespread breeding summer visitor. Numbers increased rapidly in the 1980s and the population has remained high at possibly up to 100 males singing their exquisite song.

Wood Warbler
Phylloscopus sibilatrix

At least one is noted on passage in the spring in most years with its remarkable shivering song. A few pairs stayed to nest in the mid-1980s.

Chiffchaff
Phylloscopus collybita

The first warbler to arrive in the spring and sing its name from high in a tree. A fairly common breeding bird in the closed woodland. Sometimes one spends the winter here.

Willow Warbler
Phylloscopus trochilus

A regular breeding summer visitor, previously abundant all over the birch scrub, where its sweet cadence of song is a feature of the spring; but in the early 1990s there was a dramatic crash in the population nationally, and since then there have been less than 20 pairs on the Commons.

Goldcrest
Regulus regulus

A scarce resident but a plentiful winter visitor in some years. Prefers the pine trees in the breeding season; but widespread, often with mixed tit flocks, in the woodland in winter. This tiny bird has a distinctive habit of hovering between branches when feeding.

Firecrest
Regulus ignicapillus

Equally tiny, this species is seen only occasionally, mainly on passage or in winter, but recorded in most years.

Spotted Flycatcher
Muscicapa striata

A scarce summer visitor and passage migrant in autumn. Little evidence of breeding since 1990.

Long-tailed Tit
Aegithalos caudatus

A common breeding resident, abundant and widespread after a succession of mild winters. Often seen in parties of ten or more birds in autumn.

Coal Tit
Parus ater

A fairly common breeding resident which prefers pine trees. Distinguished by its lack of blue or yellow and its white nape patch. The population was high in the 1980s but low in the 1990s.

Blue Tit
Parus caeruleus

An abundant breeding resident in the woodland.

Great Tit
Parus major

An abundant breeding resident whose two-note chiming song can fill the woodland on mild days in early spring.

Nuthatch
Sitta europaea

A breeding resident in moderate numbers. An active, vocal and dapper little bird to be looked for in the large old oaks in the woodland.

Treecreeper
Certhia familiaris

A breeding resident in similar numbers to the Nuthatch. Usually observed moving mouse-like up the trunk of a tree, but its camouflaged upper parts make it difficult to spot. Has a thin fast song.

Jay
Garrulus glandarius

A common breeding resident of the woodland. Often very evident in the autumn when collecting acorns. Shows a conspicuous white rump in flight.

Magpie
Pica pica

A common breeding resident which has been increasing considerably since about 1980. Large gatherings are regularly seen, particularly in late winter.

Jackdaw
Corvus monedula

A non-breeding visitor. These smaller black crows with grey sides to the head often visit the Commons from their extensive nesting colonies in Richmond Park. Most often seen on the playing fields in flocks of sometimes 50 or more. In June they regularly bring their fledged young to feed in the trees near there. Many accompany Carrion Crows coming to roost in the woodland, but they may fly on to their major roost at Motspur Park.

Carrion Crow
Corvus corone

A common and widespread breeding resident and probably the most conspicuous species. Up to 100 birds can often be seen on the southern part of the Plateau. Large numbers come from miles around to roost in the woodland on the western slopes and counts of well over 1,000 have been made there in mid-winter.

Starling
Sturnus vulgaris

A common, but probably declining, breeding resident, nesting in small colonies in parts of the woodland. In early summer the oak trees are alive with noisy newly fledged young birds enjoying a feast of caterpillars. A party often assembles on the Windmill sails in early morning and in the evening.

House Sparrow
Passer domesticus

A small nesting colony around the Windmill café scavenge for food at the open-air tables.

Chaffinch
Fringilla coelebs

A fairly common breeding species, but rather scarce in winter. Mainly found in the woodland, but there are usually two or three males singing in the Windmill area in the spring.

Greenfinch
Carduelis chloris

A breeding resident in small groups, which occurs mostly around the edge of the Commons, e.g. Putney Vale Cemetery and at Brook Cottage, but there are usually a few at the Windmill.

Goldfinch
Carduelis carduelis

A resident, with a few pairs nesting every year in scattered places. Most often seen in parties feeding on seeding thistles in the autumn.

Siskin
Carduelis spinus

A few of these small greeny-yellow finches are seen in late winter in most years, usually in alder trees

Redpoll
Acanthis flammea

Once a regular winter visitor in large flocks feeding on the birch seed, and a breeder in small numbers; since the 1980s this small brown streaky finch has been seen only occasionally and in smaller flocks in winter, when its chitter and whirring calls are distinctive.

Bullfinch
Pyrrhula pyrrhula

A rather scarce breeding resident which declined in numbers in the early 1990s. This white-rumped bird, with a crimson-breasted male, is usually seen in pairs in favourite patches of thorn scrub, calling to each other with soft piping.

Reed Bunting
Emberiza schoeniclus

A once quite common breeding resident on the Plateau, it did not breed from 1994-97, but a pair did so again in the last two years of the century. The black-headed male, with white collar and conspicuous white outer tail feathers, may be seen occasionally by the Bluegate Gravel Pit or Kingsmere on passage in late winter or early spring.

A selection of land birds photographed on the Commons

Figure 13.9 Female Kestrel.
Photo: Ron Kettle.

Figure 13.10 Juvenile Great Spotted Woodpecker.
Photo: Ron Kettle.

Figure 13.11 Robin.
Photo: Dave Haldane.

Figure 13.12 Song Thrush.
Photo: Ron Kettle.

Figure 13.13 Great Tit.
Photo: Dave Haldane.

Figure 13.14 Starling.
Photo: Dave Haldane.

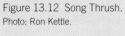

Figure 13.15 Carrion Crows near the Windmill.
Photo: Dave Haldane.

The Story of Tawny Owl Pellets

Dave Haldane

The Tawny Owl (*Strix aluco*) is the Commons' only resident owl. It is a nocturnal hunter, with a wingspan of 100 cm and a body weight of up to 400 g. in the male and 590 g. in the female. Strongly territorial, it hunts small mammals, birds and insects within its home range of approximately 10 ha. During the daylight hours the Tawny Owl seeks a roost concealed by heavy foliage, a favourite haunt being dense holly bushes.

At night the Tawny Owl is a formidable hunter and its exceptional hearing and ability to see in low light intensity allows very little to escape its attention. When a victim is identified the owl swoops through the woodland on silent wings before dropping onto its prey. Small prey is despatched swiftly under the crushing blow of its large talons, but larger animals often require the 'coup de grace' by way of the owl's strong beak.

The availability of small mammals determines the size of the owl's clutch. In a good year up to six round white eggs are laid around mid March. Incubation begins as soon as the first egg is laid, which accounts for the considerable difference in size between the first born and the last. Chicks hatch at two day intervals which means that the oldest chick has several days start on its younger siblings. The strongest chick will usually receive the lion's share of food from the parents. This strategy ensures that when food is scarce at least one chick will survive.

Its mainly nocturnal life style make the Tawny Owl an elusive subject for observation. Fortunately the familiar hooting call and strict territorial adherence allows an experienced observer to monitor breeding pairs. Once a territory has been identified, with patience the owl's daytime roost can also be located. It is here on the woodland floor, beneath the owl's perch, that pellets are found. They are usually within one to two metres of the tree trunk.

A pellet consists of the indigestible remains of the owl's prey. After the Tawny Owl has swallowed its victim (in most cases whole), it passes into the stomach. Here in a portion of the stomach called the gizzard the soft parts are

Figure 13.16 Tawny Owl in a tree on Wimbledon Common.

quickly digested and slowly pass along the gut. The parts that cannot be digested are compacted into a pellet that is later expelled through the mouth. This pellet can consist of a combination of some of the following:- fur, hair, feather, chitinous beetle remains (thorax, wing cases and legs), mammalian teeth and bone, amphibian bone, all bonded together and coated with a layer of mucus. The pellet is greyish in colour, usually pointed at one end, slightly curved, and between 4 – 6 cm in length and 2 – 3 cm across.

Many species of birds produce a form of pellet. Because the pellet passes out through the oesophagus this determines its size and shape. Identifying the bird species from the pellet is possible by its size, shape and content. A good guide to owl pellets and prey species is always consulted when identifying and analysing the contents.

When a Tawny Owl's roost has been identified, its location is recorded and if pellets are found they are measured before removal. Each pellet is placed in a separate small container and the details of where it was found recorded on the container. If an owl is present every effort is taken to avoid disturbing it. Light-weight disposable gloves are worn when handling faecal materials or disgorged pellets. It is worth remembering that fox droppings can be confused with larger bird pellets.

Dissection and analysis is best carried out in a draught free environment. It is recommended that a disposable face mask is worn to avoid inhalation of dust and hair. Pellets are easier to dissect when dry, but to avoid dust they can be immersed in water, to which a drop of clear disinfectant has been added. Remove from the water and place on blotting paper then allow to partly dry before dissecting. Six 10 cm. circles should be drawn on the work surface to receive the various remains. Use two pairs of long nose tweezers or any thin pointed object to tease the pellet apart.

The following list shows interesting remains found in four pellets from two locations on the Commons:

Bones and Jaws:	Wood Mouse (*Apodemus sylvaticus*)
	Field Vole (*Microtus agrestis*)
	Frog (*Rana temporaria*)
Thorax and leg chitin:	Minotaur Beetle (*Typhaeus typhoeus*) (These beetles bury rabbit dung in deep tunnels on which they and their larvae feed.)
Feeding on a Pellet:	Abundant springtails

Figure 13.17 Contents from Tawny Owl pellets from Wimbledon Common: (left) Wood Mouse (centre) Common Frog (right) Minotaur Beetle
Photos: Una Sutcliffe.

 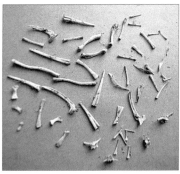 

Figure 13.18 There were hundreds of springtails (Collembola, family Hypogastruridae) feeding on one of the pellets. This specimen is 0.63 mm long. Scanning electron photomicrograph: Natural History Museum.

The study of owl pellets is not only fascinating for what the contents will reveal, but it is extremely valuable, as it identifies what the bird is feeding on, which would otherwise be very difficult in the case of a nocturnal feeder. This in turn can indicate the number and availability of prey species within the bird's territory.

Chapter 14

Mammals of Wimbledon Common and Putney Heath

Tony Drakeford and Pete Guest

Although, at the present day, the British Isles is not a region of great mammalian diversity, the number of species that make their suburbia-surrounded home on Wimbledon Common and Putney Heath is surprising. Throughout Pleistocene times Britain was repeatedly connected to and isolated from the Continent of Europe, being finally cut off only about 7000 years ago, as the result of the rise in sea level that followed the melting of the ice of the last glacial advance. Some of the mammals that were already present before this happened, including the brown bear, wolf, wild boar and beaver, subsequently disappeared, probably at the hand of Man. That beavers were still present on the Commons in historic times is nevertheless recorded in the name of the small river that traverses it – the Beverley Brook (see Chapter 8). Old English spellings give rise to "Befer" (Beaver) "Leah" (Meadow), or some scholars prefer Beaver Brook, hence the modern derivation Beaver-Ley (Beverley). The animal was still very common in Anglo-Saxon times and did not finally become extinct in Britain until the 12th century. Today, including some recent introductions, about forty-two terrestrial species occur in mainland Britain; and of these nineteen, including bats, are present on the Commons. Sadly, the last century has witnessed three losses from the Commons – the brown hare, the red squirrel and the water vole.

Although Richmond Park was a more favoured habitat, we know the red squirrel (*Sciurus vulgaris*) still lived on the Commons at the turn of the century. It was recorded in the general area as late as 1947, after which it seems to have finally given way to the alien grey squirrel, a more robust creature, far better equipped to exploit the habitat in which both existed.

The brown hare (*Lepus europaeus*) is also in serious decline nationwide, since farming practices have changed to larger fields with less variety of crops and greater use of herbicides. Open country has been lost to urbanisation and road building.

The third mammal which has disappeared on the Commons and is also in sharp decline everywhere, is the attractive water vole (*Arvicola terrestris*), often mis-named 'water rat', 'Ratty' of *Wind in the Willows* fame. This is a harmless herbivore and certainly not a rat.

A systematic small mammal survey, using Longworth traps, was conducted by Nigel Reeve of the Roehampton Institute, on Wimbledon Common and Putney Heath in 1996, using for comparison the same trapping methods and trap hours as a similar survey conducted in Richmond Park in 1994. The traps were set out in four habitats – acid grassland, heath, open woodland and dense wet woodland. Results revealed the commonest animal caught was the wood mouse (*Apodemus sylvaticus*) 103, field vole (*Microtus agrestis*) 30, bank vole (*Clethrionomys glareolus*) 13, and common shrew (*Sorex araneus*) 9. All these species were also found in Richmond Park, but the overall abundance on the Commons from this sample survey (306 captures of 155 individuals) was over three times that of Richmond Park. Reeve concluded that the dense woodland of the Commons offered habitat for these mammals that was not available in the Park. Comparing the acid grassland of the two areas, the absence of deer on the Commons leaves better cover and food for small mammals.

Non-flying Mammals

Tony Drakeford

CARNIVORES
[4 species]

Figure 14.1 Young Fox cub peeping out of its den on the Commons.
Photo: Tony Drakeford.

Fox *Vulpes vulpes*

The phenomenon of the urban/suburban fox is comparatively recent. The animal only began colonising London suburbs around the time of the Second World War, numbers building in the 1960s to the current high level. Now firmly established and an accepted part of our daily lives, many people may not realise that they are often living in close proximity to these animals.

The fox breeds from late December to February and, although it can be heard throughout the year, it is during January that vocal and sexual activity reaches a peak. The vixen emits the blood-curling screams which sometimes wake us up, particularly on cold frosty nights, while the dog fox barks his typical 'wo-wo-wo-warr'. It is thought that both sexes can utter these and other assorted cries, wickering noises and a range of contact calls in what is an extensive vocabulary.

Despite the protracted mating season, each vixen is only sexually receptive for about three days. Cubs are born in March or early April, either underground or beneath dense scrub. Fully grown by September, it is by that time difficult to differentiate between adults and juveniles. Families break up and disperse in early Autumn, and unfortunately many inexperienced youngsters are killed on roads, especially the busy A3.

Diet consists largely of earthworms, insects, fruit, small wild animals such as voles, and birds. It is not unusual to come across a scattering of grey and white feathers which is all that remains of a plump wood pigeon that has met an untimely fate at the jaws of a prowling fox. Being extremely adaptable opportunists, they also take full advantage of the rich pickings to be found in fast-food outlets such as dustbins and plastic rubbish sacks, and food is often 'cached' to be recovered later.

Mange can be a problem, recently almost eliminating the once large fox population in Bristol, but a rather scruffy thin-tailed animal seen in mid-summer is not necessarily suffering from the effects of this unsightly and distressing disease. More likely it is moulting its winter coat. Although mainly active between dusk and dawn, foxes can often be sighted during the daytime on the Commons, particularly in woodland glades, their presence betrayed by scolding calls of birds.

Scats, which are prominently and territorially deposited on grass tussocks or logs, are easy to identify, displaying a characteristic twisted tapering end. Being accomplished climbers, foxes even defaecate regularly on the bridge walls spanning the Beverley Brook.

STATUS   At an all-time high; widespread.

Badger *Meles meles*

Although so familiar to us, largely from television coverage and children's literature, the badger, or 'brock', to call it by its old English name, is a timid creature; and, being mainly nocturnal, few people have had the pleasure of seeing it in the wild. We are fortunate in having many badger setts on the Commons and certain gardens nearby are known to be visited regularly by this animal.

Badgers are very sociable and live in tight family communities comprising two or three generations but, being strongly territorial, they can nevertheless be vicious towards intruders, rivals, or if cornered. A fully grown male can weigh as much as eighteen kilos, measure nearly a metre in length and live for up to fifteen years. Most badgers display the familiar black and white striped face with a greyish black body, but variations can occur. A few years ago an albino individual resided on the Commons.

The animals mate between February and October but implantation of

Figure 14.2 A wild Badger from Wimbledon Common, eating food put out in a nearby garden, where it was a regular visitor.
Photo: Una Sutcliffe.

fertilised eggs is delayed until December. Cubs, usually numbering two to three per litter, are born between ten to twelve weeks later. Growing rapidly, they resemble their parents after about six months, but retain their feathery tails for a while longer.

Paul Rhodes, who has been studying badgers in the area for many years, has communicated the following:

"It can be a fascinating and rewarding experience watching badgers prepare for a night's foraging, although patience is required as they do not always co-operate, and on several occasions I have spent a cold, wet, miserable evening simply staring at a hole in the ground!

A sett may be either a relatively small affair with just two or three entrances or a large extensive complex network of numerous tunnels constantly in use and being enlarged for many generations. Being scrupulously clean creatures, the sett is lined with bedding consisting of moss, dried grasses and often bluebell leaves, all of which are continually renewed and left out to air.

The family usually emerge one or two at a time around sunset, and commence their time-honoured routines which are amusing to observe, with much grunting, snorting and mock battles; but at any hint of danger they will bolt back underground.

Some grooming may take place, after which the animals concentrate on the serious business of hunting for food. Being omnivorous, they will eat almost anything, but earthworms make up 50% of their diet, so they suffer badly if summer drought conditions prevail and the hard-baked ground forces the worms to dive deep. Small birds and rodents are also taken, together with eggs, plants, wasp grubs, beetles and other insects.

In my experience badgers and foxes seem to get along reasonably well together and I have watched a family foraging while a fox walked close by with no reaction whatsoever from either. The badger has not adapted to urbanisation as readily as the fox, preferring its traditional habitat. Scent is relied upon a great deal as eyesight is poor, which renders them especially vulnerable to traffic, and sadly, several animals have lost their lives in recent years on roads adjacent to the Commons. The badger's sole enemy is Man and records of badger baiting can be traced back to Medieval times. Fortunately, badgers are now protected by law".

STATUS   Common and stable.

Weasel *Mustela nivalis*

Measuring only about 20 cm in length, plus a short tail, the weasel is, in terms of size and weight, the complete opposite of the bulky lumbering badger, also a mustelid. An alert, slender, agile little powerhouse of a predator, this animal is not strictly nocturnal and can be seen during daylight hours when, snakelike, it sinuously glides and scents its way along a hedge or ditch, or moves rapidly forward in graceful leaps and bounds after its prey.

Upper parts are coloured a reddish brown, with a pure white underside, and it lacks the black tip to its tail, a factor which distinguishes it from the larger stoat. The nest, situated in a hole or hollow tree, is constructed with dry leaves and grasses and a litter of between four to six young is produced in spring or early summer.

Food consists of a mixed diet of mice, voles, frogs, rats. It is adept at

Figure 14.3 Sketch of a
Weasel.
Artist: Christiana Gilbert.

squeezing through the tiniest gaps and, being an expert climber, it will also take young birds or eggs. It is capable of killing prey much larger than itself; rabbits frequently feature on the menu, despatched by a quick bite to the neck.

Chief enemies are foxes, owls and large hawks, but the weasel is a fierce opponent and probably escapes would-be predators most of the time.

STATUS   Quite common and increasing.

Stoat *Mustela erminea*

A few brief references appear in old records, but recent sightings are limited, although in 1999 it was reliably recorded on three occasions, so perhaps it is making a recovery. However, the animal is less common than it was, and past observations could be either weasel or the much larger tame ferret, released onto the Commons on occasions.

Similar habits, but larger than the weasel; the tail of the stoat *always* has a black tip.

STATUS   Rare on the Commons.

INSECTIVORES
[4 species]

Mole *Talpa europaea*

Active all year round, the mole rarely ventures above ground during daylight. It nevertheless displays ample evidence of its subterranean activities, especially in winter, before the grass and other vegetation begins to grow and obscure the familiar molehills and tell-tale ridged runs where a tunnel has been excavated.

Although not blind, as legend has it, its eyes are very small. Large whiskers and a sensitive snout help the animal negotiate its way underground. A litter comprising three to five young are born in April or May in a nest of dry grass and leaves constructed within a large molehill.

Food consists largely of earthworms, but assorted insect larvae, including beetle larvae and leatherjackets, figure in the diet.

Preferred habitat is grassland, especially on the 'Acropolis' (see Chapter 4), but open woodland is acceptable, where the results of the animal's labours are less obvious.

STATUS   Common and widespread.

Hedgehog *Erinaceus europaeus*

Another familiar animal which needs little description. Frequently also found in large gardens, it can unwittingly be harmed there by ingesting insecticides employed to exterminate slugs and snails, which form a major part of its diet. Poorly sighted, hedgehogs rely mainly on an acute sense of smell to locate prey, foraging from dusk until dawn. In addition to a comprehensive range of insects, food can include bird's eggs, frogs, young mice and scraps put out for birds.

The animal partially hibernates in a hole or hedgebank lined with moss, dry grasses and leaves. Their nests, where up to five young are born in early summer, are similarly constructed. The spines, which are really toughened hairs, afford the creature some protection, but the young are prone to attack by badgers and foxes, which feast on all but the spiny skin.

Although present on the Commons, it is unusual to see a hedgehog during daytime.

STATUS   Common and widespread.

Common Shrew *Sorex araneus* and Pygmy Shrew *S. minutus*

Active both day and night throughout the year. These two rather mouse-like species, with long pointed noses, are more often heard than seen. Being strongly territorial and quarrelsome, they spend much time squealing at each other in high-pitched tones as they frantically scurry about in search of food.

Because of their small size, shrews need to eat continuously in order to survive. Insects, or preferably earthworms, form the main diet. The Pygmy Shrew is the smallest British mammal. Shrews burrow in leaf litter or use the tunnels of rodents.

Breeding occurs from May to November, during which time the female produces several litters of from five to seven young, born in a grass-lined underground chamber. Enemies are many, including owls, kestrels, foxes and weasels.

STATUS   Very common and widespread.

RODENTS
[5 species]

Wood Mouse *Apodemus sylvaticus*

Figure 14.4 Sketch of a Wood Mouse.
Artist: Christiana Gilbert.

With a light brown upper coat and white underside, large prominent eyes and ears, the wood mouse is an altogether much more appealing creature (prettier and more refined) than the dowdy house mouse of which we are all too familiar.

Often called the 'long-tailed field mouse', the animal is equally at home in woodland, gardens and open ground. Chiefly nocturnal, it sometimes moves around by day. It is very active and can run, leap and climb well. Food consists of nuts, seeds, fruit, insects, snails and flower bulbs. In autumn, little pieces of hazel nuts, gnawed in a characteristic way, can be found on vantage points, such as logs; a sure sign that wood mice and voles are around.

Burrows are constructed below ground or under tree roots, where food is stored, and several litters consisting of five to nine young are born during the summer in grass lined chambers. Winter is spent in partial hibernation.

Measuring approximately 9 cm from tip of long snout to base of tail, the wood mouse is probably the second commonest wild mammal in Britain. Enemies include owls, kestrels and foxes.

STATUS   Abundant on the Commons, particularly in woodland.

Figure 14.5 Chewed hazel nuts showing rodent tooth marks.
Photo: Tony Drakeford.

Field Vole *Microtus agrestis*

A recent survey estimates that the field vole, or 'short-tailed vole', as it is sometimes called, is Britain's commonest wild mammal, present in such large numbers that its population exceeds that of humans; the only mammal with that status!

Four plump inches long, with a short tail, the face is very un-mouse-like, being blunt, with small ears and tiny beady eyes. Body colour is greyish brown. Nests are constructed under logs or in grass tussocks, connected by a maze of tunnels and runways through the grass where, being very aggressive, they can be heard squealing at one another.

Main food consists of juicy grass shoots, with some seeds, roots and soft tree bark. During summer up to five litters will be produced, each with from four to six young. The field vole is the main prey item of owls, but a large number are also taken by weasels, foxes and kestrels.

Figure 14.6 Field Vole, an extremely abundant but little seen member of the Commons' fauna.
Photo: Tony Drakeford.

STATUS   Super-abundant.

Bank Vole *Clethrionomys glareolus*

Very similar to, but more agile than the field vole, with a richer chestnut brown coat. Habitat differs somewhat, with a preference for bramble thickets, light wooded areas and scrub. Bank voles climb well and feed on berries, fruit, seeds, insects, snails and nuts, frequenting wooded glades, along with wood mice.

Shallow runs are excavated in hedge banks, and several litters of between three and six young are born in lined nests, usually above ground.

STATUS   Abundant in woodland and scrub.

Brown Rat *Rattus norvegicus*

A pest species, this animal is really an alien, having been introduced into Britain in the eighteenth century from Eastern Europe. It occurs mainly around the periphery of the Commons, where nearby built up areas offer shelter and food. Rubbish tips will attract these animals, which scavenge on anything they can find.

Prolific breeders, rats produce litters of up to a dozen young, but fortunately foxes exact a heavy toll on this undesirable creature.

STATUS   Common and widespread.

Grey Squirrel *Sciurus carolinensis*

Figure 14.7 Grey Squirrel, the animal most likely to be seen when walking in the woods.
Photo: Dave Haldane.

Definitely a pest species. Introduced from the United States in the mid 19th century, it has gradually spread and colonised much of lowland Britain, forcing out our native red squirrel. Woodland areas of the Commons support large numbers, which take a toll of birds eggs and nestlings, in addition to eating nuts, beech mast, fungi, flower bulbs, fresh young shoots and the bark of many trees, particularly young beech, which are damaged in the process. Food is often buried and stored in the ground, but it is doubtful if squirrels remember the locations, thus allowing cached acorns a chance to germinate.

In early summer up to three young are born in large nests or 'dreys', constructed from twigs and leaves high up in suitable trees. Enemies are few, but being extremely agile, squirrels can escape most potential predators.

STATUS   Abundant and widespread, especially in large mature woodlands.

LAGOMORPHS
[1 species]

Rabbit *Oryctolagus cuniculus*

Although not truly native, the rabbit can justifiably claim to be an honorary alien, having become naturalised since being introduced in the 12th century as a valuable source of food and fur for clothing. The well documented disease myxomatosis almost eliminated rabbits in the mid 1950s, but during the past

Figure 14.8 The Rabbit has
become very abundant in
recent years on parts of the
Commons.
Photo: Dave Haldane.

Figure 14.8 The Rabbit has become very abundant in recent years on parts of the Commons. Photo: Dave Haldane.

forty years the population has steadily recovered across the country and within the past decade numbers have greatly increased on the Commons.

Now present in most areas, this very sociable creature occurs in greatest concentration on the wilder part of the 'Acropolis' near the A3, where many warrens exist in light woodland and at margins of open grassland. There, as elsewhere, the rabbit performs a useful function by grazing and close cropping the grass and keeping encroaching scrub at bay, thus encouraging growth of wild flowers, so useful to nectar feeding insects.

Prolific breeders, the build up of rabbits probably partly accounts for the parallel increase in their main predators, weasel and fox. Breeding commences at the beginning of the year and continues until late summer, litters consisting of three to six or seven young.

Rabbits make use of old anthills or grass tussocks as territorial markers and observation posts, and on which to deposit droppings; a sure sign that their complex warren systems are close by. Diet includes grass shoots and other green plants. Strongly aromatic plants, such as ground ivy, are not favoured.

Classed as a pests on farmland, rabbits on the whole are welcome inhabitants of the Commons, except during years of exceptional abundance, when they will overgraze important insect food plants, such as bird's-foot-trefoil. They are, nevertheless, an effective management tool, helping to control scrub and ensuring that some areas of grassland are neatly trimmed, thus maintaining the beneficial effect of mixed sward heights across the Commons.

STATUS   Very Common.

INTRODUCTIONS AND RELEASES

Mention has already been made of ferrets, which are on occasions deliberately and irresponsibly released onto the Commons, necessitating capture and removal. However, the most bizarre event took place in 1994 when two juvenile wild boars were found wandering near Springwell Cottage. After expending a great deal of effort, Keepers and Police eventually employed Rugby tackles to capture the piglets, before escorting them to Deen City Farm in Merton, where suitable accommodation was offered. The origin of the two intruders was never established.

The Bats of Wimbledon Common and Putney Heath

Pete Guest

Bats in Britain

All bats in Britain have been protected by law since 1981, but sadly this has not stopped their populations from a continued decline. These delightful little animals are very vulnerable to disturbance of their roosts, and need reliable feeding areas with high insect numbers. Of the sixteen species of bat found in Britain at least six occur on the Commons, which is encouraging considering its urban setting. All of the bats found in the British Isles are entirely insectivorous and emerge from their roosts from dusk onwards to feed on the flies, lacewings, moths and beetles that abound in naturally managed areas. During winter months bats hibernate, as there are fewer insects around, but usually wake up every couple of weeks and will emerge to feed if the weather is warm enough.

Echolocation & bat detectors

Human hearing is capable of detecting sound in the range from approximately 20Hz (cycles per second) to 20kHz, with the upper limit becoming lower as we age. Sound with frequencies above this is called ultrasound, and it is this that is used by bats for echolocation. Many bats catch their prey on the wing, using this highly sophisticated echolocation system to both find prey and to navigate in the dark when their eyesight fails – that's right, bats are not at all blind! In most species an echolocation call consists of a sweep from a high to a low frequency, and by listening to the returning echo the bat can determine where an object is, its size and even characteristics such as its having a hard or soft surface. Although we cannot hear these calls, electronic instruments called bat detectors have been developed which translate the ultrasound into sound that we can hear. This enables us to use these instruments to carry out a great deal of valuable survey work and with training it is possible to determine some species from their calls. One difficulty is that bats tend to use the type of echolocation signal that suits the environment that they are using, so a species that is feeding in an environment more usually used by another species can often sound very similar to that species. Also, some like the *Myotis* bats (Daubenton's, Natterer's, Whiskered and Brandt's) use very similar calls, so it is important to record other characteristics such as feeding habit. A *Myotis* bat feeding in a level flight about 10cm above the water surface is most likely to be a Daubenton's bat.

Pipistrelle *Pipistrellus pipistrellus*

As the majority of bats in Britain are pipistrelles it is no surprise that these are also the most frequently found bat on the Commons. The pipistrelle bat is now considered to comprise two separate species but an official name has not yet been assigned to the new species at the time of writing. The smallest bat in Britain, pipistrelles weigh a tiny 4 to 5g, with a wingspan of 18 to 24cm. Despite this small size they have been estimated to eat up to 3,000 gnats and similar insects each night, so they could be thought of as a natural insect control! Most pipistrelles roost in houses during the summer, especially the females who raise their young in large nursery roosts of which several have been found near the Commons, with up to three hundred animals in each. The pipistrelle is quite distinctive on a bat detector and fortunately the two species use different peak frequencies making them fairly easy to separate. The majority of the bats on the Commons belong to the newly described species which is strongest at 55kHz, the other being at 45kHz.

Daubenton's *Myotis daubentonii*

The second most frequent bat on the Commons is the Daubenton's bat, which weighs in at around 7 to 15g and has a wingspan of 24 to 27cm. They have sometimes been called the water bat because of their habit of flying about 10 cm above the water surface hunting for caddis flies, their favourite food, and other insects as they emerge from the water. The Daubenton's is most often seen flying over the larger ponds, Queensmere, Kingsmere and sometimes Rushmere and it usually only arrives when it is quite dark. These bats do have tree roosts on the Commons and have been observed flying on to hunt over the lake in Wimbledon Park. On a bat detector the Daubenton's echolocation call sounds like a rapid series of clicks which are strongest at 45kHz when it is in its water skimming mode of feeding.

Noctule *Nyctalus noctula*

The noctule is the largest bat in Britain, weighing around 35g, has a wingspan of 32 to 40cm and is fairly frequently seen on the Commons but appears to have suffered a serious decline in recent years. The noctule is exclusively a tree dwelling species, using woodpecker or rot holes in deciduous trees, and it is thought that their decline may be partly due to the loss of suitable trees in the storm in 1987. The best places on the Commons to see this bat are near the Windmill where one or two often hunt over the open grasslands and also near to Springwell cottage. The echolocation call of the noctule sounds typically like an irregular and metallic 'chip-chop' which is surprisingly loud and is usually best heard with the bat detector set to 20kHz.

Brown Long-eared *Plecotus auritus*

This is a fairly common bat in Britain, but the brown long-eared bat is relatively scarce in urban areas like London. It is of medium size weighing from 6g to 12g and has a wingspan of 24 to 28cm. These animals are almost impossible to observe as they fly close to vegetation, emerge very late after sunset when it is quite dark, and do not venture far from their roost. There are old records of small colonies somewhere in the 1,140 acres of the Commons, but a few were disturbed when some tree work was in progress in 1993, confirming their continued presence. This species uses houses, usually roof spaces, as well as tree holes for roosting. The usual feeding habit of the brown long-eared bat is to keep very close to vegetation using a very quiet echolocation call. This means that it is hard to see and is unlikely to be picked up on a bat detector even when flying close to the instrument.

Serotine *Eptesicus serotinus*

The serotine is nearly the same size as the noctule but is rarer, and individuals have been observed using the Commons as a feeding area, particularly over the golf links. Serotines can fly long distances from roost sites to good feeding areas and as there are other areas nearby used by this species in Beddington and Richmond their roosts could be almost anywhere. Unlike the noctule though, the serotine mainly uses buildings as roosts. The serotine typically feeds on beetles and other insects over grasslands, and uses an echolocation call that sounds like a loud 'tock' with the bat detector set to 27kHz.

Figure 14.9 Bat specialist
and photographer, Frank
Greenaway, from the Natural
History Museum, setting up
cameras for photographing
bats flying over Queensmere.
See Figure 14.10.
Photo: Antony Sutcliffe.

Figure 14.10 A Daubenton's
bat *Myotis daubentonii* flying
over Queensmere at night.
Photo: Frank Greenaway.

Where to see bats on Wimbledon Common and Putney Heath

The best places on the Commons are over water bodies like Queensmere and Kingsmere, with the former being especially good. If you do not fancy wandering too far into the Commons in the dark then you need go no further than the Windmill as there are often pipistrelles feeding over the buildings and down Windmill Road. Occasionally a noctule will feed over the grassland areas near the Windmill as well. If you want to see Daubenton's, you will have to go to Queensmere or Kingsmere, but they are occasionally found on Bluegate Gravel Pit as well. In general, pipistrelles feed all over the Commons, but are especially fond of sheltered areas of woodland edge, while the noctules and serotines more frequently feed over the open grassland areas.

Conclusion

The continued presence of bats on Wimbledon Common and Putney Heath is, we hope, fairly certain, but their needs should continue to be considered. Continued non-use of pesticides will mean that the large numbers of insects will continue, which is of course good news for the insects as well as the birds and bats that feed on them. Anyone living near the Commons and who is considering having their roof treated should consider insisting on the use of chemicals that do not harm bats. There are excellent timber treatment chemicals available that are not toxic to mammals like us, our pets and of course bats. Advice is available from English Nature and from the London Bat Group. Bat droppings can accumulate near to roosts, but these are not known to cause any health problems to humans, and being dry are easily cleared up. If you are lucky enough to be sharing your home with bats, let the London Bat Group know and arrange a visit to confirm the species. You might also like to take part in a national scheme run by the Bat Conservation Trust and monitor your roost over coming years, thus adding to our knowledge of these delightful animals.

Chapter 15

Extracts from a Keeper's Diary

Dave Haldane
Assistant Ranger, Wimbledon and Putney Commons

The following extracts are taken from my log-book at the time when I was the Head Keeper. They are seasonally arranged and location names are in accordance with those used by the Rangers' Office.

January The Running Deer

Over the centuries many crows have paid the price of their opportunism by being caught, despatched and displayed on the gamekeeper's gibbet. This picture sprung to mind as I searched the woodlands for a carrion crow reported to be hanging from a high branch. I soon discovered the bird, suspended by fishing line, some eight metres from the ground. The line had probably wrapped around its leg, while it was fishing in the shallow water of the nearby pond. Sometime later, when the bird retired to the trees, the line became entangled in the branches leaving it in its present predicament.

At first glance it appeared dead, but at that height, even from the back of my horse, which stood 17hh (68 inches), I was unable to reach it. To determine if there was life in the bird, I cut a long stick and prodded it. This soon produced a reaction, when the bird cocked its head to one side and glared indignantly in my direction. I was now faced with the task of freeing the bird and immediately arranged for a ladder.

The crow remained impassive as I climbed towards it. I could see the nylon line had bitten deeply into the leg and its attempts at freeing itself had caused the black leathery skin to peel back. The crow's mood changed at the sight of my outstretched hand hovering inches from its head and it lunged at my wrist with its beak. At the same time the claws of its free leg seized my finger and tightened into a rather painful grip. With beak and claw firmly attached and the bird unable to offer further resistance, I took its weight on my arm and carefully cut away at the fishing line.

As I worked to release the bird I became aware of another crow, hopping from branch to branch in an agitated way. It seemed very interested in what was taking place but showed no hint of aggression or indeed uttered any sound.

Upon releasing the casualty from its plight I forced a solid twig between the upper and lower beak and another under the talons, so relieving the pain on my arm. When the bird had resigned itself to its changed situation, I wrapped it in the folds of my jacket and mounted my horse. As I walked my horse towards home the companion bird accompanied me.

Back at the stable yard, the patient's wound was cleaned and dressed with an appropriate ointment. Satisfied that there were no other visible wounds and

Figure 15.1 The author, then Head Keeper, on horse patrol on the Common.

that its bones and feathers appeared intact, I released the bird. The creature was obviously weakened by its ordeal and flew but a short distance to a nearby tree. Some few minutes later it was visited by the other crow, that had faithfully waited for its companion to return. I was then entertained to a raucous reunion consisting of bowing, posturing and vocal accompaniment before both birds flew back towards the woodland.

February North View

When a wild animal looses its natural fear of humans its actions can often be unpredictable. This was the situation when a squirrel that was regularly fed by a local resident began to see everyone as a potential source of food.

I was called to an incident involving an elderly lady who while taking her afternoon stroll had been harassed by a grey squirrel. The incident occurred near a residential area just south of the Common. Unfortunately the lady was not endeared to the animal's begging antics and became very frightened. Unable to flee because of her frail condition she turned and in time honoured fashion gestured with her outstretched arms for the squirrel to shoo.

To the squirrel, the arm waving was not seen as a threat but rather a gesture associated with feeding. As the promised food failed to materialise, its natural reaction was to search for it. The lady was wearing a calf length skirt that left the lower part of her 'sapling-like' legs exposed and as such, an open invitation to this arboreal mammal. With little warning it suddenly ran up the lady's stocking leg and disappeared under her skirt. For a few seconds it foraged in the darkness of her inner clothing but finding its progress hampered by the lady's wild gyrations, it abandoned its quest. It left in similar fashion, only this time by way of the other leg.

For the elderly lady the brief encounter had been traumatic. She was left with torn stockings, deep lacerations and extremely frayed nerves. As for the grey squirrel, well, word of its misdemeanour spread among the local residents and a few days later it was successfully trapped and removed.

March Queensmere

The migration of common toads is an annual event. Males always outnumber females and competition is fierce. The male, smaller than the female by 2cm, fends off other suitors in their quest for the dominant position that will guarantee their sperm fertilising the female's spawn. Many females will die under a frenzy of multi-coupling, their pale bloated bodies littering the pond bottom. And yet even in death many will still receive the attentions of the amorous males, such is the urge to procreate.

The mating spree of both frogs and toads attracts predatory birds such as the herons and crows. Herons wade into shallow waters and gorge themselves on the amphibians, while the crows crowd the pond edge, dipping into the squirming throng and seizing and deftly disembowelling the toads. Unfortunately for the toad, a gland, which secretes a defensive fluid and deters many predators, does not seem to affect the crows.

Such a spectacular event also attracts the attention of the public. Most people are content to merely observe, but inevitably some will interfere. One of my strangest encounters was when I visited the pond early one evening and found a man in motor cycle leathers, bending over the water. As I moved towards him I noticed he was lifting paired toads from the pond and placing them into something. On closer inspection I found that his receptacle was a motor cycle helmet of the type designed to completely protect the head and lower face.

When confronted, he told me that he had chanced upon this site and not having a suitable container decided to use his helmet to carry them back to his motor cycle. When asked his reasons for removing them, he said without hesitation, "to feed my snakes".

Each year the Keepers seize containers ranging from carrier bags to motor cycle helmets, filled to overflowing with toads or frogs. Sometimes the sheer weight of cavorting amphibians, contained within such a restricted area, causes a high mortality to those at the bottom of the pile.

Notices are now displayed at the main spawning sites asking the public not to remove adult amphibians or their tadpoles.

April Ravine west

It was late afternoon and poor light forced the Keeper to ride his horse along a well defined path that bordered the old badger sett. The site had known better days and showed none of the signs associated with regular badger activity and indeed most of the mounds had been flattened and entrances partly collapsed. Sett disturbance was certainly not on the Keeper's mind as he headed his horse towards home.

Suddenly his horse lurched to one side, as the ground beneath its hind quarters gave way. The horse quickly recovered its balance and the Keeper dismounted and checked his mount for injury. Having satisfied himself there were none, he turned his attention to the hole in the path. The hole was about 30cm deep and led into an underground passage. On the floor of the passage and less than 3cm from the deep impression left by the horse's hoof, he discovered the huddled form of a badger cub. Fortunately the Keeper was wearing gloves which enabled him to gently extract the cub, thought to be about a month old.

Assistance was called and materials were conveyed to the site to effect a temporary repair. It was important that the squealing cub was returned to the run as quickly as possible. Too much handling, even with gloves, increased the risk of the parent rejecting it. We were satisfied that the cub appeared unharmed and gently placed it back in the underground run. The surface was then covered with marine ply board and hidden from view.

The following morning the temporary repair was lifted. We were pleased to see that overnight the run had been reworked and the cub had disappeared. A strong smell of adult badger wafted from the hole and led us to conclude that all had ended well. All that remained was to replace the wooden cover with a more permanent sheet of heavy metal and conceal it.

May Glen Albyn (north of the Queensmere)

The raucous cawing that accompanies the passage of crows through the woodlands is a common enough sound. It never fails to fascinate me as these pirates from the sky exercise breathtaking aerial skills between the branches of the lower canopy. And yet on this May afternoon the sound of the approaching birds was somehow different.

I gazed through the leafy woodland and focused my attention on the distant black shapes. Slowly, like leaves whisked up by the wind, the birds moved towards me and I realised that what I was witnessing was a large flock of foraging jackdaws. Because the jackdaw is a non-resident bird on the Commons, and a bit of a rarity, the sudden appearance of what I later estimated to be 200+ birds was quite startling.

The object of their attention were the thousands of tiny moth caterpillars descending from the tree canopy, each suspended by a silken line. Excited by this rich banquet, the jackdaws paid no attention to me as I moved out into the open from my place of concealment. Some birds flew so close I could feel the breeze brush my cheek but they were the exceptions, and most remained high above my head. After about ten minutes of intense activity the flock eased its way on through the woodland leaving me excited by my experience. In all my years on the Common I have never before or since witnessed such an occurrence.

Footnote: As a point of interest, I later read in Cyril Collenette's book on the History of Richmond Park, that on the 21st May 1933, he too observed what he described as a mixed flock of 200+ jackdaws feeding on descending caterpillars, and again on the 27th May 1934, noted 150 jackdaws, similarly focussed, near the Isabella Plantation. He added that these numbers were exceptional and perhaps represented the total population of the park.

June Thatched Cottages

The crows gave the fox's position away. Swooping and weaving with an agility that belied their stocky build, they repeatedly harassed the predator. The fox instinctively ducked in response to their attacks but otherwise did not appear unduly concerned. As it moved closer I could see that the animal was not in the best of health. Its muzzle was scarred with festering sores and its eyes were weeping. The coat was matted and on the hind quarters the hair had been rubbed away, exposing patches of raw flesh several centimetres in diameter.

The fox was suffering from mange, which is a condition caused by a mite that burrows beneath the epidermal layer of the skin. This sets up an intense irritation that causes the animal to repeatedly scratch or rub itself against any rough objects. As a result, hair loss is exacerbated, condition cannot be maintained and the animal loses the ability to regulate body temperature. Sadly the condition often proves fatal in the wild.

I followed the fox's progress as it slipped under the holly hedge surrounding Thatched Cottages. Entering the garden it made its way to a plastic bucket containing water placed for the benefit of local wildlife. Such was its thirst that it allowed me to move to within 5 metres of it. I noticed a continuous tremble passing along the emaciated frame and the creature's dull eye registered the hopelessness of its condition. Three days later I was informed that the lifeless body of a mange-infected fox had been found curled up under a shed at the nearby Springwell Cottage.

July West of the Wimbledon Village Pound

I had forsaken my horse for the opportunity to patrol on foot. Rambling through the undergrowth offers a different perspective to that viewed from a horse. It also offers the opportunity to crawl into out of the way places rarely visited by the public.

I positioned myself on a stump and sat back observing my surroundings. A high pitched squeal attracted my attention to a field mouse which had leapt from the grass onto a fallen tree. Using the tree as a roadway it scurried along its length, before leaping off and disappearing under a clump of tussock grass. At that very moment a weasel moving at an equally fast pace began its run along the fallen tree. On reaching the end it stopped and tested the wind with its slender nose.

Meanwhile, in the vegetation below, the mouse decide to abandon its temporary concealment in favour of the exposed roots of an old birch tree.

Sadly the move was ill-timed, for the weasel's sharp senses had picked up the sound of the fleeing prey. Leaping from the tree, hurriedly circling the tussock grass until satisfied it had the scent, it wasted little time in homing in on the birch tree with the exposed roots.

In a few seconds it was over and the triumphant weasel emerged with the hapless mouse held firmly in its mouth. With a short bounding gait it made its way back, past the tussock grass and the fallen tree, before being swallowed up by the tangle of vegetation that covered its territory.

August Queensmere

The grass snake swam towards me, gliding across the surface with such grace that I was momentarily mesmerised by its primeval beauty. It left the water and moved across the dusty path skirting the pond. Unable to resist this close encounter with such an elusive creature, I captured it.

Although I wished the creature no harm, it saw me only as a predator and lifting its head it hissed and lunged towards my outstretched hand. As grass snakes are non-venomous I was not unduly alarmed by this ploy and deftly seized the creature behind the back of its head. It was while securing my grip on the snake that I became aware of a very unpleasant smell. This I knew was a scent produced by the snake as a deterrent to hungry predators. Moving the creature away from my clothing and relaxing my hold from its head I inspected the reptile. Sixty centimetres of smooth yet muscular body squirmed in defiance. So absorbed was I with my close inspection that I failed to notice the snake allow its head to drop back, its tongue to hang out, and theatrically feign death. It remained in this position for several seconds before my stroking movements along its underside caused it to right itself.

With the snake no longer offering resistance, my intention was to place it in my jacket pocket. This would allow me to take it home, measure and sketch the creature for my records, before releasing it back into the wild. Unfortunately, I had forgotten the grass snake's ability to regurgitate its last meal. I watched helplessly as muscular body contractions assisted the delivery of several quite foul smelling small pike into my hand.

September Queensmere

As a result of the Ninja Mutant Turtle fad, which swept the country during the late 1980s, the Commons gained two new introduced species. One was the European pond terrapin and the other the red-eared terrapin, also referred to as the 'slider'.

A number of mild winters saw both species adjusting well to our climate. They were viewed initially as something of a novelty but this soon changed when it became apparent that their appetite for molluscs, tadpoles and small fish could dramatically upset the natural balance of our ponds. We were concerned at the number of fresh sightings regularly received by the Rangers' Office and took steps to control their numbers.

Responding to one such report led me to the shallows of the Queensmere. Using a large net, a colleague swept the area and was soon rewarded when a turtle rose to the surface and thrashed its way out of the ascending net. We were puzzled at the creature's strength and both agreed its habits were quite unlike the usual aquatic reptiles. It took a further thirty minutes of dragging the net before we finally landed the creature. Once on land and stripped of a veil of aquatic vegetation, we were amazed at the armoured plated little monster that stood before us. It was 25cm in length with a thick shell, the upper plates of which were folded into raised points. The tail had a serrated central comb and its head was far wider than the turtles we had previously encountered. When we attempted to handle it, the turtle raised itself up by straightening its legs and lifting its shell clear of the ground. From this defensive position it was able to lunge out with a formidable beaked mouth at anything that moved within range.

Although I had never encountered one before I realised that what we had before us was a 'snapping turtle'. This was later confirmed from an identification chart. Here was a creature capable of inflicting a serious wound, irresponsibly dumped in a public pond, with no thought to the consequences. On this occasion, because of the exotic nature of the creature, we were able to pass it on to the RSPCA. Later, they, and many animal rescue centres were inundated with terrapins and unable to offer their services to land owners faced with the removal of these aliens.

Footnote: This was just one of many unwanted pets abandoned to their fate each year on the Commons.

October Stag Ride north

It was my mount's enquiring gaze and suspicious snort that alerted me to the movement in the undergrowth. Trusting his instincts I urged him on a few steps and well away from the distraction before dismounting. Leaving the horse happily picking at the hazel shrubbery I moved towards the source of its concern.

Alongside the horse ride a thick tangle of bramble effectively hides a metre deep drainage ditch. Peering into the shadows I was able to make out a colour which did not fit in with the surrounding autumnal tints. On closer investigation, and after removing a considerable amount of bramble, I came across a very distressed heron. The bird had probably been hunting along the ditch when its long neck became entangled in the bramble.

Extracting the heron from its plight was quite easy although the bird seemed very confused at 'being pulled through a hedge backwards'. With the bird freed, I took a firm grip on its wings and menacing beak, before recovering my horse. The intention was to mount up without alarming the horse and convey the heron to the stable yard. Unfortunately this was not to be as horse and bird reacted in classic style. The heron, frightened and desperate, forcefully freed itself from my grasp and, uttering a war cry, stabbed at the neck of my horse. The horse in true equine style issued a terrific blast of wind from its rear end and tore off at the gallop, heading for home.

Sometime later, after a healthy walk and many enquiring glances from Commons users, the heron and I arrived at the stables. The bird was given the customary once over but appeared none the worse for wear. To test its flight muscles it was taken out onto an open expanse of grassland and 'launched'. This was achieved by running with the bird firmly held while allowing it to exercise its wings. After a couple of abortive attempts, it finally managed to keep itself airborne, slowly gaining height and heading off towards Richmond Park.

November South of the KRR Stone

Rabbits are great survivors. Fitness and stamina is the key to their success and ailing animals stand no chance in the wild. The healthy rabbit is a joy to behold with senses honed to perfection and the ability to out-run and out-manoeuvre its adversary. Occasionally they also seem to possess a large slice of luck.

It was 0630hrs as I positioned myself in the fork of a tree some 6 metres above and 20 metres away from an active rabbit warren. I was soon rewarded by the sight of two adult and three young rabbits. They appeared relaxed and grazed the lush tussock grass that was a feature of the area.

The largest member of the group was a fine buck, who remained alert and occasionally sat bolt upright to view the surrounding area. Its attention was repeatedly drawn to a nearby gorse bush and in time the buck rabbit bounded cautiously towards it. Until that moment I was completely unaware of the fox, lying low in the bushes and watching. About three metres from the bush the rabbit stopped and stared in the direction of its arch adversary. Neither creature stirred as both remained locked in eye contact.

The minutes ticked by and then suddenly, as though snapped out of a trance, the rabbit hopped to within a metre of the fox. In response the fox laid back its ears and stretched its nose forwards, gently inhaling the rabbit's scent. I feared that this bold guardian of the warren would soon hang limply from the fox's mouth. But this was not to be and to my amazement the fox narrowed its eyes, yawned and slowly, indeed almost submissively, turned and melted into the surrounding shadows.

December Thatched Cottage

Birds that have fallen from their nest are frequently encountered during the nesting season. Often they are so small and helpless that they have little chance of survival. For the larger fledglings, with a healthy compliment of feathers, the odds are better, and they instinctively hide themselves away and continue to be cared for by the parents. Occasionally birds are found injured or abandoned and brought to the Rangers' Office.

The pair of young pigeons handed to me were sparsely feathered and had been abandoned to their fate when the only known parent was killed. Deprived of the mothers' 'pigeon milk' I did not rate their chances but felt my effort at nurturing them would be better than abandoning them to their fate. For several days I fed them biscuit meal and well crushed oats doused in baby milk. They prospered well with this regime and soon progressed to soft pulses and seed. In time I cut back on the feed and allowed them to free range the garden. Slowly, as their stamina increased and flying abilities improved, I considered myself relieved of my parental duties.

The days rolled by, and my feathered friends, now capable of sustained flight, regularly circled the cottage but never ventured far from the roof. Each time I went out into the garden they would fly to my side, sometimes actually landing on my head or shoulders. When I dug my plot they inspected the earth for seeds and insects and when I retired to the house they returned to the eves to await my reappearance. Meanwhile, their droppings piled up under my porch and it was evident that some form of drastic action was needed to evict my squatters.

One morning, as they flew down to greet me, I bundled both into a box and transported them to a faraway Common. Upon release they flew into a nearby tree and, avoiding their enquiring gaze, I drove away. My journey home took almost thirty minutes and, with a feeling of remorse still gnawing away at my conscience, I entered my driveway. I could not believe the sight that greeted me, for there on the roof, diligently preening their flight feathers, were the two pigeons. They remained with me for several weeks, taking advantage of the seed regularly scattered for the winter birds, before finally flying off to pastures new.

Figure 16.1 Ravine Pond, 1999.
Photo: Tony Drakeford.

Chapter 16

Habitat Creation and Habitat Restoration

Tony Drakeford and Pete Guest

Habitat Creation – Ravine Pond

Tony Drakeford

Nature itself is the finest creator of habitats. However, in certain circumstances the hand of man can and has influenced, moulded, and enhanced suitable areas to help the situation along. A prime example of the way in which the environment can be improved is to introduce a new permanent water body.

In 1998 the Conservators of the Commons decided to celebrate the coming Millennium by constructing a new pond; especially bearing in mind how the severely drought ridden years of the early to mid 1990s had adversely affected the wildlife of several ponds. Some had reached unacceptably low levels or had even dried out entirely. Creation of the pond was funded by the Countryside Commission, with the full endorsement of English Nature.

It was decided that the location of the new pond would be in an already marshy area situated in the attractive valley now known as 'the Ravine'. The stream forming this valley rises from a spring close to the junction of Gravelly Ride and Windmill Road and flows northwards to Queensmere. The pond was to occupy what had been a crossing point for golfers, so provision had to be made for their access from one side of the valley to the other.

Using local materials, including surplus clay from the old Putney Heath Reservoir, work commenced with the construction of a clay embankment to hold in the water on the down-stream side of the proposed pond. This would, of course, also serve as a path for the golfers. To ensure that the bed and sides of the pond would be leak proof, a considerable time had to be allowed for the clay to consolidate.

Finally in November 1998 the dam was plugged. Heavy rains at the time ensured that the pond filled quickly and within two weeks water levels reached the overflow pipe built into the dam. The surplus water could rejoin the brook which bubbles on down to Queensmere. Shaded by mature trees, an attractive open wooden fence was constructed along the top of the dam, both for safety and aesthetic reasons, and similar fencing was also used for the path at the upstream end of the pond.

Mallard, coot and moorhen quickly adjusted to the new habitat, which became a watering hole for foxes and badgers, as well as the large local dog population!

Naturally, any new pond requires time to settle down, and during the first winter falling leaves and decaying submerged vegetation had acidified the water. Nevertheless, the spring of 1999 saw frog spawn laid there, and by May of that year damselflies and dragonflies appeared in surprisingly large numbers. This coincided with a revival on the Commons of the fortunes of Azure, Common Blue, Large Red and Blue-tailed damselflies and Broad-bodied Chaser dragonflies. On one hot June morning ten male Broad-bodied Chasers were observed indulging in territorial skirmishes, while three females, accompanied by guarding males, busied themselves ovipositing around the perimeter. The remainder of the summer encouraged other species of Odonata to colonise Ravine Pond, together with pond skaters, whirligig beetles and water boatmen.

At first a decision was taken not to introduce aquatic plants so that the rate of natural colonisation could be studied. However, it now seems necessary to stabilise some of the edges and banks, which suffer considerable disturbance by dogs. Also, at times of low water the pond becomes increasingly anaerobic, through the accumulation of detritus from fallen leaves. Thus, a few marginals have been planted to help it on its way.

Ravine Pond is already a valuable new habitat for wildlife and a most picturesque feature for lovers of the Commons.

Habitat Restoration in Fishpond Wood and Beverley Meads Local Nature Reserve

Pete Guest

The areas about to be described lie just outside the south western boundary of Wimbledon Common and are owned by the London Borough of Merton and managed by the London Wildlife Trust. With the strip of woodland and Beverley Brook known as Mill Corner lying to its west, the Common abuts the reserve on two sides (Fig.2.17). As wildlife does not recognise our artificial boundaries, the larger the area that is sensitively managed the better, so the restoration of the habitats in the reserve benefits the Common, and of course vice-versa.

If you were able to go back in time to the reign of Elizabeth I and stand near Mill Corner, a completely unrecognisable scene would lie before you. Not surprisingly, given the name of the area, you would see a wooden furling mill used to prepare sheep's wool standing nearby, presumably run by waterpower from Beverley Brook. Perhaps more surprisingly there are fewer trees around you, with much of the area being wildflower rich meadows, grazing marsh and ponds. Beverley Brook would have been a more natural stream with overhanging alder and willow trees, not at all like the present day deep and gloomy channel that dates from 1887. Where Fishpond Wood stands now you would see a series of ponds, possibly associated with the mill but which might have been used as fishponds. Beverley Meads was likely to have been a series of small open fields used either for grazing or perhaps as arable with hedges and ditches between them.

So how do we know so much about such a long time ago? In 1989 a student from Nene College, Northampton, took a sample of the sediment in the area of the northern pond in Fishpond Wood, and analysed the pollen found at various depths. This shows that there have been major changes in the vegetation in the area from mainly grasses, sedges and wetland plants in the oldest deposits, to many more trees and shrubs indicated by the more recent ones.

Comparison of amounts of Tree, Shrub and Non-Tree Pollen

From pond deposit in Fishpond Wood (Adapted from – Christian Smillie 1990. BSc. Report, Nene College)

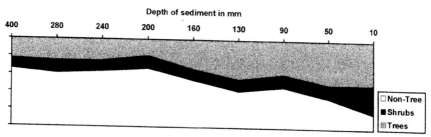

The chart shows a plot of the relative amounts of pollen at different depths of sediment in the pond which represent a time sequence, the oldest being the deepest of course. No precise dating is possible from such basic data, but a general idea of time can be inferred by correlation with known facts. For a more refined pollen analysis of a 2m core from Farm Bog, refer back to Chapter 3. In Fishpond Wood the best estimate for the dates of the sediments is that the bottom 100mm was deposited in the 14th or 15th century when the mill was in operation. The next 100mm could show the use of Warren Farm in the 16th/17th Century, after which there is a steady rise in tree and shrub pollen as the area turns into the more wooded landscape we are familiar with today.

Another valuable source of information is historical documents. These suggest that the mill may have burnt down in Elizabethan times, and they tell us that the area was considered as "waste" in the Wimbledon Manorial Rolls of 1763. The origin of the name Fishpond Wood is not certain, and could be simply a mistake! There are records of fishponds somewhere in the area during medieval times that belonged to Merton Abbey, but no one then thought it necessary to record exactly where they were situated. From such limited information we can attempt to uncover the past history of an area, particularly the land use patterns, which are useful in planning the best way to manage a site for nature conservation for the future

Up to the 1930s, Fishpond Wood and Beverley Meads were a part of Warren Farm, and were purchased by Wimbledon Borough Council in the 1950s. During the 1980s Merton Council agreed that the London Wildlife Trust should adopt and manage Fishpond Wood as a Nature Reserve. Almost all work on this area is carried out by volunteers from the Merton local group who would welcome help in this never ending task.

There were a number of problems to be solved before the objective of restoring the ponds and wet woodland could be achieved, of which the most serious was the constant loss of water through breaches in the bank. Only when the worst of these was completely dug out and refilled with waterproof clay did water remain in the pond for most of the year; occasional drying out in late summer is both normal and even desirable for ponds like this. In late 1989 a bulldozer was used to de-silt and deepen the pond and, although the immediate result looked rather devastating, subsequent spread of vegetation

Figure 16.2 General view of Fishpond Wood.

Photo: Tony Drakeford.

Figure 16.3 Hazel coppice, Fishpond Wood.

Photo: Tony Drakeford.

has been rapid. The pond has large amounts of soft rush (*Juncus effusus*), branched bur-reed (*Sparganium erectum*), reedmace (*Typha latifolia*) and yellow flag (*Iris pseudacorus*) and some less common species like bogbean (*Menyanthes trifoloiata*) and common water plantain (*Alisma plantago-aquatica*). Many dragonflies like the emperor (*Anax imperator*), broad-bodied chaser (*Libellula depressa*), the common darter (*Sympetrum striolatum*) and damselflies like the common blue (*Enallagma cyathigerum*) and large red (*Pyrrhosoma nymphula*) are often seen round the pond and breed here. In spring large numbers of frogs (*Rana temporaria*), toads (*Bufo bufo*) and smooth newts (*Triturus vulgaris*) lay their eggs in the pond; and the tadpoles can be seen at the pond edge feeding on the algae. The stream that feeds the pond passes under the path down the east side of the reserve, and crosses Beverley Meads from a source near to Warren Farm. This needs to be cleared out regularly to maintain the flow into the Reserve.

The southern section of Fishpond Wood is very different and the management methods adopted are consequently also different. The woodland is of a type known as "coppice with standards" and has an understorey of hazel (*Corylus avellana*) with large oak trees (*Quercus robur*), and would have provided the farm with fencing materials and fuel by regular coppicing of the hazel. The cutting to stumps called stools at ground level is a method of woodland management that has been used in Britain since prehistoric times. The technique produces a multitude of thin and long shoots that after only a few years are ideal for weaving into many useful items, or if left for ten to fifteen years can be used for fence panels. Indeed, there are still commercial sweet chestnut coppice woodlands in Sussex for making fencing. The hazel in

Fishpond Wood had not been cut for around 50 years and was very derelict and so the London Wildlife Trust has begun to cut selected areas on a rotational basis. The reason for restoring this technique was not to make fences however, but because cutting the hazel increases the light at ground level which encourages woodland flora such as bluebell (*Hyacinthoides non-scripta*) and foxglove (*Digitalis purpurea*) which abound in the area. This section has an area of wet woodland, which usually floods in winter to spring and which is fed by several streams and the overflow from the main pond. A number of wetland plants thrive on this regime, including yellow flag and bladder sedge (*Carex vesicaria*).

Beverley Meads lies to the east of Fishpond Wood and consists of 4.5 acres of acid grassland and woodland with lines of old oak trees showing the line of the ancient field boundaries. The area was grazed by horses until the late 1960s but in the 1970s was turned into a nine hole pitch and putt golf course. Much disturbance of the site was caused by this work, including importing of soil and re-seeding which resulted in much of the acid grassland being converted into less interesting neutral grassland. The golf course was abandoned in the early 1980s due to lack of use and you can still see the position of many of the greens and tees. In 1993 Merton Council designated both sites as a statutory Local Nature Reserve, giving the area formal protection, and the London Wildlife Trust adopted Beverley Meads, making the two areas into a single Reserve. The LNR designation demonstrates Merton

Figure 16.4 Stream at Beverley Meads.
Photo: Tony Drakeford.

Figure 16.5 Foxgloves, Beverley Meads.
Photo: Tony Drakeford.

Council's commitment to the area being managed for the benefit of wildlife and the enjoyment of people.

Beverley Meads is a haven for many grassland butterfly species, such as meadow brown (*Maniola jurtina*), small copper (*Lycaena phlaeas*), common blue (*Polyommatus icarus*), and the small (*Thymelicus sylvestris*), Essex (*T. lineola*) and large (*Ochlodes venatus*) skippers. These can be seen variously from June to August depending on the species, and in July onwards are joined by large numbers of grasshoppers, principally the common green (*Omocestus viridulus*) and meadow (*Chorthippus parallelus*). Acid grassland is important because of its high insect value, but has a lower floral diversity than some other grassy habitats. Nonetheless, there are many flowers to be seen including meadow buttercup (*Ranunculus acris*), bird's-foot-trefoil (*Lotus corniculatus*), common sorrel (*Rumex acetosa*), perforate St. Johns-wort (*Hypericum perforatum*) and the uncommon heath bedstraw (*Galium saxatile*). Much of the management work on Beverley Meads consists of preventing trees and shrubs from invading the grasslands by cutting and raking off the grass in summer after seed has been set. It is hoped that we might be able to increase the areas of acid grassland by removing some of the dumped soil and allowing the adjacent areas to re-invade their old territory.

In autumn a great many fungi appear in most years, with the most obvious being the toxic fly agaric (*Amanita muscaria*) under birch trees, with which it has a symbiotic relationship. The attractive bright red cap often covered with white shreds of the veil makes this one of the most recognisable of our fungi, and is of course the one most often depicted in fairy stories. Others often seen include the common yellow russula (*Russula ochroleuca*), blackening russula (*Russula nigricans*) and fragile russula (*Russula fragilis*), the ugly milk cap (*Lactarius turpis*) and amythyst deceiver (*Laccaria amethystea*), as well as a great many others.

The birds found in the area all year include finches, thrushes, starlings, robins and all three species of woodpecker. The great spotted woodpecker (*Dendrocopus major*) is often easily seen and especially heard as it gives its "chip chip" call from high in a tree or flying with the typically undulating flight of the woodpeckers. The green woodpecker (*Picus viridis*) may be seen flying up from ground level where it would have been feeding on ants, its favourite food, or giving its laughing "keu-keu-keu" call from a treetop. The much rarer lesser spotted woodpecker (*Dendrocopus minor*) is sparrow sized and occasionally can be seen up in the tree tops in Fishpond Wood especially in spring when, like the great spotted, it drums on the dead branches of trees. A favourite area for bullfinches (*Pyrrhula pyrrhula*) is the southern end of Beverley Meads in the scrub along the stream. Listen out for its soft "heu" calls.

In summer the resident birds are joined by chiffchaffs (*Phylloscopus collybita*) and blackcaps (*Sylvia atricapilla*), which have become quite frequent in recent years. Both these members of the warbler family arrive from their wintering quarters in April, and the chiffchaff is easily distinguished by its clear "chiff-chaff" song. In contrast, the blackcap is one of the finest avian songsters in Britain, with a delightfully varied warble heard during spring and early summer. The winter months often bring redwings (*Turdus iliacus*) into the area; these thrushes from northern Europe winter in Britain and are particularly fond of the berries found in the scrubby areas. They can sometimes be seen feeding on the rugby pitches next to Beverley Meads. Small flocks of redpolls (*Carduelis flammea*) have in the past fed in the high branches of the many birches across the Meads.

In general, the Reserve is richer than many other similarly sized sites in London, mainly because of its proximity to Wimbledon Common. The large continuous area this creates means that wildlife, which of course has no concept of our artificial boundaries but is severely affected by our built up areas, has more space, which significantly increases the diversity of species. This means that there is usually something to see and even listen to at any time of the year, and the regular visitor can observe the passing of the seasons in a lovely area of ancient countryside, whose only slight defect is the all too obvious traffic noise from the nearby A3.

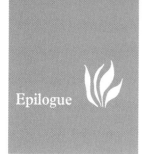

Figure E.1
Female wolf spider (*Pisaura mirabilis*) carrying its egg cocoon to ensure a future generation.
Photo: Charlie Wicker.

Figure E.2
The end of another day. We can thank past Conservators for what the Commons are today. Tomorrow rests in the hands of those who read this book and care about the future.
Photo: Tony Drakeford.

Further Reading

BAKER, C.A., MOXEY, P.A. & OXFORD, P.M. (1978) Woodland continuity and change in Epping Forest. *Field Studies.* **4**, 645-669.

BRIDGLAND, D.R. (1994) *Quaternary of the Thames.* Geological Conservation Review Series, Chapman and Hall, London.

BRIDGLAND, D.R. & GIBBARD, P.L. (1997) Quaternary River Diversions in the London Basin and the Eastern English Channel. *Géographie Physique et Quaternaire.* **51**, 337-346.

COOPE, G.R. & ANGUS, R.B. (1975) An ecological study of the temperate inter-lude in the middle of the Last Glaciation, based on fossil Coleoptera from Isleworth, Middlesex. *Journal of Animal Ecology.* **44**, 365-391.

CURRY, C. (1988) *Memories of my side of the Common.* Senol Printing Ltd.

DRAKEFORD, T. (1987) *A Field Guide to the Butterflies and some Day-flying Moths of Wimbledon Common and Putney Heath.* Wimbledon and Putney Commons Conservators, London.

DRAKEFORD, T. (1999) *The Wildlife of Cannizaro Park, a concise pocket guide.* Friends of Cannizaro Park. Wimbledon.

ENVIRONMENT AGENCY (1998) *The Beverley Brook Catchment Strategic River Corridor Survey. Thames Region.* (Final Report) Babtie Group Ltd., Reading.

GIBBARD, P.L. (1986) *The Pleistocene History of the Middle Thames Valley.* Cambridge University Press, Cambridge.

JOHNSON, W. (1912) *Wimbledon Common; its Geology, Antiquities and Natural History* (1912) Fisher Unwin, London.

JOHNSON, W. (1937) Wimbledon Common – a Retrospect; 1888-1937. *Journal of the Wimbledon Natural History Society*

JONES, A.W. (1952) *Flowers, Ferns and Horsetails of Wimbledon Common.* (unpublished)

JONES, A.W. (1954) The Flora of the Golf Course on Wimbledon Common. *London Naturalist. L.N.H.S.* **34**, 141-145.

JONES, A.W. (1954) Notes on the Butterflies of Wimbledon Common. *London Naturalist. L.N.H.S.* **34**, 108-114.

KERNEY, M.P., GIBBARD, P.L. *et al.* (1982). Middle Devensian river deposits beneath the 'Upper Floodplain' terrace of the River Thames at Isleworth, West London. *Proceedings of the Geologists' Association.* **93**, 385-393.

MILWARD, R.J. (1989) *Historic Wimbledon: From Caesar's Camp to Centre Court.* Fielders & Windrush Press.

MILWARD, R.J. (1997) *Wimbledon 1865 – 1965.* Chalford Publishing Co. Ltd. Gloucestershire.

MILWARD, R.J. (1998) *Wimbledon Past.* Historical Publications, London.

MONCKTON, H.W. (1893) Boulders and pebbles from the Glacial Drift. *Quarterly Journal of the Geological Society of London.* **49**, 316-317.

MOORE, P.D, WEBB, J.A. & COLLINSON, M.E. (1991) *Pollen Analysis* (2nd edition). Blackwell Scientific Publications. Oxford.

NICHOLSON, G. *et al* (1971) *Walks on Wimbledon Common.* Wimbledon & Putney Commons Conservators, London.

PEARSON, A.A. (1918) *The Flora of Wimbledon Common*. An address given to the Members of the John Evelyn Club on the 14th December, 1917. Taylor & Francis.

PLASTOW, N. (1986) Ed. *A History of Wimbledon & Putney Commons*. Wimbledon and Putney Commons Conservators, London.

POWELL, A. & SOUTH, A. (1978) Studies of the Mollusc faunas of gravel-pit lakes in S.E. England. *Journal of molluscan Studies*. **44**, 327-339.

RILEY, N. (1971) Insects. pp. 69-73 *in* Nicholson, *et al. Walks on Wimbledon Common*. Wimbledon & Putney Commons Conservators, London.

STUBBS, D. (1989) *Beverley Catchment Ecological Survey – A report by the London Wildlife Trust for National Rivers Authority, Thames Region*.

SUMBLER, M.G. (1996) *British Regional Geology: London and the Thames Valley* (4th edition). London H.M.S.O., for the British Geological Survey.

SUTCLIFFE, U. (1991) *A study of the soil hydrology of Farm Bog, Wimbledon Common and its effect on the distribution of plant species*. M.Sc. dissertation, University of London.

WANDSWORTH NATURE CONSERVATION UNIT (c.1983) Unpublished systematic list of fauna, produced under the direction of Dr James Whitelaw, which includes the fauna from Wimbledon and Putney Commons. Wandsworth Borough Council.

WANDSWORTH NATURE CONSERVATION UNIT (1983) *Putney Heath Nature Trail*. Wandsworth Borough Council.

WANDSWORTH NATURE CONSERVATION UNIT (1985) *Kingsmere Nature Trail*. Wandsworth Borough Council.

WANDSWORTH NATURE CONSERVATION UNIT (1988) *Mill Corner Nature Trail*. Wandsworth Borough Council.

WILLS, D.L. (1999) *The Birds of Wimbledon Common and Putney Heath*. Unpublished Report.

WILLS, D.L. & KETTLE, R.H. (1997) The Birds of Wimbledon Common and Putney Heath, 1974 to 1996. *London Bird Report. London Natural History Society*. **61**, 212-228.

WIMBLEDON AND PUTNEY COMMONS CONSERVATORS (1999) *Windmill Nature Trail*. (pamphlet).

YARHAM, I., DAWSON, D., BOYLE, M. & HOLLIDAY, R. (1998) *Nature Conservation in Merton*. Ecology Handbook **29**. London Ecology Unit.

Index

Compiled by Antony and Una Sutcliffe

Bold type indicates an illustration   [ ] indicates Farm Bog pollen